Introduction to
STATISTICS FOR BUSINESS DECISIONS

Introduction to

STATISTICS
FOR BUSINESS DECISIONS

Robert Schlaifer

PROFESSOR OF BUSINESS ADMINISTRATION
HARVARD UNIVERSITY

McGRAW-HILL BOOK COMPANY, INC.

New York   Toronto   London

1961

INTRODUCTION TO
STATISTICS FOR BUSINESS DECISIONS

THE MAPLE PRESS COMPANY, YORK, PA.

IV

55308

Preface

The primary objective of this book is twofold: first, to set forth as simply as possible the basic principles of the classical decision theory of Neyman and Pearson; second, to show, again as simply as possible, how this classical theory is completed rather than contradicted by more recent developments based on the concepts of utility and personal probability. The problem of reaching a decision on the basis of sample evidence is first analyzed in the traditional manner by choosing a suitable form of decision rule or test and then examining the operating characteristics or error functions of all possible rules of this suitable form. After discussing some of the traditional methods of choosing among operating characteristics—or equivalently, of deciding on the exact point and level at which to test— losses are introduced explicitly in the manner of Wald; operating characteristics or error functions are converted into risk functions. Finally, it is shown how a reasoned choice among risk functions can be made by assigning a weight or "probability" to each possible value of the parameter under test and then computing the weighted-average or "Bayes" risk of the various decision rules or tests among which a choice must be made.

The present book differs in three fundamental respects from the author's "Probability and Statistics for Business Decisions." First, it aims at a *unified* treatment of classical and Bayesian statistics, intended to bring out from the very first the essential agreements between the two schools, whereas the earlier book relied essentially on a form of analysis which tends to conceal this unity even though it leads to the same results. Second, the present book aims solely at teaching how to deal with samples, whereas the earlier book dealt with a wide variety of decision problems in which samples were not involved. Finally, the present book has been organized in such a way as to facilitate the use of only a part of it in a short course. The teacher who wants to give a short introduction to both classical and Bayesian decision theory can do so by using only Chapters 1 through 4 and 8 through 13; he will find all essential principles covered in these ten chapters, and the skipping of Chapters 5 through 7 will create no pedagogical difficulties.

Because a good deal of teaching experience has convinced the author that it is hopeless to try to explain the analysis of decisions involving samples before the student has some familiarity with the basic concepts of probability and decision under uncertainty, the first four chapters of the book are devoted to a discussion of these necessary foundations in terms of examples which do not actually involve samples.   The concepts thus introduced are probability and probability distributions, expected value, utility, and loss (or "regret").

The next three chapters (5 through 7) are essentially an excursus into "descriptive statistics" and can be omitted by the teacher who wishes to proceed directly to the study of the use of samples.   The real purpose of these chapters is the discussion in Chapter 6 of the uses and misuses of measures of location: the mean, the median, and other fractiles.   Chapter 5 provides the motivation for the use of fractiles, while Chapter 7 provides supplementary exercise in their use in practical decision problems.

The main attack on the use of samples begins in Chapter 8, and all the essential ideas are presented, illustrated by examples, and fully discussed in this chapter and the five following.   Chapters 8 an 9 present conditional, joint, and marginal probability and then use these concepts to derive the binomial distribution.   Chapter 10 presents the classical statistical problem of choice between two hypotheses or acts, introduces the concepts of decision rules and tests of significance, and discusses the use of operating characteristics or error functions as a basis for choice among possible rules or tests.   In Chapter 11 the error characteristics of the previous chapter are converted into risk functions showing conditional loss or regret under the various decision rules being compared, and both the minimax and Bayes principles for choice among these risk functions are explained.   Chapter 12 introduces Bayes' theorem for the first time and shows that, after a sample has already been taken, the use of this theorem to choose a terminal act is equivalent to selection of a decision rule with minimum expected loss.   Finally, Chapter 13 takes up situations in which the decision maker is *not* obliged to choose a terminal act immediately but can if he likes suspend judgment until further evidence has been obtained.   After it has been explained how tests of significance are used for this purpose, the problem is reexamined in terms of the economics of a second sample and in this way is related to the study of optimal decision rules in Chapters 10 and 11.   Chapter 13 then closes with a brief examination of the problem of "scientific reporting"—i.e., the problem of simply indicating what is known about some parameter when no real choice between terminal acts has to be made.   Confidence intervals are presented as one possible solution of this problem, after which the relation between confidence intervals and posterior probability is explained.

The student who completes Chapter 13 (possibly having omitted Chapters 5 through 7 on the way) has thus already been presented with the principal techniques and concepts of both classical and Bayesian statistics. The remainder of the book merely extends the varieties of situations in which the student can apply these concepts and techniques by introducing him to the Normal distribution and some of its principal uses.

To avoid introducing too many novelties at one time, the Normal distribution is first introduced merely as a method of approximating the binomial probabilities with which the student is already familiar. Chapter 14 defines and explains variance and standard deviation; Chapter 15 explains how a binomial distribution can be approximated by a Normal distribution with the same mean and variance.

The last six chapters of the book (16 through 21) are then devoted to applications of large-sample theory to the same basic kinds of statistical problems which were studied with the aid of the binomial distribution in Chapters 8 through 13. Chapter 16 develops the foundations of large-sample theory: the approximate Normality of the means of large samples, and the legitimacy of using a large-sample estimate of the population standard deviation as if it were the actual value of this standard deviation. Chapter 17 parallels Chapter 10 in expounding decision rules for two-action problems in terms of their operating characteristics or error functions and reviews what was explained in Chapter 10 about the relation between decision rules and tests of significance. Chapter 18 parallels Chapter 12 in converting error functions into risk functions and showing how the introduction of weights makes it possible to choose among rules on the basis of weighted-average expected loss.

Chapter 19 corresponds to Chapter 12 on Bayes' theorem; but instead of again expounding the basic logic of the theorem through the use of discrete prior distributions, Chapter 19 gives the student a taste of the power of analytical methods by introducing continuous (Normal) prior distributions and showing how in this case the complete posterior distribution can be obtained by using a very simple formula. This device makes it possible to include in the chapter some discussion of the conditions under which very large disagreements about prior distributions will be of virtually no importance at all once a substantial amount of sample information is at hand. The last two chapters of the book continue to exploit the tractability of continuous prior distributions so that the student can obtain quantitative answers to realistic decision problems with only a reasonable computational burden. Chapter 20 shows how to compute the expected opportunity loss—in one sense, the "risk"—of acting without obtaining further information and also how to compute the expected value of the information to be obtained from a sample of any given size.   Chapter 21 completes this line of development by showing how to determine the best possible sample size, and the solution to this problem of course includes a solution to the problem of deciding whether or not any sample should be taken at all.

The text contains no "references for further reading" by the student simply because the author does not believe that a logically precise subject like decision theory can be taught by assigning small extracts from each of a large number of books.   It contains no account of the historical development of the subject because it is a text in decision theory and not in intellectual history; any really meaningful history—one which amounts to more than name dropping—would be nearly as long as the present book.   Students who seriously wish to continue their study of decision theory beyond the very elementary level reached in the present book can study the philosophical foundations in L. J. Savage's "Foundations of Statistics,"† they can study its history by looking up the references in Savage's very complete bibliography, and they can find applications in the periodical literature.   The student or teacher who wishes proofs of results given without proof in the present book can find them in Raiffa and Schlaifer's "Applied Statistical Decision Theory."‡

Robert Schlaifer

† John Wiley & Sons, Inc., 1954, New York.
‡ Division of Research, Graduate School of Business Administration, Harvard University, Boston, 1961.

Contents

Preface v

Introduction. The Problem of Decision under Uncertainty

1. The Meaning of Probability 3
2. Expected Value and Utility 24
3. Random Variables and Probability Distributions 49

Part One. The Use of Probabilities Based Directly on Experience

4. Opportunity Loss and the Cost of Uncertainty 67
5. Incremental Analysis 80
6. Measures of Location: Fractiles and Expectations; Linear Profits and Costs 89
7. Assessment of Probabilities by Smoothing Historical Frequencies . . . 104

Part Two. Binomial Sampling

8. Conditional, Joint, and Marginal Probability 121
9. The Binomial Distribution 136
10. Statistical Decision Rules and Their Error Characteristics 150
11. Evaluation of Statistical Decision Rules in Terms of Expected Loss . . 169
12. Revision of Probabilities in the Light of New Information 188
13. Suspension of Judgment and Summarization of Information 198

Part Three. Introduction to the Normal Distribution

14. Measures of Variability: Variance and Standard Deviation 223
15. The Normal Distribution and the Normal Approximation to the Binomial
Distribution 233

Part Four. Sampling of Measured Values

16. The Central Limit Theorem and Large-sample Theory 249
17. Statistical Decision Rules with Normal Sampling 268
18. Expected Loss with Normal Sampling 289
19. Normal Prior Distributions; Statistical Significance and Confidence
Intervals 296
20. The Economics of Two-action Problems with Linear Profits or Costs and
Normal Distributions 316
21. Optimal Sample Size in Two-action Problems with Linear Profits or Costs
and Normal Distributions 329

x   *Contents*

Tables

I. Cumulative Binomial Distribution. 344
II. Unit Normal Probability Distribution 366
III. Cumulative Unit Normal Distribution 368
IV. Unit Normal Loss Integral 370
V. Random Digits 372
VI. Square Roots 373
VII. Cube Roots 374

Chart I. Optimal Sample Size . . . . *facing page* 374

Index of Symbols 375

Subject Index 377

INTRODUCTION

The Problem of Decision under Uncertainty

CHAPTER 1

The Meaning of Probability

1.1 The Problem of Decision under Uncertainty

When all of the facts bearing on a business decision are accurately known—when the decision is made "under certainty"—careless thinking is the only reason why the decision should turn out, after the fact, to have been wrong. But when the relevant facts are not all known—when the decision is made "under uncertainty"—it is impossible to make sure that every decision will turn out to have been right in this same sense. Under uncertainty, the businessman is forced, in effect, to gamble. His previous actions have put him in a position where he *must* place bets, hoping that he will win but knowing that he may lose. Under such circumstances, a right decision consists in the choice of the best possible bet, whether it is won or lost after the fact. The following examples are typical of situations in which business decisions must be made and judged in this way.

An Inventory Problem. A retailer is about to place an order for a number of units of a perishable commodity which spoils if it is not sold by the end of the day on which it is stocked. Each unit costs the retailer $1; the retail price is $5. The retailer does not know what the demand for the item will be, but he must nevertheless decide on a definite number of units to stock.

A Scrap-allowance Problem. A manufacturer has contracted to deliver at least 100 good pieces of a nonstandard product at a fixed price for the lot. He feels virtually sure that there will be some defectives among the first 100 pieces produced; and since setting up for a second production run to fill out a shortage would cost a substantial amount of money, he wishes to schedule some additional pieces on the original run as a scrap allowance. On the other hand, once 100 good pieces have been produced the direct manufacturing cost of any additional production will be a total loss, and therefore he does not wish to make the scrap allowance excessively large. If the manufacturer knew exactly how many pieces would have to be produced in order to get exactly 100 good pieces, it would be easy to set the "right" size for the production order;

3

but he must decide on some definite size for the order even though he does not know the "right" size.

An Investment Problem.   A manufacturer is about to tool up for production of a newly developed product.   This product can be manufactured by either of two processes, one of which requires a relatively small capital investment but high labor cost per unit produced while the other will have much lower labor costs but requires a much greater investment.   The former process will thus be the better one if sales of the product are low while the latter will be better if sales are high; but the manufacturer must choose between the two processes without knowing what his sales will actually be.

A Marketing Problem.   The brand manager for a certain grocery product is considering a change of package design in the hope that the new package will attract more attention on the shelf and thereby increase sales.   He has done a certain amount of store testing and has found that during the test weeks sales of the new package were greater than sales of the old in some stores but that the contrary was true in other stores.   He still feels uncertain whether adoption of the new package will increase or decrease his total national sales, but he must nevertheless either decide on one package or the other or else decide to spend more money on additional testing; in the latter case he must decide whether he should simply continue the test for a few more weeks in the same stores he has already used or spend still more money to draw new stores into his sample.

1.1.1   The Payoff Table

The essential characteristics of all four of these problems, and of all problems which we shall study in this course, are the following.

1. A choice must be made among several possible *acts*.
2. The chosen act will ultimately lead to some definite profit (possibly negative), but for at least some of the acts the amount of this profit is unknown because it will be determined by some *event* which cannot be predicted with certainty.

The first step in analyzing any such problem is to lay out all the possible acts and all their possible consequences in some systematic fashion, and we shall do this for the inventory problem as an example.

In the inventory problem, an "act" is a decision to stock some particular number of units; the "event" is the number of units which the customers will actually demand.   If we suppose that the retailer's space limits the number of units stocked to a maximum of 5, then remembering that each unit stocked costs $1 while each sale brings in $5 of revenue we can describe the whole problem by a table like Table 1.1, where each column corresponds to a particular act while each row corresponds to a particular event. Such a table is known as a *payoff table*.

Table 1.1
Payoff Table for the Inventory Example

Event (number demanded)	Act (number of units stocked)					
	0	1	2	3	4	5
0	$0	−$1	−$2	−$3	−$4	−$5
1	0	+ 4	+ 3	+ 2	+ 1	0
2	0	+ 4	+ 8	+ 7	+ 6	+ 5
3	0	+ 4	+ 8	+12	+11	+10
4	0	+ 4	+ 8	+12	+16	+15
5 or more	0	+ 4	+ 8	+12	+16	+20

1.1.2   Comparison of Acts

If we compare any two acts (columns) in Table 1.1, we see that one of the two will be more profitable if certain events occur while the other will be more profitable if other events occur; but when we actually choose among these acts we are implicitly if not explicitly making a single, unconditional evaluation of each act.   We are saying that in some sense one of the acts is "better" than any of the others.

The Minimax Principle.   One *possible* way of evaluating acts under uncertainty is to follow the so-called *minimax* principle, according to which the decision maker should look only at the *worst* possible consequence of each act and then choose the act for which the worst consequence is *least bad*.   He should, in other words, *min*imize the *max*imum damage which the world can do him.   Use of the minimax principle has been seriously advocated for problems involving sampling, but we can see its basic implications very clearly by applying it to the problem of Table 1.1.   What it says there is that the retailer should choose the act "stock 0," since with this act the worst that can happen is that he will make no money, whereas any other act *might* result in an actual *loss* of money. Observe that, since the same conclusion would apply to any other item the retailer might stock, the minimax principle implies that the retailer should simply go out of business.

The Principle of Weighing the Possibilities.   We shall examine another version of the minimax principle in Chapter 4 and find that it too leads to completely intolerable results.   Any sensible businessman will of course immediately reject not only the minimax principle but *any* purely *arbitrary* principle of action under uncertainty and will say that even though the retailer cannot predict demand with *certainty* he ought to know enough about his business and the product in question to have some convictions about what the demand is *likely to be.*   If after weighing all the available information the retailer decides that there is very little chance that customers will demand less than 3 or more than 4 units, he will conclude that the only reasonable act is to stock either 3 or 4 units. Choice between these two acts will be a little more complex, since the larger stock will be only $12 − $11 = $1 less profitable than the smaller if there is a demand for only 3 units while it will be all of $16 − $12 = $4 more profitable if 4 units are demanded.   Consequently the retailer will want to stock 4 units even if he believes that the chance of a demand for 4 is somewhat less than the chance of a demand for 3; it is only if he believes that the chance of a demand for 4 is relatively *very* slight that he will reduce his stock to 3 units.

Now this informal kind of reasoning works very well when the decision problem is relatively simple, but one quickly becomes confused when the problem is even slightly more complex.   Even in our very simple example, it will be hard for the retailer to see through to a satisfying conclusion if he thinks that there is a substantial chance that demand may have any of three or four different values, and in larger problems of the same sort he may well consider a hundred or a thousand different values as possible.   What we would like to do, therefore, is find some way of *systematizing* the kind of analysis which a reasonable man uses in simple problems so that it can be effectively applied in more complex problems.

If we look back at the reasoning used by our hypothetical retailer, we see that in essence he proceeded in two steps: he first gave a numerical *value* to the consequence of each possible act given each possible event, but he then attached more *weight* to the consequences corresponding to certain events (demand 3 or 4) than he did to the others.   This suggests that it may be possible to systematize the reasoning underlying *any* decision under uncertainty by proceeding as follows:

1. Attach a definite numerical *value* to the consequence of every possible act given every possible event.
2. Attach a definite numerical *weight* to every possible event.
3. For each act separately, use these weights to compute a *weighted average* of all the values attached to that act.
4. Select the act whose weighted-average value is highest.

Our hope is that we can find rules for using the businessman's own knowledge and beliefs in carrying out steps 1 and 2 in such a way that he will *want* to choose the act with the highest computed value instead of relying on mere inspection of a mass of numbers and informal reasoning of the kind described above. If we are to have confidence in these rules in complex situations, they must yield values which seem reasonable to us when applied in very simple situations, and for this reason many of the examples which we shall use in developing these rules will be artificial ones which avoid the complexities of practical business decisions in order to present their really essential features in the simplest possible form. Because the heart of the problem is the uncertainty concerning the event, we shall begin by developing the rules for attaching weights to events.

1.2 Events

Before we even start to assign numerical weights to a set of events some one of which will determine the consequence of any act we choose, we obviously must have in mind a clear and complete description of the events which may occur. We usually have considerable latitude in defining the possible events in a given problem, but certain rules must be followed if we are to avoid hopeless confusion.

1.2.1 Collectively Exhaustive Events

If before we started to analyze the inventory problem of Table 1.1 the retailer had told us that he was absolutely convinced that there would be a demand for at least 2 units, we could just as well have simplified Table 1.1 by eliminating the rows describing the consequences of the events "demand 0" and "demand 1." In general, impossible events may be totally disregarded if it is convenient to do so, and it is to be emphasized that there is no need to "prove" that an event is impossible before it is eliminated. Our object is to arrive at results which the businessman *wants to accept*, and therefore an event is impossible for our purposes whenever the businessman wants to treat it as impossible.

It is obvious, on the other hand, that we must keep *all* the *possible* events in mind in analyzing any decision problem, since if we fail to include some of the possible events in the payoff table the corresponding consequences will not be duly considered in evaluating the various acts. The same thing can be stated the other way around: the basic list of events must be complete in the sense that *some one of the events on the list is bound to occur*. The events on such a list are called *collectively exhaustive*.

1.2.2 Mutually Exclusive Events

In the inventory example of Table 1.1, demand for each specific number of units from 0 to 4 inclusive was treated as a separate event but demands for all numbers of units above 4 were treated as constituting the same event "demand for 5 or more." Obviously we *could* have treated a demand for exactly 5 units as a separate event and assigned it a separate line in Table 1.1, and similarly for any larger number of units, but nothing was to be gained by so doing because for every act under consideration the consequences of the event "demand for 5" were identical to the consequences of the event "demand for 6" or the event "demand for 7" and so forth.

Careless grouping of events can easily lead to confusion, however. It is obvious that potentially separate events must not be grouped if their consequences differ for any act under consideration. We cannot treat "demand for 3 or 4" or "demand for 4 or more" as a single event in constructing a payoff table for our inventory example. What is often less obvious is that we must not have events with *overlapping definitions* on our list even if it is possible to give a clear description of the consequences of all acts in terms of such a list.

Suppose, for example, that we are given a choice of one or the other of two tickets in a lottery to be conducted by drawing one ball from an urn containing four kinds of balls: dotted red, striped red, dotted green, and striped green. The first ticket entitles the holder to a prize of value V if the ball drawn from the urn is either red or striped; the second entitles the holder to the same prize if the ball is dotted green. Table 1.2

Table 1.2

Event	Act (choice of ticket)	
	1	2
Red	V	0
Striped	V	0
Dotted green	0	V

gives a perfectly clear description of the conditions under which the prize will be awarded, but confusion is bound to arise if we base our analysis of this decision problem on this table because the events "red" and "striped" will *both* occur if a striped red ball is drawn. To illustrate the difficulty by an extreme case, suppose that we know that *all* the red balls are striped and that all the striped balls are red. Then the events "red" and "striped" are really the same event counted twice, and any weight which we attach to this event will be counted twice in evaluating the acts under consideration.

This kind of difficulty can be avoided by basing our analysis on any of the three lists of events shown in Table 1.3, since the occurrence of any one event on any of these lists means that *no other event on the same list can possibly occur.* The events on any such list are said to be *mutually exclusive*.

Table 1.3

A	B	C
Striped red	Red	Red or striped
Dotted red	Striped green	Dotted green
Striped green	Dotted green	
Dotted green		

1.2.3   Elementary and Compound Events

The importance of mutual exclusiveness is so great that it is worth the trouble to find a way of visualizing it. The events on list *A* of Table 1.3 are obviously mutually exclusive because they have been defined

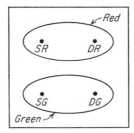
Figure 1.1

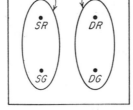
Figure 1.2

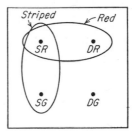
Figure 1.3

without any grouping at all—balls which differ in *any* respect have been classified as separate events in this list. These four events will be called the *elementary events* of this problem.

Any set of *elementary* events can be visualized as a set of *points* in a diagram like Figure 1.1, 1.2, or 1.3, where the points represent the four elementary events of list *A* in Table 1.3. Events such as "red" or "striped" can then be visualized as corresponding to a *group of points* representing elementary events: the events "red" and "green" are depicted in Figure 1.1, the events "striped" and "dotted" in Figure 1.2. Such events will be called *compound events*, and it is obvious that

Two compound events are mutually exclusive if they contain no elementary events in common.

In Figure 1.3 we illustrate the difficulty with the events used in Table 1.2: the point corresponding to the elementary event "striped red" is included in *both* the compound events "red" and "striped."

1.3   The Basic Rules Governing the Assignment of Weights

We are now ready to develop rules for using a definite number to represent the weight which a decision maker attaches to each of the events in a set of mutually exclusive and collectively exhaustive events. Since we propose to use these numbers in computing weighted averages, our rules must be such that these weighted averages will "make sense"— i.e., they must be such that the decision maker will *want* to choose the act with the highest weighted-average value. On the other hand, this is the *only* way in which we shall use these weights; and if we find that the requirement just stated can be met by more than one set of rules, we are free to choose the one which is most convenient.

To see whether we do have any such choice, let us review the way in which any weighted average is computed. In the first two columns of Table 1.4a we show a set of four values with a weight attached to each value; the meaning of the values and the weights is irrelevant for our present purpose. The weighted average is computed in three steps:

1. Each value is multiplied by its weight to form the products shown in the third column of Table 1.4a.
2. Both the weights and the products are added to obtain the sums shown at the bottoms of their respective columns.
3. The sum of the products is divided by the sum of the weights to obtain the weighted average.

Table 1.4a			Table 1.4b		
Value	Weight	Product	Value	Weight	Product
3	2	6	3	.2	.6
2	1	2	2	.1	.2
7	3	21	7	.3	2.1
5	4	20	5	.4	2.0
	10	49		1.0	4.9

$$\text{Weighted average} = \frac{49}{10} = 4.9 \qquad \text{Weighted average} = \frac{4.9}{1.0} = 4.9$$

Observe now that exactly the same weighted average is obtained in Table 1.4b by using weights each of which is one-tenth as large as the corresponding weight in Table 1.4a. It is obvious that this example can be generalized: dividing every weight in a set by the same nonzero number has no effect on any weighted average computed by use of these weights. In other words, *weighted averages are affected by the proportions among the weights attached to the values being averaged but not by the absolute sizes of the weights.*

This means that we are free to specify that the weights assigned to a set of mutually exclusive and collectively exhaustive events shall add up to any amount we choose, and unless we do make such a specification it will be possible to represent the same beliefs by many different sets of weights. If we allow this, confusion is bound to arise, and we shall therefore adopt the following *fundamental convention* as the first of our basic rules for assigning weights to events:

Rule 1. The sum of the weights assigned to any set of mutually exclusive and collectively exhaustive events shall be 1.

The choice of 1 rather than some other number for the specified total is purely a matter of convenience; it eliminates the need to divide by the sum of the weights in order to convert the sum of products into a weighted average.

Having adopted this fundamental convention, we are now ready to develop rules which *must* be observed in assigning weights if the resulting weighted averages are to make sense. In so doing it will be well to have an extremely simple decision problem actually before us, and we may as well use the same problem which we have already used to illustrate the concept of mutually exclusive events. Three lists of collectively exhaustive and mutually exclusive events suitable for analysis of this problem were shown in Table 1.3; payoff tables based on two of these three lists are shown in Tables 1.5a and 1.5b.

Table 1.5a

Event	Act (choice of ticket)	
	1	2
Striped red	V	0
Dotted red	V	0
Striped green	V	0
Dotted green	0	V

Table 1.5b

Event	Act (choice of ticket)	
	1	2
Red or striped	V	0
Dotted green	0	V

Let us first consider the problem of evaluating ticket number 2. Since this ticket pays off only if the event "dotted green" occurs, three facts are immediately obvious about the value we will assign to this ticket.

1. If we are absolutely convinced, for whatever reason, that the ball will *not* be dotted green, we will value the ticket at 0.
2. If we are absolutely convinced that the ball *will* be dotted green, we will value the ticket at V—it is just as good as the prize itself.

3. If we are uncertain about the event, we will value the ticket at something between 0 and *V*.

Now if we assign numerical weights to the events in Table 1.5*a* or 1.5*b* and use these to compute a weighted average of the values in the column describing ticket number 2, this weighted average will be simply *V* times the weight we assign to the event "dotted green"—recall that by Rule 1 the sum of the weights assigned to all the events in either table must be 1 and therefore that as in Table 1.4*b* the sum of products is left unchanged when it is divided by the sum of the weights. But if this is so, then our weighted-average valuation will agree with the three direct valuations listed just above only if we assign weight 0 to an event which we believe impossible, weight 1 to an event which we believe certain, and some intermediate number to any doubtful event. We thus arrive at our second fundamental rule:

Rule 2. The weight assigned to any event shall be a number between 0 and 1 inclusive, 0 representing complete conviction that the event will not occur and 1 representing complete conviction that it will occur.

We now turn our attention to the valuation of ticket number 1. If we compute a weighted average of the values in the column describing ticket number 1 in Table 1.5*a*, we will have the sum of three terms:

V × weight of "striped red,"
V × weight of "dotted red,"
V × weight of "striped green,"

and this sum is equal to *V* times the sum of the three weights. If on the other hand we compute a weighted average of the values in the corresponding column of Table 1.5*b*, we will have simply *V* times the weight of the compound event "red *or* striped." We conclude that the weight assigned to the event "red or striped" must be the sum of the weights assigned to the three mutually exclusive events of which it is composed, and we generalize this example to obtain our last basic rule:

Rule 3. If two or more mutually exclusive events are grouped into a single event, the weight attached to this single event shall be equal to the sum of the weights attached to the original events.

Observe that this rule does *not* hold for events which are not mutually exclusive. Suppose, for example, that for some reason or other we have assigned the weights shown in Table 1.6 to the four mutually exclusive events of Table 1.5*a*. We can use Rule 3 to show that the weight assigned to "red" must be .4 + .3 = .7 or to show that the weight

Table 1.6

Event	Weight
Striped red	.4
Dotted red	.3
Striped green	.2
Dotted green	.1
	1.0

assigned to "striped" must be .4 + .2 = .6, but we *cannot* add these two results to obtain .7 + .6 = 1.3 for the weight to be assigned to "red or striped"; if we do, we are double-counting the .4 weight originally assigned to the event "striped red."

1.4 The Standard Lottery

Although the three basic rules which we have derived above may seem so broad that they fail to specify exactly what set of numbers should be used as the weights in any given problem of decision under uncertainty, we shall now see that this is not so. In any situation there will exist one and only one set of weights which will both comply with these rules and express the decision maker's attitudes toward a set of collectively exhaustive and mutually exclusive events.

Suppose that we are offered a free chance at a prize of value V under the following conditions. Balls numbered 1 to 100 have been placed in an urn and one of these balls has then been drawn and put in a closed box. We are presented with 100 tickets numbered from 1 to 100 and are allowed to choose one of them. If the number we choose matches the number on the ball which has been drawn from the urn, we will receive the prize; if not, we receive nothing. Suppose further that even though the prize is one which we are extremely anxious to win, we do not feel that it is worth the slightest effort to look for a ticket with any particular number on it; we simply take the first one which comes to hand.

In such a situation we shall say that *in our opinion* the 100 possible events are *equally likely*. Notice very carefully that we do not and *cannot* "prove" that the events are "in fact" equally likely: the fact is that the ball which has been drawn has some one particular number and no other. But even though anyone who *knew* which ball has been drawn would not be indifferent among the 100 tickets, *our* decisions must be based on what *we* know or believe about the facts of the world—they *cannot* be based on the unknown truth about these facts. Therefore if <u>*we* are indifferent in the way described, then *for us* the 100 events are equally likely *by definition*.</u>

Now if our state of mind as just described is to be described by numerical weights attached to the 100 possible events 1, 2, . . . , 100, it is clear that *these weights must all be equal.* If the sum of these 100 equal numbers is to be 1, as required by Rule 1, it is also clear that the number attached to each event must be $\frac{1}{100}$. Rule 3 then tells us that events such as "ball number 2 or 7" must have weight $\frac{1}{100} + \frac{1}{100} = \frac{2}{100}$, that events such as "any ball numbered between 1 and 37 inclusive" must have weight $\frac{37}{100}$, and so forth. Thus while Rule 2 specified only that the weight attached to any event must be a number between 0 and 1 inclusive, we have found a way of selecting a specific number within this range to describe our attitude toward any conceivable event in this lottery.

What is more important, a *businessman can find the unique set of weights which describes his attitudes in a more complex situation by using a lottery of this sort as a standard of comparison.* In order to decide what weight to assign to the event "demand 0" in our inventory example, the retailer can imagine that he is given a choice between a certain number of tickets in the standard lottery with a prize of value V as described above and the right to receive *this same prize* in the event of "demand 0." If in his opinion the right to receive this prize in the event of "demand 0" has exactly the same value as 18 tickets in the standard lottery, then *by definition* he considers these two events equally likely and he should assign weight $\frac{18}{100}$ to the event "demand 0." (It goes without saying that if the standard lottery with 100 balls does not offer a fine enough division, the retailer can substitute a similar lottery with more balls. If he feels that the right to receive the prize in case of demand 0 is worth more than 18 tickets but less than 19 in a lottery with 100 equally likely events, he may decide that it is equivalent to 183 tickets in a lottery with 1000 equally likely events.)

Having assigned a weight to the event "demand 0," the retailer can proceed in the same way to assign weights to all the other events in Table 1.1. These weights must of course be such that their total is 1, and therefore what the retailer is really doing is placing the set of collectively exhaustive and mutually exclusive events shown in Table 1.1 into one-to-one correspondence with a set of collectively exhaustive and mutually exclusive events in the standard lottery. When he is through, the event "demand 0" will correspond, say, to the event "ball numbered between 1 and 18 inclusive," the event "demand 1" to balls 19 to 52, and so forth. It is perhaps worth remarking that we are in no sense assuming that a businessman will actually be as ready to gamble on balls drawn from an urn as to make decisions concerning his regular business. We are simply assuming that a rational person can with practice *think abstractly about his feelings of certainty and uncertainty in any given situation*, regardless of any feelings he may have about any other aspects of the situation.

1.5 Logical Consistency and the Mathematical Theory of Probability

In addition to checking to see that the weights assigned to the events of Table 1.1 obey the fundamental convention expressed by Rule 1, the retailer may do well to check whether he is satisfied with some of the logical consequences which result when Rule 3 is applied to these weights. It is easy to assign either too small or too large a weight to an individual event in a long list of events, and after assigning weight .18 to "demand 0" and weight .34 to "demand 1" the retailer may find that the weight .18 + .34 = .52 which he has thus *implicitly* assigned to the compound event "demand less than 2" is not what he would have assigned if he had thought directly about that event.   If so, he must reconcile this *logical inconsistency* before proceeding further with the analysis of his problem.

In many problems such checks for logical consistency are of really crucial importance.   To cite a very simple but famous example, the mathematician D'Alembert assigned weight ⅓ to the occurrence of one heads in two tosses of a coin, arguing that the pair of tosses must produce 0, 1, or 2 heads and that in his opinion these three events were equally likely.   To see whether we would share this attitude we may reason as follows.   An *elementary* event of a pair of tosses of a coin is described by stating the results of each of the two tosses in the order in which they occurred.   If we use HT to denote the elementary event "heads on first toss, tails on second toss" and similar notation for all the other possibilities, the four possible elementary events of the double toss are HH, HT, TH, and TT.   If we feel that *these* four events are equally likely and therefore assign weight ¼ to each of them, we can add the weights assigned to HT and TH and find that we have implicitly assigned weight ½ rather than ⅓ to the compound event "one heads."   To state the conclusion the other way around, D'Alembert implicitly assigned the same total weight to the *two* events HT and TH that he assigned to each of the single events HH and TT.

Assignments of weights in more complex problems are still more in need of this kind of check.   As a practical business example, consider the scrap-allowance problem which was sketched at the beginning of this chapter.   The actual payoff table for this problem is too complex to discuss at this point, but it is easy to see that because a new setup will be required if less than 100 good pieces are produced on the first run, it will be necessary to assign weights to such events as "more than 80 defectives in a production run of 180 pieces."   An elementary event of a run of 180 pieces can be described by a sequence of 180 g's and d's, g denoting a good piece and d a defective; and in some cases the manufacturer may be able to check any weight he assigns directly to the event "more than

80 defectives" by assigning weights to these elementary events just as we assigned weights to sequences such as HT in order to check D'Alembert's probability.   To consider only the simplest possible case, suppose that the manufacturer feels that any one of the 180 pieces is as likely to be defective as it is to be good and assigns *equal* weight to every possible elementary event.   The weight which he has implicitly assigned to the event "more than 80 defectives" can then be computed by simply counting the total number of possible sequences of 180 g's and d's, counting the number of sequences which contain more than 80 d's, and dividing the latter of these two counts by the former.

It is true that this counting would take a very great deal of time, since it can be shown that the total number of sequences is roughly 1 followed by 54 zeros and a substantial fraction of these sequences contains more than 80 d's.   Fortunately, however, actual counting is unnecessary. By the use of simple mathematical short cuts which we shall study later in the course, we can very quickly determine that $922/1000$ of the total number of sequences contain more than 80 d's and therefore that the weight which has implicitly been assigned to the event "more than 80 defectives" is .922.   We shall also see later in the course that these same mathematical short cuts can be used to compute implicit probabilities when the businessman does not think that each piece produced is as likely to be defective as it is to be good, even though the reasoning about the weights to be assigned to the elementary events is more complex in that case.

The whole body of mathematical short cuts used in computations of this kind is known as the *theory of probability*.   Like any *mathematical* "theory," the theory of probability is simply a set of logical deductions from certain basic axioms; the axioms of this particular theory are the following:

1. A probability is a number between 0 and 1 assigned to an event.
2. The sum of the probabilities assigned to a set of mutually exclusive and collectively exhaustive events must be 1.
3. The probability of an event which is composed of a group of mutually exclusive events is the sum of their probabilities.

We are justified in using the theory of probability to calculate "weights" in the way in which we have just used it because we have agreed to assign weights in accordance with these three axioms; the axioms are simply our three "basic rules" for assigning weights presented in slightly different language and with the order of the first and second rules reversed.   Henceforth we shall use the word *probability* in exactly the same sense that we have hitherto used the word "weight."

1.6   Relative Frequency and the Rational Assessment of Probabilities

Although we have just seen that the theory of probability can be used to show that certain probabilities are mutually inconsistent and although we have said that such inconsistencies must be reconciled before final assignments of probabilities are made, we have as yet said nothing about the way in which a reasonable man will reconcile the inconsistencies he discovers. We have seen that it is inconsistent to assign probability $\frac{1}{3}$ to the event "one heads" and at the same time to assign probability $\frac{1}{4}$ to each of the events HT and TH, but we have given no reason for preferring either one of these assignments to the other. It is to this problem that we now turn our attention.

In our original discussion of the meaning of "weights" or probabilities, we emphasized that any probability is necessarily an expression of a personal judgment and is therefore necessarily *subjective* in the sense that two reasonable men may assign different probabilities to the same event. This by no means implies, however, that a reasonable man will assign probabilities *arbitrarily*.

Reasonable men base the probabilities which they assign to events in the real world on their experience with events in the real world, and when two reasonable men have had roughly the same experience with a certain kind of event they assign it roughly the same probability.

1.6.1   *Overwhelming Common Experience*

As an extreme example of this principle, consider the assessment of the probability of heads on the toss of a coin which has been very carefully inspected and found to be perfectly symmetric and which is to be tossed in such a way that it will spin an extremely large number of times before it falls. Although we may or may not have had direct experience with this particular coin and this particular tossing procedure, almost everyone has observed that other coins tossed in more or less the same way seem to turn up heads roughly half of the time. We have further observed that although the ratio of heads to tosses is often very far from $\frac{1}{2}$ in short sequences of tosses, it is usually much closer to $\frac{1}{2}$ in long sequences. Still further, we have observed that heads occur about as frequently on tosses which follow heads as on tosses which follow tails, and more generally that heads occur about half the time *whatever* the pattern of heads and tails on previous tosses. Finally, all this experience with coins agrees with our experience with other symmetric objects—all the above statements apply to the event "ace" on the roll of a perfectly symmetric die if $\frac{1}{6}$ is substituted for $\frac{1}{2}$, and so forth.

On the basis of all this experience we proceed to construct a *physical* theory of the behavior of a tossed coin; in other words, we proceed to make *predictions* about the behavior of a tossed coin.   This theory asserts that the fraction of tosses resulting in heads is almost certain to be almost exactly ½ if the coin is tossed indefinitely, and it asserts further that in a very long run half the heads will be followed by heads, half the runs of two heads will be followed by a third head, and so forth.   We expect, furthermore, that any reasonable man either will adopt this same theory on the basis of his own experience or will adopt it as soon as he is informed of the very great amount of experience which other people have had on the point.

Now such a theory or model of the real world says nothing directly about the *probability* of heads.   It predicts what would happen in a very large number of tosses and says nothing whatever about any individual toss.   Such a prediction is exactly analogous to a prediction that the average diameter of parts produced by a certain machine will be 1.037 inches, and it is obvious that a predicted average diameter and a probability are not the same thing.   On the other hand, a reasonable man will clearly take account of long-run relative frequency in assigning probabilities.   If he believes that a certain coin would fall heads half the time when tossed repeatedly under a certain set of conditions, and if he has no way of predicting which particular tosses will be heads, he will assign probability ½ to the event "heads" on any one toss—he will pay neither more nor less for a chance at a prize conditional on heads on a particular toss than he will pay for a chance at the same prize conditional on tails. In general, we shall assume it to be a characteristic of rational behavior that:

> If a person assessing the probability of a given event under a given set of conditions feels absolutely sure that the event would occur with relative frequency p in a very great number of trials made under these same conditions, he will assign probability p to the event.

It is important to make clear the meaning of the words "under these same conditions."   In one sense it is tautologically true that if conditions were *really* the same from trial to trial, the same event would always occur.   If a coin were tossed several times in *exactly* the same way, it would either always fall heads or always fall tails.   What we actually mean when we say that conditions are "the same" is that there is no *observable* difference from one trial to the next which *enables us to predict* the fall of the coin on any particular trial.

We are now able to say something definite about the probability which it is reasonable to assign to "one heads" in D'Alembert's problem. If we have adopted a model of coin behavior in which heads occur in the long run on one-half of all tosses and in which half the heads are followed by heads, and so forth, it is easy to see that in a long run of *pairs* of tosses the events *HH*, *HT*, *TH*, and *TT* will each occur $\frac{1}{4}$ of the time. Any reasonable man who has adopted this model of the behavior of a given coin will therefore assign the same probability to each of these events and therefore must assign probability $\frac{1}{2}$ rather than $\frac{1}{3}$ to the compound event "one heads." In actual practice, we would not even go through the process of first assigning a probability directly to "one heads" and then checking this against the implications of probabilities assigned to the four elementary events. We know in advance that our assignment of probabilities to the elementary events can be based on experience which is extremely extensive in comparison with the number of times that we have tossed a coin twice and counted the number of heads in the pair of tosses, and therefore we would start by assigning probabilities to the elementary events and stop when we had computed the probability which we had thus implicitly assigned to the event "one heads."

In more complex problems such as the scrap-allowance example we will proceed in the same general way: we will ask the businessman to assign probabilities to those events on which his experience bears most directly and we will then use the theory of probability to compute the probabilities of the events with which he has had less extensive experience. It is for this reason and this reason alone that the theory of probability is of use in making practical business decisions:

The theory of probability allows the businessman to assign probabilities to those events on which his experience and judgment bear most directly rather than to the events which will actually determine the profit or cost of his decision but with which he has had little or no direct experience.

1.6.2 Limited Experience

It is only rarely that experience with a given kind of event will be as overwhelming as it is for "heads" on the toss of a coin, but even when experience is limited it is still a guide to the rational assessment of probabilities. Suppose, for example, that we wish to assess the probability of ace on the roll of a die which has been deformed in such a way that it is no longer symmetric. In this situation general experience with rolled objects will usually lead a reasonable person to adopt a model of die behavior which is like the coin model except that the fraction of aces is unknown. Our experience is sufficient to lead us to predict that in the long run the relative frequency of ace will become and remain nearly equal to *some* fraction p, that ace will be followed by ace with this *same* relative frequency, and so forth; but our experience is *not* adequate for a prediction of the exact value of this frequency.

Obviously such a model does *not* tell us exactly what probability to assign to ace.   We can say that *if* we had had enough experience with the die to feel sure that the long-run relative frequency of ace would be .15, *then* we would assign probability .15 to ace on any one roll, and so forth; but our problem is not to make statements of this sort.   If the consequences of a decision depend on the occurrence of ace on the next roll of the die, we must assess the probability of this event in the light of whatever experience we actually have.   Two reasonable people may well disagree concerning the probability to be assigned to ace in a situation like this, since neither of them will have had any great amount of experience with the behavior of a die deformed in exactly the way this one is. Observe, however, that this does not mean that there is *no* relevant experience: if the deformation of the die is slight, we will *not* consider a person reasonable if he assigns probability .01 or .99 to ace.

1.6.3   Learning from Additional Experience

The case of the perfectly symmetric coin and the case of the deformed die differ not only in the amount of agreement to be expected in the initial assessment of the probabilities of heads or ace but also in the way in which further experience affects any one individual's assessments of these same probabilities on subsequent trials.

In the case of the perfectly symmetric coin, we might still assess the probability of heads on the next toss at ½ even though we had just observed a large number of consecutive heads or tails; our model of the long-run behavior of the coin rests on an extremely great amount of evidence and we may consider this new evidence negligible in comparison. In the case of the asymmetric die, on the contrary, we will use any experience we gather by rolling the die to modify the probability we originally assigned to ace.   Notice, however, that we usually will *not* simply equate the probability of ace to the fraction of aces observed in a limited number of rolls.   If we roll the die once and it comes up ace, we will not assign probability 1 to ace; if we roll it six times and get no ace, we will not assign probability 0 to ace.

Our assessment of the probability of ace will continue to be substantially influenced by our observation of the shape of the die, and the relative importance we attach to the observed shape of the die in comparison with the importance we attach to the observed frequencies is necessarily a matter of subjective judgment.

1.6.4   Application to Business Problems

In exceptional circumstances the probabilities involved in a business problem can be simply equated to "known" relative frequencies in the way probability ½ is assigned to heads on the toss of a very symmetric coin.   If 50 per cent of the last 100,000 parts produced by some machine have been defective, if we have no reason either in theory or in observation to believe that defectives occur in "streaks," and if a new production run is to be made under the same conditions as all these past runs, we will be strongly tempted to adopt a model of the behavior of the machine which is exactly like the model of coin behavior discussed above.   We will be willing to predict that 50 per cent of all future parts will be defective, that 50 per cent of the defectives will be followed by defectives, etc., and we will not change these predictions whatever the pattern of quality in the next few hundred pieces produced.   We will then be *justified* in assigning equal probabilities to all possible elementary events in the way we did in Section 1.5 above.

In the majority of cases, however, the problem will not be so simple. If the machine is new or has just been repaired, or if a new operator is employed or a slightly off-standard batch of raw material is received, we will be in the same position that we are when we assess the probability of ace on a slightly deformed die.   The probability assigned to defective on the first piece will depend on "judgment" in the sense that two reasonable men may well assign different values.   This probability will be revised as more experience is gained, and again judgment will determine the relative weights given to the observed frequencies on the one hand and to other kinds of evidence on the other.

1.6.5   Mental Processes and Relative Frequency

The examples which we have discussed above of the way in which models predicting relative frequencies can be of use in assessing probabilities all involved the relative frequencies of physical phenomena, but the same kind of argument can be of use in connection with mental phenomena.   Frequency models of mental processes usually involve uncertainty about the actual value of the long-run frequency in exactly the same way that most frequency models of physical processes do; but in both cases the frequency model is useful even though it is not completely decisive.   The value of a large tract of timber is often assessed by having it visually inspected by an experienced timber cruiser whose judgment has previously been calibrated by comparing his estimates of the amount of timber in a number of tracts with accurate measurements made on the same tracts.   The probability that his present estimate will be low by 10 per cent, say, is then assessed largely on the basis of the relative frequency of errors of this magnitude on previous occasions.

In the same way a sales manager who bases sales forecasts on his "feel of the market" can very usefully be treated as a "process."   If we have extensive records of the errors he has made in his past forecasts, we will assess the probability that his current forecast will be low by 10 per cent almost entirely on the basis of the relative frequency with which this event occurred in past forecasts.   If on the other hand we have very little previous experience with his forecasts, or if the nature of the product or the market has been radically changed, we will have to make much larger use of other kinds of experience in assessing this probability, just as we have to depart from exclusive reliance on observed frequencies when we assess probabilities concerning the performance of a new machine or of an old machine under new conditions.

1.7   Relative Frequency and the Mathematical Theory of Probability

If we think back to the three axioms of the mathematical theory of probability as stated in Section 1.5 above, we will see that relative frequencies—either those predicted for the long run or those actually observed in a finite number of trials—are numbers which agree with these axioms.   The relative frequency of any event is a number between 0 and 1 inclusive, the sum of the relative frequencies of all possible events is 1, and the relative frequency of a compound event such as "either ace or deuce" is the sum of the relative frequencies of the mutually exclusive events of which it is composed.

This means that the theory of probability can be used to deduce relative frequencies from other relative frequencies in exactly the same way that it can be used to deduce probabilities (i.e. subjective weights) from other probabilities.   When we first discussed the scrap-allowance example, in Section 1.5, we assumed that the manufacturer assigned equal *probability* to every possible elementary event, i.e., to every possible sequence of 180 *g*'s and *d*'s, and from these probability assignments we deduced that the probability of the compound event "more than 80 defectives" was .922.   We pointed out in Section 1.6.4, however, that the assignment of equal probabilities to the elementary events was warranted only on the basis of a "model" of the production process which implies that these events would occur with equal *relative frequencies* in a very great number of runs of 180 pieces, and this gives us an alternative way of expressing the same calculation.   Given that the elementary events occur with equal relative frequencies, the theory of probability can be used to show that the *relative frequency* of the compound event "more than 80 defectives" must be .922; we can then assess the probability of this compound event by equating it to its *own* relative frequency.

A relationship of this kind between probabilities and relative frequencies can be imagined even in a problem where the probabilities of the elementary events have *not* been assessed by reference to any frequency model. In other words, we can *visualize* all the probabilities involved in *any* problem as being equal to relative frequencies in an imaginary sequence of trials whether or not the particular trial with which we are dealing is of such a nature that it could conceivably be repeated. Since relations among actual numbers of events are easier to grasp than relations among abstract numbers called probabilities, we shall often make use of this device to "explain" the results of calculations involving probabilities; but the student must always remember that such "explanations" do not imply either that probabilities *are* relative frequencies or that they are necessarily *equal* to *real* relative frequencies.

PROBLEMS

1. Five different lotteries *i* through *v* are to be conducted according to rules given below. Any one of these lotteries will pay the player either a $100 cash prize or nothing. Answer the following three questions for each of the five lotteries separately.

a. How much would you personally be willing to pay for the right to play?

b. What probability would you assign to the event "win" if you played?

c. Try to imagine what would happen if the lottery were repeated over and over with the same player, not necessarily yourself, and say what you can about the relative frequency with which the player would win in the long run. To what extent does your answer depend on the way in which the person conducting the lottery behaves? On the way in which the player behaves?

Description of the Five Lotteries

i. Fifty red and fifty black balls will be placed in an urn and stirred thoroughly. The player will then be allowed to draw one ball without looking and will receive the prize if the ball he draws is red.

ii. Same as *i* except that the person conducting the lottery may place in the urn any mixture of red and black balls that he pleases and the player will *not* be told what the mixture actually is.

iii. Same as *i* except that the player may call either "red" or "black" just before drawing the ball and will receive the prize if the ball is of the color he calls.

iv. Same as *ii* except that the player may call his color.

v. Same as *iv* except that the player must toss a coin and call "red" if the coin falls heads, "black" if it falls tails.

CHAPTER 2

Expected Value and Utility †

At the beginning of Chapter 1 we said that any problem of decision under uncertainty can always be described by a payoff table in which there is a column for every possible *act* and a row for every possible *event;* each cell in the table describes the *consequence* of a particular act given a particular event. We said that we would try to find a way of choosing among the acts in the face of uncertainty concerning the events by:

1. Assigning a definite numerical *value* to every consequence (every cell in the table),
2. Assigning a definite numerical *weight* to every event,
3. Evaluating each act by taking a *weighted average* of all the different values which might result from that act.

In the remainder of Chapter 1 we concentrated our attention on the second of these three steps; we now go on to consider how we can carry out the first step in such a way that the result of the third step will in fact be a "correct" guide to action.

2.1 Definitions of Conditional and Expected Value

Conditional Value. Each of the values which have to be assigned in step 1 of the procedure outlined just above is the value which some particular act will have *on condition* that some particular event occurs, and therefore these values will be called *conditional values.* We define

Conditional value of an act given a particular event: the value which the person responsible for a choice among acts attaches to the consequence which that particular act will have if that particular event occurs.

Expected Value. After probabilities have been assigned to events in step 2 of the procedure we propose to use, step 3 consists in obtaining a *single* value for each act by taking a weighted average of all the various

† The contents of Sections 2.3 and 2.4 of this chapter are not required in any subsequent chapter.

24

conditional values of that act, each conditional value being weighted by the *probability* that the act will in fact have that value. The standard name for an average in which all possible values are weighted by their probabilities is *expected value;* we define

> *Expected value* of an act: a weighted average of *all* the conditional values of the act, each conditional value being weighted by its probability.

Such a weighted average is also called the *expectation* of the conditional values of the act.

Mistakes are bound to occur unless we adopt some kind of systematic procedure for the actual computation of expected values according to the definition just given. We have already said that the analysis of any decision problem must start by (1) drawing up a *payoff table* showing the *conditional value* of every act given every event and (2) assigning a *probability* to every event in the payoff table. After both these steps have been completed, we shall take the acts of the payoff table *one at a time* and compute the expected value of each one on a work sheet like the one shown in Table 2.1, filling out this work sheet according to the following rules:

1. List every possible *event* in column 1.
2. Enter the *probability* of each event in column 2.
3. Enter the *conditional value* of the act given each event in column 3.
4. For each event *multiply* probability times conditional value and enter the product in column 4, *taking care to preserve the algebraic sign.*
5. *Add* the products in column 4 *with due regard to algebraic sign.*

Table 2.1
Computation of the Expected Value of an Act

Event	Probability	Value	
		Conditional	Expected
A	.3	+5	+1.50
B	.3	+3	+ .90
C	.4	−4	−1.60
	1.0		+ .80

2.2 Expected Monetary Value

The definition of expected value which we have given above applies no matter what *kind* of value is assigned to each consequence in a decision problem. If in an inventory problem like the one discussed in Section 1.1.1 we take the net cash receipts shown in Table 1.1 as representing the value of each consequence, then a computation like the one illustrated in Table 2.1 will give us the expected net cash receipts of any act. If we value each consequence according to the number of units sold, application of the same rules of computation will give us the expected number of units sold; and so forth. We now turn to our real problem, which is to find out exactly how each consequence must be valued if the businessman is to feel that the act with the highest expected value is really the act he wants to choose.

Our first inclination, of course, is to think that at least in most business problems the value of a consequence can properly be represented by a sum of money, and our first step will be to inquire to what extent this proposition is true. What we shall see is that while expected monetary value is in fact a valid guide to action in the great majority of practical business problems, there are some very important problems in which it would be an extremely misleading guide.

2.2.1   The Importance of the Individual's Attitude toward Risk

Consider two businessmen each of whom believes that if he submits the proper proposal he has a 50-50 chance of being awarded a contract which is sure to yield a $35,000 gross profit, and suppose that preparation of the proposal will cost either of these men $10,000 out of pocket. The expected monetary value of the act "submit the proposal" is shown in Table 2.2 to be a positive $7500 for either of these two men while the

Table 2.2
Expected Monetary Value of Making the Proposal

Event	Probability	Monetary value	
		Conditional	Expected
Get contract	½	+$25,000	+$12,500
Do not get contract	½	− 10,000	− 5,000
	1		+ $7,500

corresponding figure for not making the proposal is obviously $0, and yet the two men may quite reasonably come to opposite conclusions. If one of them is extremely hard pressed for cash and could easily be bankrupted by the loss of $10,000, he may well decide to let this opportunity go; if the other man has adequate working capital he may with equally good reason decide to make the proposal.

This example obviously implies that there are situations in which expected monetary value is not a valid guide to action if by "valid" we mean a guide which accords with the businessman's own judgment and preferences, but if we look a little more closely we will see that it implies much more than this. What must be decided is simply whether it is worth risking a loss of $10,000 in order to have an even chance of a $25,000 profit, and there is *no conceivable* computation or method of analysis which will be of the least help to anyone in making such a decision—it *must* turn *entirely* on a direct expression of personal preference.

The student may well ask at this point how we propose to help a businessman in any situation whatever if we can be of no help at all in a situation as simple as the one just described, and the question deserves an answer before we proceed further. The answer is this: we propose to show the businessman how he can make a fully reasoned analysis of a *very complex* decision problem—one in which there are many possible acts each of which has many possible consequences—by in effect reducing this very complex problem to a number of separate problems every one of which is just as simple as the one we have just discussed.

Suppose, for example, that our two businessmen are given the opportunity of submitting proposals for another contract and that in this case they both assign to the act "submit the proposal" the whole set of possible consequences and associated probabilities shown in Table 2.3.

Table 2.3
Description of Act "Submit the Proposal"

Event	Consequence	Probability
A	+$25,000	.1
B	+ 20,000	.1
C	+ 15,000	.1
D	+ 10,000	.1
E	+ 5,000	.1
F	− 10,000	.5
		1.0

Comparison of this table with Table 2.2 shows that the act "submit" is clearly less desirable in the present example than in the original example, and consequently the businessman who was hard pressed for cash and therefore refused to submit the proposal in the original example can quickly arrive at the same conclusion in the present example; in other words, he can solve a complex decision problem by referring it to a simple decision problem in which he can easily see exactly what is at stake. The choice is by no means so clear for the other businessman, however, and he *will* be substantially aided if we can find some systematic technique of analysis which in effect reduces his complex problem to a simple problem in which he can see exactly what is at stake. We shall now investigate the conditions under which the computation of expected monetary value will be a suitable technique.

2.2.2 Conditions under Which Expected Monetary Value Is a Valid Guide to Action

If we think for a moment about what we know about the way in which businessmen in fact make very simple decisions under uncertainty, we will realize that whether or not they formally compute expected monetary value they act in accordance with expected monetary value when the amounts at stake are not too large. If a businessman believes that there is 1 chance in 1000 that his million-dollar plant will burn down during the next year, he may be willing to pay $1500 as a premium for an insurance policy even though the expected monetary value of his loss if he does not insure is only $1000; but if the same businessman believes that he runs a 1-in-1000 chance of suffering $100 worth of damage to his machinery because of tramp iron in a particular batch of raw material, he is very likely to be unwilling to pay a cent more than the $.10 expected value of this loss for insurance against it. Remembering that a cash outlay is to be given a minus sign, we see that in the former case he chooses an act with a monetary value of $-\$1500$ even though the alternative act has the greater monetary value $-\$1000$ but that in the latter case he says that he will take the act with expected monetary value $-\$.10$ if the monetary value of the other act is the least amount lower.

This general kind of behavior is not restricted to situations in which the monetary values of all possible consequences are negative or at best zero. A businessman with net assets of $500,000 who must choose between a deal which is certain to result in a profit of $50 and another which in his eyes is equally likely to result in a profit of $0 or a profit of $110 is likely to choose the latter act in accordance with the fact that its expected monetary value is $55; but if this same businessman is given the happy opportunity to choose between a deal which is certain to net him $5 million and another which has equal chances of yielding $0 and $11 million, he is very likely to take the $5 million.

To sum up: businessmen tend to treat acts which must have one or the other of just two possible consequences as being "really worth" their expected monetary value as long as the worst of the two consequences is not too bad and the best of the consequences is not too good. This immediately suggests that a businessman who must evaluate an act or acts with a great number of possible consequences can decide whether or not he should use expected monetary value as the basis of his evaluation by looking only at the best and the worst of the consequences and asking himself whether he would act in accordance with expected monetary value if these were the *only* possible consequences. More specifically, it would seem reasonable for a man faced with a very complex decision problem to decide whether or not he should take expected monetary value as his guide by applying the following very simple

> *Test for the Validity of Expected Monetary Value as a Guide to Action:*
> Expected monetary value should be used as the decision criterion in any real decision problem, however complex, if the person responsible for the decision would use it as his criterion in choosing between (1) an act which is certain to result in receipt or payment of a definite amount of cash and (2) an act which will result in either the *best* or the *worst* of all the possible consequences of the real decision problem.

Later in the chapter we shall see that the correctness of this rule can be "proved" in the sense that we can show that any person who does not follow the rule will end up by making choices which in the opinion of most reasonable people are logically inconsistent.

As an illustration of the application of this rule, let us return to the businessman who must decide whether or not to submit a proposal for a contract when the possible consequences of this act are as described in Table 2.3. The best and worst possible consequences of this act are +$25,000 and −$10,000; and since the consequence of not submitting the proposal is certain to be $0, the two consequences previously named are the best and worst of the entire decision problem. As an initial test, the businessman can therefore ask himself the following question: "Suppose that *I* had to choose between (1) receiving a definite amount of cash and (2) being awarded a contract such that *I* assigned probability ½ to the consequence +$25,000 and probability ½ to the consequence −$10,000, making the expected monetary value of the contract $7500. Would *I* (*a*) prefer the contract to the cash if the specified amount of cash was less than $7500 and (*b*) prefer the cash to the contract if the specified amount of cash was over $7500?" If the answer to this question is yes, expected monetary value will almost certainly be a correct guide to this businessman's action in his real problem; but in principle he must go on to ask himself whether he would answer yes to *any* question of this type *whatever* the probability he assigned to the $25,000 profit. He should, for example, suppose that he had already signed a contract with probability .1 assigned to the consequence +$25,000 and probability .9 assigned to −$10,000, so that the expected monetary value of the contract was −$6500, and then ask himself whether in fact he would (*a*) prefer to pay any amount of cash less than $6500 for a release rather than perform the contract but (*b*) prefer to perform the contract rather than pay any sum greater than $6500 for a release.

If the businessman's answer to any of these questions is no, a little common sense is required. Such an answer implies that expected monetary value will not give an *exactly accurate evaluation* of any act which may result in the $25,000 profit or the $10,000 loss, but this does not mean that expected monetary value will necessarily lead to the *wrong choice of act*. In our example, the expected monetary value of the act "submit the proposal" is +$2500, as shown in Table 2.4, and this is very substantially greater than the value $0 of the act "do not submit the proposal." If then the businessman feels that he would value a contract which gave him even chances of +$25,000 and −$10,000 at only slightly less than its expected monetary value of +$7500, he can feel quite sure that the act "submit the proposal" in the real problem is better than an act which is certain to have the value $0 even though he could not be sure that it would be better than an act which was certain to have the value $2400.

Table 2.4

Event	Probability	Monetary value	
		Conditional	Expected
A	.1	+$25,000	+$2500
B	.1	+ 20,000	+ 2000
C	.1	+ 15,000	+ 1500
D	.1	+ 10,000	+ 1000
E	.1	+ 5,000	+ 500
F	.5	− 10,000	− 5000
	1.0		+$2500

2.2.3 Delegation of Routine Decision Making

Systematic use of expected monetary value actually simplifies practical business decisions even more than this example suggests, and for two reasons.

1. The person who is ultimately responsible for a certain class of decisions does not have to look at each decision problem individually in order to decide whether expected monetary value is a proper guide to action, as we can easily see by considering the decision which had to be made by the retailer of the example originally discussed in Section 1.1.1. This retailer will presumably have larger numbers of decisions of exactly this same kind to make daily, and he can settle the question of the validity of expected monetary value as a guide to all these decisions once and for all by simply asking himself how large the worst possible loss and the

greatest possible profit would have to be before he would *refuse* to use expected monetary value as a guide in a simple two-consequence problem. If he has $10,000 of working capital, he may well decide that he would take expected monetary value as a guide in any inventory-control problem where the worst possible loss did not exceed, say, $100 and where the greatest possible profit did not exceed, say, $500. If his preferences are of this sort, then a simple statement of policy to this effect will enable his subordinates to solve virtually all of his stock-control problems without having to ask him any further questions about the "value of money," while at the same time he can feel absolutely sure that his preferences are respected.

2. In principle, the person ultimately responsible for a class of risky decisions must himself evaluate the probabilities or weights which he himself attaches to the various possible events in any problem, but this evaluation can also be delegated in the great majority of practical business problems. In most routine problems the executive would follow some systematic procedure for assessing these probabilities if he did assess them himself; and whenever this is true he can delegate the assessment by simply prescribing the assessment procedure or even the general type of assessment procedure to be used. Thus probabilities may be assessed in routine inventory-control problems by examining the record of demand over the past several periods and using this record in some systematic way; probabilities in routine quality-control problems may be assessed by standard statistical procedures which we shall study later in this course, and so forth.

Once the executive has specified the range of problems within which he wants to have expected monetary value taken as a guide to action and the procedures by which probabilities are to be assessed in routine situations, he will be free to make a careful personal analysis of those problems where such an analysis is really worth the effort: problems in which the possible losses and gains are so great that expected monetary value ceases to be a proper guide to action, and problems in which business judgment of a kind not expected of clerks and statisticians is required to assess the probabilities of the events.

2.3 Expected Utility

In the remainder of this chapter we shall study the problem of choice in situations where the amounts at stake are so large that the test described in Section 2.2.2 tells the businessman that he should *not* use expected monetary value as a guide to action, and we shall see that even in these situations the businessman can reach a fully reasoned solution of the most complex problem by deciding how he would want to act in a number of very simple problems.   More specifically, we shall see that his decisions in the simple problems can be used as the basis for assigning a *utility value* to each possible consequence in the real problem and that once this has been done the real problem can be solved by the mere mechanical computation of the *expected utility* of every possible act.

This means that the *only* difference between analysis of a problem in which expected monetary value is a valid guide to action and analysis of a problem in which it is not is that in the latter case we must replace the monetary payoff table by a table showing conditional utilities.   Once this has been done, probabilities are assigned to the events in the utility table exactly as they would be if the table showed monetary values rather than utilities, and the expected utility of each act is computed from the conditional utilities in exactly the same way that expected monetary value is computed from conditional monetary values.   For this reason we shall talk exclusively in terms of the more familiar monetary values in all future chapters, leaving it to the student to remember that in any real problem he must apply the test of Section 2.2.2 and substitute utilities for monetary values if necessary.   It follows that the remaining sections of the present chapter can be read just as well at the end of this course as at the present time.

2.3.1   Outline of the Method of Analysis

Suppose that the businessman with limited working capital who refused the contracts described in Tables 2.2 and 2.4 is offered two other contracts to whose possible consequences he assigns the probabilities shown in Table 2.5.   It is easy to calculate the expected *monetary* value of contract M as +\$3825 and that of contract N as +\$2025, and the expected monetary value of taking neither contract is obviously \$0; but we assume that the businessman tells us that he would certainly *not* be willing to accept any deal in which there was an even chance of making or losing \$9000, and this by the rule of Section 2.2.2 means that expected monetary value is of no help to him in choosing among the three acts actually open to him.

Table 2.5

Contract M			Contract N		
Event	Probability	Consequence	Event	Probability	Consequence
A	.30	+\$9000	Q	.25	+\$7500
B	.45	+ 7500	R	.60	+ 2000
C	.25	− 9000	S	.15	− 7000
	1.00			1.00	

If the two contracts offered to the businessman had been those described in Table 2.6 rather than those described in Table 2.5, his decision problem would obviously have been much easier. Each of these contracts has only two possible consequences and these consequences are the same for both contracts; the *only* difference between the two contracts is in the probabilities attached to the consequences, and it is obvious that the more desirable contract is the one with the higher probability of obtaining the $10,000 profit. All that the businessman has to do to make a completely reasoned analysis of this problem and reach a decision is to make up his mind whether or not he prefers a certainty of $0 to the combination of a .8 chance of $+$10,000 and a .2 chance of $-$10,000 which he will obtain if he accepts contract X.

Table 2.6

Contract X		Contract Y	
Consequence	Probability	Consequence	Probability
$+$10,000	.8	$+$10,000	.7
$-$ 10,000	.2	$-$ 10,000	.3
	1.0		1.0

We shall now show that the problem of deciding whether to take contract M, contract N, or neither can be reduced to a number of problems every one of which is just as simple as the problem of choosing between contract X and $0 cash certain. To do this we proceed as follows.

1. Simply to make the reasoning concrete, we *represent* each real contract by an *equivalent lottery* which in the businessman's own judgment has exactly the same value as the real contract, whatever that value may be.

2. We select two "reference consequences," one of which is at least as bad as the worst possible consequence in the real decision problem and one of which is at least as good as the best, and we show that each of the lotteries representing real contracts must have the same value in the businessman's own judgment as a ticket with a certain probability of winning in a *reference lottery* in which these two "reference consequences" are the *only* prizes.

Once this has been done, all that is left is to select the real contract which corresponds to the *highest probability of winning* in the reference lottery.

2.3.2   The Equivalent Lotteries

As our first step in the procedure we have just outlined we represent the real contract M by the following equivalent lottery. An urn contains 1000 balls of which 300 are marked A, 450 are marked B, and 250 are marked C. A single ball is to be drawn from this urn; and *if* the businessman chooses to participate in the lottery he will *receive* $9000 if the ball is marked A or $7500 if it is marked B but will be obliged to *pay the bank* $9000 if the ball is marked C. The businessman is to imagine that this imaginary drawing will be made in such a way that every ball has an equal chance of being drawn, whereupon he will see that the probability of winning any one of the three prizes in the lottery is exactly the same as the probability which *he himself has assigned* to obtaining the same prize by signing contract M. We may therefore say that *this imaginary lottery M has exactly the same value as the real contract M in the businessman's own opinion.*

We next proceed to represent contract N by an equivalent lottery N involving an urn of appropriate composition—*not* the same urn that represents contract M. The two urns are both described in Table 2.7, and the

Table 2.7
Equivalent Lottery Tickets

Lottery M			Lottery N		
Label on balls	Number of balls	Prize	Label on balls	Number of balls	Prize
A	300	$+$9000	Q	250	$+$7500
B	450	$+$ 7500	R	600	$+$ 2000
C	250	$-$ 9000	S	150	$-$ 7000
	1000			1000	

student will see that we have completed the first step in our procedure: we have reduced the businessman's problem of choosing between contracts M and N to a completely equivalent problem of choosing between lotteries M and N.

2.3.3   Evaluation of Consequences in Terms of Tickets in a Reference Lottery

We must next select two "reference consequences," one at least as good as the best consequence in the decision problem and one at least as bad as the worst. The best and worst of the real consequences are respectively +$9000 and −$9000, and these could be taken as the reference consequences; but just to emphasize that we are not bound to this choice we shall actually take +$10,000 and −$10,000 as our reference consequences.

We next set up our *reference lottery* by imagining an urn containing a number of balls some of which are marked "win," the remainder "lose." A ticket in *this* lottery entitles the holder to receive $10,000 if a ball marked "win" is drawn from this urn, but obliges him to pay the bank $10,000 if the ball is marked "lose."

We are now able *to evaluate each possible consequence* in the decision problem by equating it to a ticket in a reference lottery in which the mix of balls is such as to give the "right" probability of winning in the *businessman's own opinion*. Starting with the consequence $0 of the act *"sign neither contract"* or the equivalent act *"accept neither lottery M nor lottery N,"* we address the businessman as follows.

"Imagine that you have refused both lottery *M* and lottery *N* but that you are now offered, at a price of exactly $0, a ticket in a *reference lottery* in which you will either win $10,000 or lose $10,000. Just how good would the chances of winning have to be to make you *just indifferent* whether you took this free ticket or not?"

The businessman will see at once that the *expected monetary value* of this ticket will be equal to its $0 price if the chances of winning are 50 in 100; but we shall imagine that he would by no means accept the ticket if these were in fact the chances of winning. He feels that losing $10,000 is a very good deal worse than winning $10,000 is good; and we shall therefore suppose that after careful reflection he decides that he would barely be willing to accept the ticket if the chances of winning were 85 in 100—he *really* dislikes the idea of losing $10,000. Given this answer, we can say that *the consequence $0 has exactly the same value in this particular businessman's own personal opinion as a ticket in a reference lottery with probability $\pi = .85$ of winning.*

We next make a similar evaluation of the consequence +$9000, which may occur if the businessman chooses act *M*, by asking him: "Imagine that you have already accepted lottery *M* in Table 2.7, that a ball marked *A* has already been drawn from the urn, and that you have accordingly received the $9000 prize. Imagine further that you are now offered a chance to exchange this $9000 for a ticket in a reference lottery in which you will either win $10,000 or lose $10,000. How good would the chances of winning in this reference lottery have to be to make you *just indifferent* about trading your $9000 cash for the lottery ticket?"

We can imagine the businessman starting to think out his answer by quickly computing that the *expected monetary value* of the ticket in the reference lottery would be exactly $9000 if the chances of winning were 95 in 100, since

$$.95(+\$10{,}000) + .05(-\$10{,}000) = \$9000;$$

but we already know that this particular businessman is very averse to risk, and we shall therefore suppose that he finally answers that he would be barely willing to pay $9000 for the ticket if the chances of winning were 99 in 100.

We have thus established that *the consequence +$9000 has exactly the same value in this particular businessman's own personal opinion as a ticket in a reference lottery with probability $\pi = .99$ of winning;* and without repeating the details of the questioning procedure we shall suppose that we can similarly establish that +$7500 is equivalent to a reference lottery with $\pi = .98$, while +$2000 is equivalent to $\pi = .90$. Our man is *very* averse to risk.

We must now evaluate the *negative* consequences which may occur if the businessman chooses act M or N, and to do so we start with the following question.

"Imagine that you have already accepted a ticket in lottery M, that the ball has already been drawn from the urn, and that you have unfortunately found yourself with an *obligation to pay* $9000 to the bank. Imagine further that someone offers to relieve you of this obligation provided that you will accept in its stead a lottery ticket which may win you $10,000 but may oblige you to pay out $10,000 instead of $9000. How good would the changes of winning have to be to make you just indifferent between (1) actually paying the $9000 you now owe and (2) accepting the ticket?"

The businessman may calculate that the expected monetary value of the ticket would be −$9000 if the chances of winning were 5 in 100, since

$$.05(+\$10{,}000) + .95(-\$10{,}000) = -\$9000,$$

but if losing the extra $1000 would put him in a really tight position, he will not be at all willing to accept the ticket in the reference lottery with the chances of winning being actually .05. We shall suppose that he finally says he would be barely willing to trade if the chances of winning were .24. We have thus established that for *this* businessman the consequence −$9000 is equivalent to a reference lottery with $\pi = .24$, and we shall suppose that we similarly establish that −$7000 is equivalent to $\pi = .50$.

All of our results to date are summarized in Table 2.8, where we replace the monetary *consequences* of Table 2.7 by the π's of the equivalent *reference* lottery.

Table 2.8

Lottery M			Lottery N		
Label on ball	Number of balls	Reference π	Label on ball	Number of balls	Reference π
A	300	.99	Q	250	.98
B	450	.98	R	600	.90
C	250	.24	S	150	.50
	1000			1000	

Act "do nothing": $\pi = .85$

2.3.4   Reduction of Lotteries to Reference Lotteries

We now come to the last stage of the procedure outlined in Section 2.3.1: we must reduce the "complicated" and incomparable lotteries M and N to *reference* lotteries which *can* be directly compared in terms of the probability of winning.

Starting with act M and event A in Table 2.8, we argue as follows. *If* the businessman takes lottery M and if the ball which is drawn from the urn is one of the 300 marked A, he has already told us that he would value the consequence of A neither more nor less than a ticket in a reference lottery with probability $\pi = .99$ of winning. Such a lottery can be constructed by drawing one ball from among 300 balls 297 of which are marked win and 3 marked lose, and we now come to the crucial step in our reasoning. We assume that

> Since *this* businessman is just indifferent between the actual consequence of drawing a ball marked A and a ticket in a reference lottery with 297 balls marked "win" and 3 marked "lose," the value of lottery M will be completely unchanged for *this* businessman if we remove the 300 balls which are marked A from the urn for lottery M and replace them with 300 balls of which 297 are marked "win $10,000$" and 3 are marked "lose $10,000$."

By similar reasoning we will leave the value of lottery M unchanged if we replace the 450 balls marked B by 450 balls of which $.98 \times 450 = 441$ are marked "win $10,000$" and 9 are marked "lose $10,000$"; and the value of M will still be unchanged if we replace the 250 balls marked C by $.24 \times 250 = 60$ balls marked "win $10,000$" and 190 marked "lose $10,000$."

Without in any way changing the value of lottery M for this particular businessman, we have now reduced it to a form in which *it will result,* *not in any of its three original consequences, but in one or the other of our two reference consequences.* If we count up the number of winning balls, we find there are $297 + 441 + 60 = 798$ out of the 1000 total; and one conclusion emerges immediately. Since the probability of winning in lottery M is only $\pi = {}^{798}\!/_{1000} = .798$, whereas this businessman has already told us that he would be barely willing to accept a ticket at a price of $0 if the probability of winning were $\pi = .85$, we can say that $0 cash certain *should* logically be worth more to this businessman than lottery M. Then since lottery M has the same value as contract M in the real problem and the real act "do nothing" is certain to have the consequence $0, it follows that the businessman *should not* sign contract M if he wants to behave in a way which is *logically consistent with his own basic judgments and preferences.*

It is still possible, of course, that the *other* contract is *better* than "do nothing," and it turns out that it actually is, although not by much. We leave it to the student to show that lottery N can be reduced to a reference lottery in which the probability of winning is

$$\pi = {}^{860}\!/_{1000} = .86,$$

which is just slightly better than the $\pi = .85$ which is equivalent to "do nothing."

2.3.5   Utility

At the beginning of this section we said that when expected monetary value was not a valid guide to action the person responsible for a decision could always find a valid guide by assigning utility values to the various possible consequences of his acts and then choosing the act with the highest expected utility. We shall now see that this is simply another way of describing the calculation of the π's of the several reference lotteries to which the several real-world acts can be reduced.

In Table 2.9 we show the *same* calculation of the reference π corre-

Table 2.9
Evaluation of Act M

Label	Number N	P	Reference π	Number marked "win $10,000" N	P	π	N	$P\pi$
A	$1000 \times$	.30	.99	$1000 \times .30 \times .99$		$=$	$1000 \times$	.297
B	$1000 \times$	.45	.98	$1000 \times .45 \times .98$		$=$	$1000 \times$	.441
C	$1000 \times$	.25	.24	$1000 \times .25 \times .24$		$=$	$1000 \times$	.060
	$1000 \times$	1.00					$1000 \times$	.798

sponding to lottery M which we carried out in the text of the preceding section, the only difference being that we have written the number of A balls in the form $1000 \times .30$ rather than in the form 300, and similarly for other numbers of balls. It is completely obvious at once that the fact that we had $N = 1000$ balls in the urn is irrelevant to the final probability of winning $\pi = .798$; it is only the *proportions* P and π which count. Now P is simply the original *probability* of each *event* and π is simply the *break-even probability* which makes a reference lottery just equivalent to each *consequence*. Since it is customary in technical subjects to assign curious names to things, we may if we like give the name "utility" to these "break-even probabilities" π and say, for example, that the *utility* of the consequence $+\$9000$ corresponding to act M and event A is .99.

Now the utility π attached to any act-event combination can if we like be called the *conditional* "value" of that act if that event occurs; and then, following the definition of expected value in Section 2.1, we can say that the expected value or *expected utility* of any act is the number found by multiplying each conditional utility by the corresponding probability and adding the products. The last column of Table 2.9 shows that the result $\pi = .798$, which gives the probability of winning in a reference lottery that is just equivalent to act M, is exactly such a sum of products—i.e., *the expected utility of act M is* .798; and since we have already seen that, to be logically self-consistent, the businessman *should* choose the act which corresponds to the *highest* probability of winning in a reference lottery, we can say that

> Any decision maker who wishes to choose among acts in a logically self-consistent manner must choose the act which has the greatest expected utility.

2.3.6 Establishment of Utility Curves

The way in which we have hitherto questioned the businessman of our example has served the purpose of making clear the reason why an intelligent businessman will *want* to choose the act with the highest expected utility, but is actually a very poor way of proceeding in practice because it forces the businessman to evaluate lotteries with extreme probabilities such as $\pi = .99$ and it is very difficult for most people to do this. A much better quantification of a businessman's really basic attitudes toward risk and uncertainty can be obtained by proceeding as follows.

1. We start exactly as in Section 2.3.3 by asking what the π of a reference lottery would have to be to make the businessman just willing to accept a free ticket.

2. We then ask a series of questions about gambles in all of which

there is an *even* chance of winning either some prize or *nothing*, since such gambles are in general the easiest kind to evaluate.

Thus suppose that our businessman has answered our first question as before and told us that the utility of the consequence $0 is $\pi = .85$. We know automatically that the utility of the consequence +$10,000 is $\pi = 1$, since *anyone* would be willing to pay $10,000 for a lottery ticket which is sure to win $10,000; and similarly we know that the utility of −$10,000 is 0. We can now proceed as follows.

We first ask the businessman how large a premium he would pay for insurance against a $10,000 loss if he felt that there was an *even* chance that this loss would occur. From his previous answers that the utility of −$10,000 is 0 and that the utility of $0 is .85, we know that the expected utility of *not* insuring is $\frac{1}{2}(0) + \frac{1}{2}(.85) = .425$; and if he now answers this new question by saying that a loss of $10,000 would put him in so tight a position that he would be willing to pay up to, say, $7700 for insurance against it, then we have established that the utility of −$7700 is .425.

Now that we know the utility of −$7700, we can calculate the expected utility of *not* insuring against an even chance of losing $7700; it is $\frac{1}{2}(.425) + \frac{1}{2}(.85) = .6375$. We therefore next ask the businessman how much he would just be willing to pay for insurance against *this* risk; and if he answers that he would be just willing to pay $5200, we have established that the utility of −$5200 is .6375.

By next asking about insurance against a 50-50 chance of losing $5200, and continuing in this way to build on each previous answer, we can end up by establishing the utilities of a large number of *negative* consequences or losses.

We then turn to *positive* consequences or profits and proceed similarly. The utility of a deal in which the businessman feels that he has an even chance of *winning* either $10,000 or $0 can be calculated as

Table 2.10

Question number	Gamble between		Utility π	Equivalent consequence
	−$10,000 and	+$10,000	0	−$10,000
	− 10,000	+ 10,000	1	+ 10,000
1	− 10,000	+ 10,000	.85	0
2	− 10,000	0	.425	− 7,700
3	− 7,700	0	.6375	− 5,200
4	− 5,200	0	.74375	− 3,100
5	0	+ 10,000	.925	+ 3,300
6	0	+ 3,300	.8875	+ 1,600
7	0	+ 1,600	.86875	+ 600

½(.85) + ½(1) = .925; and if the businessman tells us that he would be just willing to exchange such a deal for receipt of $3300 certain, we have established that the utility of +$3300 is .925.   We next ask about the cash value of a 50-50 chance of winning $3300 or $0, which has a utility of ½(.85) + ½(.925) = .8875; and we then make use of this answer to obtain the utility of another consequence, and so forth.

Suppose then that our successive questions have established the utilities shown in Table 2.10.   If now we plot each utility against the corresponding consequence, we obtain the points shown as heavy dots in Figure 2.1, and we can then fair in a smooth curve and read from it *this* businessman's utility for *any* monetary consequence between −$10,000 and +$10,000.

> Such a procedure makes it easy to evaluate utilities in problems where there are hundreds of possible consequences and where it would therefore be completely impossible for the businessman to take the time to assign a utility π to each consequence individually.

2.3.7   *Differing Attitudes toward Risk*

In Figure 2.2 we reproduce with the label *A* the utility curve of the businessman whose preferences in risky situations we have been examining thus far, and we also show utility curves which we might have obtained from two *other* businessmen with quite *different* preferences in risky situations.   Utility as we have defined it above is to be read from the *left*-hand vertical scale in this figure; the use of the *right*-hand scale will be explained later on.

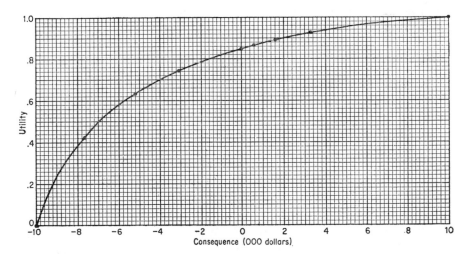

Figure 2.1. Utilities of consequences from −$10,000 to +$10,000.

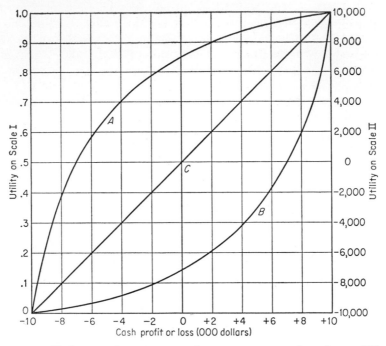

Figure 2.2. Utilities of various cash consequences for three different businessmen.

From the curves in Figure 2.2 we now read off and show in Table 2.11 the amount of cash which each of the three men would be willing to pay for tickets in reference lotteries with three different probabilities of winning rather than losing $10,000. The differing evaluations of the various lotteries can then be explained as follows.

Table 2.11
Cash Values of Reference Lotteries
for Three Different Businessmen

Probability of $10,000 profit	Cash equivalent for Mr.		
π	A	B	C
¾	−3000	+9000	+5000
½	−7000	+7000	0
¼	−9000	+3000	−5000

Because a loss of $10,000 would put Mr. A's business in an extremely critical position, he feels that he would rather pay $3000 out of pocket

than run a risk of a $10,000 loss even though he thinks that there is only
one chance in four that this loss will actually occur against three chances
in four that there will be a $10,000 profit. As the chance of the loss
becomes larger and the chance of the profit smaller, Mr. A naturally
becomes willing to pay even more to avoid the risk: he will pay $7000
for a release when the probability of the loss is $\frac{1}{2}$, and when it is $\frac{3}{4}$
he will even pay $9000 certain rather than run the risk of losing the
extra $1000 which might put him in bankruptcy.

Mr. B has attitudes diametrically opposed to those of the very
cautious and conservative Mr. A; he represents the player of long shots,
the man who feels that even a large loss could not make things much
worse than they are now whereas a large profit would very substantially
improve his whole situation. This attitude is more commonly found
among players of numbers pools and the like than it is among business
executives, but it is perhaps worth pointing out that even the extremely
conservative Mr. A might take this attitude if his misfortunes continued
to the point where he would not be able to meet his next payroll unless
something extremely fortunate happened between now and Friday.
Whatever his motives, Mr. B wants an additional $10,000 so badly that
he would consider a $\pi = \frac{1}{4}$ chance of making it to be worth as much to
him as $3000 cash certain even though this chance was accompanied by
a $\frac{3}{4}$ chance of taking a $10,000 loss; by the time $\pi = \frac{3}{4}$ and $(1 - \pi)$ is
only $\frac{1}{4}$, he would not sell his chance at $10,000 for less than $9000.

The attitudes of Mr. C will serve as a kind of standard of comparison. Mr. C represents a businessman well supplied with working
capital who believes in self-insurance against moderate risks, considers
$10,000 to be in fact a very moderate risk, and is therefore willing to use
expected monetary value as his guide to action in any problem where the
stakes do not exceed plus or minus $10,000. When the chances of a
$10,000 profit and a $10,000 loss are equal, Mr. C does not care whether
he takes the gamble or not. When the probability of winning is $\frac{3}{4}$, he
would be willing, but not eager, to trade the gamble for its expected
monetary value of $5000; if the probabilities of winning and losing were
reversed, he would be willing, but not eager, to pay $5000 to avoid the
gamble.

2.3.8   The Interpretation of Utility

In a certain sense analysis of a problem in terms of conditional and
expected utilities rather than in terms of reference lotteries enables us to
gain a better feeling for the reasons behind a given person's preferences,
but unless we are very careful this feeling will do our real understanding
more harm than good.

Let us look first at the advantages to be gained from the use of the concept of utility.   Looking at curve A in Figure 2.2 we can "explain" Mr. A's extremely cautious attitude toward all risky contracts by observing that moving any given distance to the right of 0 on the horizontal axis increases his utility by much less than moving a corresponding distance to the left decreases it—a profit of any specified amount increases his utility by less than a loss of the same amount decreases it.   For Mr. B, on the contrary, the situation is just the reverse: a profit of any given amount increases his utility by more than a loss of the same amount decreases it; while for Mr. C a dollar lost is worth neither more nor less than a dollar gained.

Now it is true that most people will actually think in terms much like these when they are deciding how to evaluate risky acts.   A person is likely to say that he would prefer \$1 million certain to a 50-50 chance of \$2 million or nothing because he would be almost as well off with \$1 million as with \$2 million and "therefore" the chance at the extra million is not worth the risk of losing the first one.   Similarly a person who buys life insurance despite the fact that the premium is always larger than the expected monetary value of the benefits by the amount of the insurance company's costs and profits will explain his action by saying that the dollars he now uses to pay the premium are worth much less to his family than the dollars which would be paid as benefits in case of his death.

We must be very careful, however, not to lose sight of the fact that all utilities are and must be evaluated by looking at *particular types* of risky acts or reference contracts and that a person may well have one attitude toward risk in one situation and a quite different attitude in a different situation.   The businessman who decided to submit the proposal under the conditions described in Table 2.2 is in effect betting \$10,000 against \$25,000 in a situation where he thinks that he has an even chance of winning his bet; but the same businessman might flatly refuse to make the same bet on the toss of a coin even though he was absolutely convinced that the coin was fair and therefore that he had an even chance of winning the bet.

Curves like those shown in Figure 2.2 do *not* purport to represent the "value of money" as such; they reflect an indecomposable mixture of attitude toward risk, profit, and loss in a particular kind of situation.

Finally, we warn the student emphatically against two common interpretations of the meaning of utility which are totally false.

First, the utilities of two separate consequences cannot be added to obtain the utility of both consequences together—the utility of an apple plus an orange is usually *not* equal to the utility of an apple plus the utility of an orange.   All that is required to understand this assertion is to look at curve A or B in Figure 2.2, observe that the utility of a $10,000 profit is not equal to twice the utility of a $5000 profit, and remember the reason why.

Second, we cannot use curves like those in Figure 2.2 as the basis for an assertion that any given consequence is worth less or more to one man than to another if by this we mean that one of the two men "really needs" the money more than the other or that the money will do more "real good" to one man than to another; nor can we say for example that because a loss of $10,000 would reduce Mr. C's utility by only .5 utile while a profit of $10,000 would increase Mr. B's utility by .85 utile, therefore there would be a net social gain if Mr. C were taxed $10,000 and the proceeds handed over to Mr. B. *All* that we can say on the basis of curves like those of Figure 2.2 is that one man will *want to behave* differently from another when faced with choices under uncertainty. Ethical and social issues cannot be handled by the methods we shall use in this course.

2.4   The Justification for the Use of Expected Monetary Value

2.4.1   Alternative Scales for Measuring Utility

Suppose now that we were to *rescale* the numerical values of the utilities in Figure 2.2 by first multiplying every number on the left-hand scale by 20,000 and then subtracting 10,000. The result of such a change of scale is shown on the right-hand side of the figure.

If now we were to evaluate act M for our old friend Mr. A by reading the "value" of each consequence from the right-hand rather than the left-hand scale and then taking the expectation of these values, we would obtain the result shown in the last column of Table 2.12 in place of that

Table 2.12

Expected Utility of Contract M to Mr. A

Event	Probability	Expected utility on scale I	Expected utility on scale II
A	.30	$.30 \times .99$	$-10{,}000(.30) + 20{,}000(.30 \times 99)$
B	.45	$.45 \times .98$	$-10{,}000(.45) + 20{,}000(.45 \times .98)$
C	.25	$.25 \times .24$	$-10{,}000(.25) + 20{,}000(.25 \times .24)$
	1.00	.798	$-10{,}000(1) \quad + 20{,}000(.798)$

obtained in Table 2.9 and shown again in the next to the last column of Table 2.12. Comparing the sums of these two columns we see that the only element which depends on *either* the probabilities or the consequences of this particular act M is the factor .798 which appears in *both* column sums; it is obvious that if we were to reevaluate act N in this way we would get the same factor .86, instead of .798, in *both* column sums; and finally, the utility of the consequence $0 of the act "do nothing" is .85 on the left-hand scale and $-10,000 + 20,000(.85)$ on the right-hand scale.

Clearly, then, use of the right-hand scale for evaluation of acts will lead to exactly the same *results* as use of the left-hand scale, and therefore we can if we like say that the right-hand scale measures "utilities" of consequences just as well as the left-hand scale.   The whole problem is exactly like the problem of scaling a thermometer: no matter what numerical values we give to the top and bottom of the scale, the thermometer will give just as good *comparisons* of the temperatures of various objects. To sum up:

> A utility scale can always be transformed by *multiplying or dividing* every value by the *same* constant, or by adding the *same* constant (positive or negative) to every value, or by both these operations together.

2.4.2   Expected Utility When Conditional Utility Is Linear in Money

We are now able to prove the correctness of the rule which we gave in Section 2.2.2 for testing whether expected *monetary* value would be a correct guide to action in a given complex decision problem.   What we shall show is that a person who chooses the act with the highest expected monetary value when this rule tells him to do so will necessarily choose the act with the highest expected utility; the student will follow the argument more easily if he first observes that the utility which Mr. C assigns to any consequence on scale II is numerically equal to the monetary value of the consequence and therefore that the expected monetary value of any act involving these consequences will be numerically equal to its expected utility on scale II.

Letting $W denote the monetary value of the worst possible consequence of any complex decision problem and $B that of the best, the rule given in Section 2.2.2 said in effect that expected monetary value would be a valid guide to action if and only if the person responsible for the decision would use this guide in simple problems involving a choice between (1) a specified amount of cash certain and (2) a reference lottery which would result with probability π in $B and with probability $(1 - \pi)$ in $W.   Such a person is saying that for him the cash equivalent of the reference lottery is given by the formula

$$\$W(1 - \pi) + \$B\pi.$$

Since the choice of the end points of a utility scale is always arbitrary, this person can always choose a scale in which the number W without the dollar sign represents the *utility* of the consequence whose monetary value is $\$W$ and in which the number B represents the utility of the consequence whose monetary value is $\$B$. On this scale the utility of the reference lottery and therefore of its cash equivalent is *by definition*

$$W(1 - \pi) + B\pi,$$

and we conclude that *a person who values all reference lotteries at their expected monetary value* can always find a utility scale such that the utility of every consequence between the reference consequences is numerically equal to the monetary value of the consequence and therefore such that *the expected utility of any act involving consequences within this range is numerically equal to the expected monetary value of the act.* By choosing the act with the highest expected monetary value, such a person automatically chooses the act with the highest expected utility.

PROBLEMS

A. Problems on Expected Monetary Value

1. Assuming that the retailer of the example discussed in Section 1.1.1 has decided to use expected monetary value as his criterion of choice in any problem where the greatest possible loss does not exceed $50 and the greatest possible profit does not exceed $100, and assuming that he assigns to the events of Table 1.1 the probabilities shown in Table 2.13, how many units should he stock and what is his expected gross profit?

Table 2.13

Event (number demanded)	Probability
0	$\frac{1}{20}$
1	$\frac{3}{20}$
2	$\frac{6}{20}$
3	$\frac{5}{20}$
4	$\frac{3}{20}$
5 or more	$\frac{2}{20}$
	1

2. *a.* A roulette wheel of the kind used at Monte Carlo has 37 numbered positions on which one may bet. Those who bet on the winning number get back their bets and 35 times as much in addition. What is the value to the house of a 1000-franc bet on number 17?

b. Of the 37 positions, 18 are red, 18 black, and 1 green. A player can bet on red or black but not green. Those who bet on a winning color get back their bets and an equal amount in addition. What is the value to the house of a 1000-franc bet on red?

c. "There is little possibility of the exercise of skill in roulette, though a certain judgment is advisable in betting; it would, for example, be unwise to place a bet on red and also on the number 17, which is black, for if one bet wins the other must lose." (*Encyclopaedia Britannica*, edition of 1953, s.v. "Roulette.") Discuss.

3. A company has $100,000 available to invest in a new plant. If business conditions continue as they are, the investment will return 10 per cent, but if there is a mild recession, it will return only 2 per cent. Alternatively the money can be invested in government bonds for a sure return of 3 per cent. What probability must management assign to a recession to make the two investments have the same expected monetary value?

B. Problems on Utility

4. Verify the assertion in Section 2.3.4 that a reference lottery with $\pi = .86$ is equivalent *in the opinion of Mr. A* to the real contract N.

5. Show that *in the opinion of Mr. B* contracts M and N will be respectively equivalent to reference lotteries with $\pi = .48$ and $.27$ rather than $.798$ and $.86$, even though he assigns to the *events A, B, C, Q, R,* and S the same *probabilities* that Mr. A assigns. Explain in nontechnical language why Mr. B prefers M to N when Mr. A prefers N to M.

6. *a.* What are true cash equivalents of contracts M and N for Mr. B?

b. What are their expected utilities for Mr. B on scales I and II?

7. By subtracting an appropriate constant amount from every one of Mr. A's scale II utilities it is possible to define a third scale such that the utility of $0 is 0 utiles.

a. Make a rough graph showing the utility of every consequence from $-$10,000 to $+$10,000 on this new scale.

b. Compute the expected utility of contracts M and N for Mr. A on this new scale.

c. Show that the *relative* ratings of the acts "take M," "take N," "take neither" are exactly the same on this new scale as they were on scale II.

8. Mr. A is presented with a deal which in his opinion has probability $\frac{2}{3}$ of resulting in a $10,000 profit but probability $\frac{1}{3}$ of resulting in a $10,000 loss.

a. Show that Mr. A should refuse the deal.

b. Suppose that five people with utility curves exactly like Mr. A's all assign the same probabilities to the possible consequences of this deal. Show that if they agree to share the profit or loss equally, the deal becomes attractive for all of them.

CHAPTER 3

Random Variables and Probability Distributions

3.1 Random Variables

In Chapter 1 we saw that the first step in the analysis of a problem of decision under uncertainty is always to draw up a list of mutually exclusive and collectively exhaustive events. In this chapter we shall introduce the important concept of a *random variable* which assigns a "value" to an event and is often more convenient to work with than the event itself, and we shall then see how the probabilities assigned to the possible values of a random variable may be laid out systematically in a *probability distribution*.

Suppose that a manufacturer is about to manufacture a cylindrical shaft, that he intends to use go and no-go gauges to check both the diameter and the length of the finished piece, and that we wish to use every bit of information supplied by the gauging to describe the outcome of this "trial." If we let g, u, and o respectively denote that the *diameter* is good, undersize, or oversize, and if we let G, U, and O convey the same information for the *length*, we can say that the possible events of this trial are the nine which are listed in the first column of Table 3.1. In the

Table 3.1

Event	Probability
gG	.55
gU	.07
gO	.03
uG	.10
uU	.08
uO	.02
oG	.05
oU	.04
oO	.06
	$\overline{1.00}$

second column of the table probabilities have been assigned to each of these events for use in our further discussion; these probabilities are completely arbitrary except that they add to 1 as all good probabilities must—how they were assessed is irrelevant for our present purpose.

Suppose now that it will cost the manufacturer $1 to rework either an oversize diameter or an oversize length and that it will cost $4 to replace a piece which is undersize and must therefore be scrapped. Since we are looking only at costs incurred *after* the original piece has been produced and inspected, we can say that the cost due to a good piece will be $0.

These statements suffice to assign a *value* to every elementary event in Table 3.1. The value $0 is assigned to the event gG, the value $1 to the events oG and gO, the value $2 to the event oO, and the value $4 to all other events. The probability of each of these four *values* is obtained in exactly the same way that we obtained the probabilities of *compound events* in Chapter 1, by adding the probabilities of the corresponding elementary events; the results are shown in Table 3.2.

Table 3.2

Value	Elementary events	Probability
$0	gG	.55
1	oG, gO	.08
2	oO	.06
4	All others	.31
		1.00

Monetary values are not the only interesting values which may be attached to events. In our example, the manufacturer may be interested not only in costs but in the amount of raw material which will be used in manufacturing replacements for pieces which cannot be reworked and must be scrapped. Suppose that it takes .3 pound of bar stock to manufacture one piece: if we recall that a piece which is undersize in either dimension must be scrapped, we see that a "value" of .3 pound is attached to the events gU, uG, uU, uO, and oU of the list in Table 3.1 while the value 0 pound is attached to all the other elementary events. Adding the probabilities of these two groups of elementary events we obtain the probabilities for the two possible values of the quantity "amount of raw material" shown in Table 3.3.

Quantities such as cost and amount of material in these two examples are known as random variables; in general, we define

> *Random variable:* any quantity which has a definite value corresponding to every possible event.

A list of the possible values of a random variable can be regarded as being simply a list of elementary and/or compound events defined in a special way; but it is important to realize that while a particular value of a random variable can always be regarded as an event, it is *not* true that all events can be regarded as values of random variables.   First, the values of a random variable have a *meaningful order* whereas events like those of Table 3.1 do not.   "More than \$1" makes sense but "more than gU" does not.   Second and much more important, the concepts of average value and *expected value* have meaning when applied to a random variable but not when applied to events in general.   We have already applied these concepts to monetary random variables and to the random variable "utility" in Chapter 2, and in Chapter 6 we shall see that they apply to all random variables without exception.

Table 3.3

Value	Probability
0 pound	.69
.3 pound	.31
	1.00

Observe on the other hand that the existence of a meaningful order and a meaningful average or expected value are the *only* properties which we require of the "values" of a random variable.   If the manufacturer of our example is interested in the quality of the work done in his shop as measured by the number of individual defects produced, we may consider "number of defects" a random variable describing the outcome of each trial (each piece produced) even though we have attached no economic worth to a defect and even though the economic worth of one defect may be quite different from that of another.   The probability distribution of this variable is shown in Table 3.4.

Table 3.4

Value of the random variable	Elementary events	Probability
0	gG	.55
1	gU, gO, uG, oG	.25
2	All others	.20
		1.00

Observe also that in many cases the *value* of a random variable may be identical to the natural *description* of an event.   If the manufacturer had measured his pieces instead of using gauges, an "event" would have been described by a pair of numbers—e.g., diameter 1.23 inches, length 2.07 inches.   These two numbers can equally well be regarded as "values" of two random variables "diameter" and "length," and we shall ordinarily so regard them.   In just the same way we can regard the various possible events in the inventory problem described in Table 1.1 as values of the random variable "demand."

3.2   Probability Distributions and Frequency Distributions

A table like Tables 3.2 through 3.4 which assigns a probability to every possible value of a random variable is called a *probability distribution* of that random variable.   Since by the definition of a random variable every possible elementary event corresponds to *some* value of the variable, the sum of the probabilities in any probability distribution must be 1.

3.2.1   *Assessment of Probability Distributions*

Although a random variable is *defined* in terms of values attached to the elementary events of a trial, it is not to be assumed that the probability distribution of a random variable must necessarily be *assessed* by first assigning probabilities to elementary events and then adding the probabilities of a number of elementary events to obtain the probability of each value of the variable as we did in the examples of the previous section.   It has already been pointed out that in some cases a random variable will attach a different value to each elementary event (e.g., the random variable "demand" in the inventory example), so that there is only a verbal difference between assigning probabilities to elementary events and assigning probabilities directly to the possible values of the random variable.   Later in the course we shall see that even when each value of a random variable does correspond to a large number of elementary events, it is often better to proceed by using our experience to make a direct assessment of the distribution of two or more random variables and then to use these distributions to compute the probabilities of the elementary events if they are needed in the problem at hand.

Whenever probabilities are assigned *directly* to the values of some random variable, we shall refer to this variable as a *basic random variable* in order to distinguish it from other random variables which may be involved in the same problem.   Suppose, for example, that a can of coffee is to be filled by an automatic machine and that a loss will be incurred if either more or less than 1 pound of coffee is put into the can.   What we really want in such a problem is a probability distribution for the random variable "loss," but the most effective way of using our experience may well be to start by assessing the distribution of the random variable "weight."   If we do proceed in this way, "weight" is the basic random variable of the problem.

3.2.2 Frequency Distributions

The *probabilities* which a reasonable man assigns to the values of a basic random variable will often (though by no means always) be largely if not wholly determined by consideration of the *relative frequencies* with which these values have occurred in past trials.   To continue with the example of the coffee, suppose that the net weight of the coffee in each of the last 50 cans filled by the machine has been determined to the nearest $\frac{1}{100}$ pound with the results shown in the first two columns of Table 3.5. By dividing the *number of occurrences* of each value by the *total number of trials* we obtain the *relative frequency* of each value as shown in the last column of the table.

Table 3.5

Value of the random variable	Number of occurrences	Relative frequency
.98	2	.04
.99	6	.12
1.00	7	.14
1.01	10	.20
1.02	9	.18
1.03	8	.16
1.04	5	.10
1.05	3	.06
	50	1.00

The first and last columns of Table 3.5 together constitute a *frequency distribution* of the random variable "weight," and in general any complete list of the relative frequencies of all the values of any random variable will be called a frequency distribution.   Since it is only in relative frequencies that we are interested, the word "relative" will often be omitted in future discussions: "frequency" will *always* mean relative frequency.   Observe that the total of the frequencies in a frequency distribution must always be 1, just as the total of the probabilities in a probability distribution must always be 1.

Now a frequency distribution like the one shown in Table 3.5 is most definitely *not* in itself a probability distribution for the random variable "weight" on the next trial.   If, however, we have *no other information about the can-filling process which we consider to be of any real importance,* we *may* decide to assign probabilities which are *numerically equal* to the relative frequencies shown in Table 3.5.   In other words, we *may* decide on the basis of the evidence summarized in Table 3.5 that we would be indifferent between the right to receive a certain prize if the next can weighs .98 pound and the right to receive the same prize if a particular ball is drawn in a "standard lottery" with 25 balls in the urn. In Chapter 7 we shall return to this subject and look at some of the questions we should ask before actually proceeding in this way, particularly when the available frequency distribution is based on only a few trials.

3.3   Graphic Representation of Distributions

Our thinking about a probability or frequency distribution can often be considerably clarified if we represent the distribution graphically, and in Chapter 7 we shall also see that graphical representation is often of

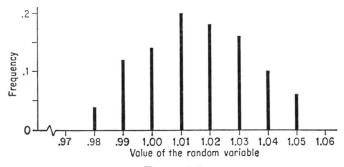

Figure 3.1

considerable help when we try to assess a probability distribution rationally. Frequency distributions and probability distributions can both be represented by exactly the same devices; we shall use the frequency distribution of Table 3.5 as an example.

One form of graphic representation is shown in Figure 3.1. The horizontal axis shows the various *values* of the random variable; the height of the vertical line at any particular value represents the *frequency* with which that value occurs.

Another form of representation is shown in Figure 3.2, where the frequency of each value of the variable is shown by the height of a point and the points are then joined by straight lines. Since values of this variable other than .97, .98, .99, etc., are meaningless—the measurements were made to the nearest $\frac{1}{100}$ pound—the lines have no meaning except at those points; in between, they serve simply as guides to the eye.

Histograms. Frequencies or probabilities can be represented by areas as well as by heights, and the histogram of Figure 3.3 is such a representation for the data of Table 3.5: the frequency of each value of the random variable is represented by the *area* of the bar centered on that value. Some problems which we shall encounter later in the course will be far easier to understand if we visualize probability distributions in terms of histograms than if we visualize them in any other way, and we therefore advise the student to pay close attention to the rules which we shall now give for the construction and interpretation of graphs of this sort even though these rules may seem needlessly complex at the moment.

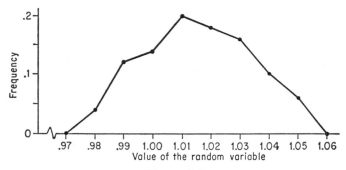

Figure 3.2

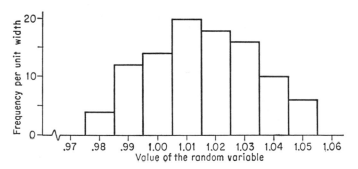

Figure 3.3

Observe first that the edges of the bar for any value of the variable in Figure 3.3 are halfway between the location of that value and the adjacent values of the variable. Thus the edges of the bar for the value 1.02 are located at 1.015 and 1.025. This means that the width of this bar can be taken as $1.025 - 1.015 = .01$, and in general *the width of any bar in any histogram can be taken as equal to the difference between two successive possible values of the variable.*

Now since it is the *area* of a bar which represents the frequency or probability of the corresponding value of the variable, and since the area of a bar is equal to its width times its height, we must interpret the *height* of a bar as showing *frequency or probability per unit width.* In Figure 3.3 the height of the bar for the value 1.02 of the variable can be read as 18 on the vertical axis; the width of this bar is .01 as we have already seen; and therefore

$$\text{Area} = \text{frequency} = 18 \times .01 = .18$$

in agreement with Table 3.5. *It is exactly this trick of interpretation which will make the use of histograms so useful a little later on, and we urge the student to fix it firmly in his mind.*

3.3.1   Grouped Distributions

When a random variable has a very large number of possible values, it becomes bothersome to tabulate or graph all the small individual frequencies occurring in a historical frequency distribution, and often we find ourselves forced to deal with historical data in which some of this detail has been suppressed. We may be presented, for example, with a historical record of daily sales in which the possible values of the variable have been grouped into "brackets" and the frequencies of all values within each bracket have been added together as in Table 3.6.

Table 3.6

Sales	Relative frequency
55–59	.05
60–64	.09
65–69	.18
70–74	.27
75–79	.21
80–84	.14
85–89	.06
	1.00

By far the best graphical representation for a grouped distribution is a histogram, since the grouping into brackets can be directly represented by the widths of the bars. A histogram for the data of Table 3.6 is shown in Figure 3.4. The bar representing the frequency of sales from 55 to 59 units inclusive is represented by a bar with its left edge at 54.5 and its right edge at 59.5—*the bar covers exactly the same interval on the horizontal axis which would have been covered by the individual bars for the values in question.* The *width* of this bar is thus $59.5 - 54.5 = 5$ units, and since its *area* is .05 by Table 3.6 it has been drawn with a *height* of $.05/5 = .01$.

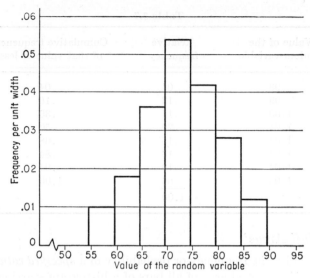

Figure 3.4

Similarly the frequency of values from 60 to 64 units inclusive can be read from the graph as

Area = frequency = height × width = .018 × 5 = .09.

3.4 Cumulative Distributions

We are often interested, not in the frequency or probability of an *individual* value of a random variable, but in the frequency or probability of *all values less than* some specified value or of *all values greater than* some specified value.   In the example of the cans of coffee which were supposed to contain exactly 1 pound, we may want to know the probability that the next can will contain less than 1 pound or the probability that it will contain more than 1 pound.   For other purposes we may want to know the probability that a variable will be *equal to or less than* some specified value or that it will be *equal to or greater than* the specified value.

Cumulative frequencies or probabilities of this sort are computed from individual frequencies or probabilities in a way which is perfectly obvious.   In the example of Table 3.5, the frequency of values equal to or less than .98 is simply the frequency of .98 itself, or .04.   The frequency of values equal to or less than .99 is the frequency of .98 plus the frequency of .99 or .04 + .12 = .16.   Proceeding systematically in this way we can compute the complete *cumulative distribution* of this random variable with the results shown in Table 3.7, where the individual frequencies are repeated from Table 3.5 for the student's convenience.

Table 3.7

Value of the random variable	Relative frequency	Cumulative frequency of that value or less
.98	.04	.04
.99	.12	.16
1.00	.14	.30
1.01	.20	.50
1.02	.18	.68
1.03	.16	.84
1.04	.10	.94
1.05	.06	1.00
	1.00	

3.4.1 "Tail Areas"

Graphically, the frequency or probability of a *specified value* or less is represented by the total area of all bars of a histogram starting from the extreme left and continuing *up to and including* the bar representing the specified value.   This area will frequently be called the area of the *left tail* of the distribution; the corresponding *right-tail* area represents the frequency of values *greater than* the specified value.   We are not compelled, however, to include the area of the bar representing the specified value itself in the left tail of the distribution.   We can equally well define the right tail as including this bar, in which case the area of the left tail represents the frequency or probability of values *less than* the specified value.   The proper definition of a tail area—the proper specification of a cumulative probability or frequency—depends on the way in which the probability or frequency is to be used in a particular problem, and care must be taken both in deciding on the proper specification and in computing the probability or frequency so that it actually corresponds to the specification.

3.4.2 Direct Graphic Representation of Cumulative Distributions

It is often convenient to have a graph from which cumulative probabilities or frequencies can be read directly rather than as the sum of the areas of a number of bars of a histogram.   Figure 3.5 is such a graph for the data of Table 3.7: for every value of the random variable, Figure 3.5 shows the relative frequency of *that value or less* and thus conveys exactly the same information which is conveyed by the last column of Table 3.7. Three points need special attention in constructing or reading a graph of this sort.

First, the graph of any *cumulative* distribution has meaning for *every* value of the variable and not just for those values which the variable did or could actually take on.   Even though the value 1.003 itself neither occurred nor could occur when the weighing was done only to the nearest ⅟₁₀₀ pound, it is perfectly sensible to say that the frequency with which the random variable had values of 1.003 pounds or less was .30.   Similarly we can read from Figure 3.5 the meaningful information that values of .97 or less occurred with frequency 0 and that values of 1.06 or less occurred with frequency 1.

Second, a special convention is needed to draw and read a graph like Figure 3.5 at those values of the variable which actually did occur or to which a nonzero probability is assigned, since at each such value the

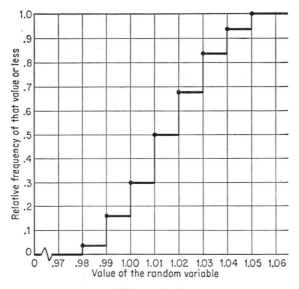

Figure 3.5

graph necessarily makes an abrupt vertical jump of an amount equal to the individual probability or frequency of the value in question.   Thus the cumulative frequency of all values up to and including 1.00999 · · · is .30, no matter how many 9's we write down; but as soon as we reach 1.01 itself, the cumulative frequency jumps to .50.   For this reason a heavy dot is used in Figure 3.5 to indicate which of the two horizontal lines should be read at each point of this sort.

Finally, observe that a graph showing the frequency of all values *less than* a given value would look exactly like Figure 3.5 except that the heavy dot would be on the lower of the two lines at each jump rather than on the higher of the two lines.   The frequency of all values *less than* an impossible value like 1.003 is exactly the same as the frequency of all values *equal to or less than* such a value; but whereas the frequency of all values *less than* 1.01 is .30, the frequency of 1.01 *or less* is .50, the difference being the frequency of this value itself.

3.5   Notation

Finally, let us introduce some shorthand notation which will be very convenient in writing about probabilities and random variables.   Any *probability* will be denoted by a capital P followed by parentheses showing the *event* whose probability is in question.   Thus P(red) will denote the probability that a ball is red, P(defective) will denote the probability that a manufactured part is defective, and so forth.

A *random variable* will be denoted by a letter with a "tilde" above it; thus we may use $\tilde{z}$ to denote the random variable "tomorrow's demand" or $\tilde{r}$ to denote the random variable "number of defectives in the next lot received."   We have already seen in Section 3.1 that any value of a random variable is an event, and therefore we may write

> $P(\tilde{z} = 4)$ or $P(4)$: the probability that the random variable $\tilde{z}$ has the value 4.

The symbol $<$ means "less than," $>$ means "greater than," $\leq$ means "less than or equal to," and $\geq$ means "greater than or equal to."

> $P(\tilde{z} < 4)$: the probability that the random variable $\tilde{z}$ has a value less than 4.

The following relations between the tails of a distribution will give an example of the use of this notation.

> $P(\tilde{z} \leq 4) = 1 - P(\tilde{z} > 4)$.
> $P(\tilde{z} < 4) = 1 - P(\tilde{z} \geq 4)$.
> $P(\tilde{z} < 4) + P(\tilde{z} = 4) + P(\tilde{z} > 4) = 1$.

In many cases we shall need a symbol which denotes *any* value of a random variable, and for this purpose we shall use the same letter we use to denote the random variable itself but without the tilde.   Thus the horizontal axis of a cumulative probability distribution may be labeled z while the vertical axis is labeled $P(\tilde{z} < z)$.   We can write

> $P(\tilde{z} \leq z) = 1 - P(\tilde{z} > z)$

because this relation between the tails of the distribution holds for *any* specified value z and not just for the value 4 used in our previous illustration.

When the probability distribution of a random variable is represented by a histogram, the heights of the bars represent probability *per unit width*, and to denote this quantity we shall use the symbol P′ (P prime):

P′(z): probability per unit width (height of the histogram) *at the point z* on the horizontal axis.

For any *possible* value z of the random variable $\tilde{z}$,

P(z) = P′(z) × (width of bar corresponding to the value z).

For impossible values this equation is of course meaningless.

PROBLEMS

1. The number of units sold by the XYZ Company on 20 successive days was 4, 3, 1, 3, 2, 0, 4, 5, 3, 1, 2, 3, 6, 2, 4, 5, 3, 1, 4, and 3 units.

a. Make a (relative) frequency distribution of this data in the form of a table, a graph like Figure 3.2, and a histogram.

b. Make a table showing both the left-tail and the right-tail cumulative frequencies of the data, defining the left tail as "specified value or less" and the right tail as "specified value or more."

c. Make a graph like Figure 3.5 of the left-tail cumulative frequencies, defining the left tail as in part *b* of this question.

2. An automobile dealer sold 21 cars on Monday, 9 on Tuesday, 13 on Wednesday, 7 on Thursday, and 9 on Friday.

a. Graph the cumulative daily sales as they occurred chronologically.

b. Graph the left-tail cumulative distribution of the same data considered as a frequency distribution, defining the tail as in Problem 1*b*.

3. A company which has been basing its production scheduling on demand forecasts made by the sales department decides to investigate the accuracy of these forecasts. The record for the past 10 months turns out as follows:

Forecast demand	Actual demand	Discrepancy
22	23	+1
20	18	−2
17	19	etc.
20	15	
19	19	
19	22	
23	28	
25	21	
23	18	
20	19	

Graph the frequency distribution and left-tail cumulative distribution (defined as in Problem 1*b*) of the *discrepancies* between actual demand and forecast demand. In so doing define the discrepancy as *actual minus forecast,* and *do not neglect or reverse the algebraic signs.*

4. Figure 3.6 is a histogram showing the number of cars sold daily by an automobile salesman.

a. What fraction of the time did he sell between **7** and **9** (inclusive) **cars?**

b. What fraction of the time did he sell more than 9 cars?

c. What fraction of the time did he sell more than 2 cars?

5. Figure 3.7 is a cumulative frequency distribution of per cents defective in samples of 100 drawn from lots of a product manufactured on an automatic screw machine.

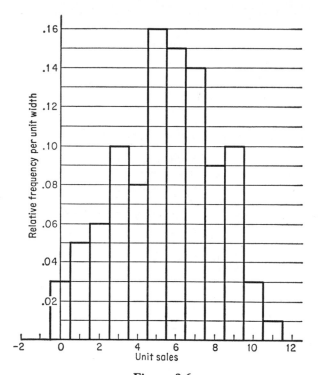

Figure 3.6

a. What fraction of samples was 5 per cent or less defective?

b. What fraction was more than 12 per cent defective?

c. What fraction was 7 per cent defective?

d. What fraction had per cents defective between 3.5 and 10.8 per cent inclusive?

6. Figure 3.8 is a frequency distribution of daily sales volume for a certain product.

a. On what fraction of all days were sales below 15 units?

b. On what fraction of days were sales between 15 and 24 units inclusive?

c. On what fraction of days were sales at least as high as 20 units?

7. Graph in histogram form the probability distributions corresponding to the following statements.

a. "Our experience with this supplier has been such that I believe that only a quarter of the relays we buy from him next year will contain no defective contacts, half will contain one, and another quarter will contain two."

b. "I believe that there is 1 chance in 5 that sales next month will be between 0 and 3 units inclusive, 2 chances in 5 that they will be between 4 and 7 units, and

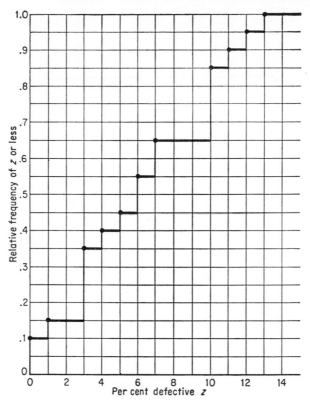

Figure 3.7

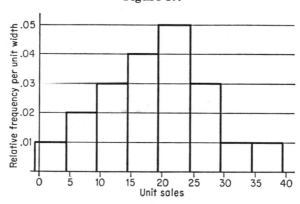

Figure 3.8

2 chances in 5 that they will be between 8 and 11 units." (Be careful in labeling the vertical scale of this graph.)

8. Under what conditions would you use the frequency distributions given in Problems 1 through 6 as probability distributions on which you would be willing to base a decision?

PART ONE

The Use of Probabilities
Based Directly on Experience

CHAPTER 4

Opportunity Loss and the Cost of Uncertainty

4.1 Construction of Payoff Tables

In Chapter 1 we defined a payoff table as a table showing the consequence of every possible *act* given every possible *event*. The fact that the decision is being made under uncertainty has no bearing whatever on the *construction* of the payoff table, since *the entries in the row describing any particular event are exactly the same as they would be if that event were certain to occur*, and consequently we shall pause only briefly to remind the student of the basic principle which must be observed in making *any* economic comparison of two or more possible acts.

This basic principle states simply that before choosing among two or more acts we must take into account *all present and future flows of cash which are affected by the decision* and that these cash flows are the *only* elements of profit or cost which we should take into account. If a certain act involves the consumption of materials already in inventory, then according to circumstances these materials should be considered as the *equivalent* either of the cash for which they could otherwise have been sold or of the cash which will ultimately be spent in order to replace them, but their value as thus determined should not be inflated by allocations of fixed costs or expenses whose total amount will actually remain the same whether these materials are used or not.

The one rule to follow in drawing up a payoff table is therefore the following:

> For each act-event combination, list every item of cash or the equivalent which will flow out of the business and every item of cash or the equivalent which will flow into the business; the net of all these amounts is the amount to enter in the table.

If the payoff table is being drawn up in terms of *profit*, the outflows are subtracted from the inflows; if the table is being drawn up to show *costs*, the reverse procedure is followed. In either case, some of the entries in the table may be negative; and if they are, *the minus signs must not be neglected:* they must be entered in the table and observed in all subsequent computations.

An Example. As an example, let us take a slightly more complex version of the kind of inventory problem which we discussed in Chapter 1. Once a week a retailer stocks a perishable commodity which deteriorates on the shelf so that stock which remains unsold at the end of the week must be salvaged at a fraction of its full value; he has space in his freezer to stock up to 5 units. The commodity is bought by the retailer for $2.50 per unit and is offered for sale at a price of $3.70 per unit during the week in which it is stocked; leftover stock has a salvage value of $.50 per unit. The retailer's rent, insurance, etc., average $.12 per dollar of total sales of all commodities; clerks' wages, delivery expenses, etc., average $.41 per dollar of total sales. The retailer assigns the probability distribution shown in Table 4.1 to the basic random variable "next week's demand" and consults us to determine how many units he should stock.

Table 4.1

Demand z	Probability $P(z)$
0	.05
1	.10
2	.25
3	.30
4	.20
5	.10
6+	0
	1.00

Our first step in analyzing this problem is to draw up the payoff table, and in so doing we should recognize immediately that the fact that overhead and selling expense have *averaged* $.12 + $.41 = $.53 per dollar of sales in no way implies that these expenses are *variable* with sales. On the other hand we *do* have to inquire whether there are any costs or expenses which are directly attributable to sales of this commodity, and we shall suppose that our inquiries lead to the information that special materials costing $.20 are used to package each unit sold at full price.

We are now ready to construct the payoff table. If Q is the number stocked and z is the number of fresh units demanded, the *net* cash *inflow* or "gross profit" will be:

For $z \leq Q$ (demand no greater than stock on hand)

Sale of fresh units:	$+ \$3.70\,z$
Wrapping fresh units:	$- \quad .20\,z$
Salvage of leftovers:	$+ \quad .50\,(Q - z)$
Purchase cost of stock:	$- \quad 2.50\,Q$
Net inflow:	$\$3.00\,z - \$2.00\,Q$

For z > Q (demand exceeds stock)

Sale of fresh units:	$+\$3.70\,Q$
Wrapping fresh units:	$-\ .20\,Q$
Salvage of leftovers:	0
Purchase cost of stock:	$-\$2.50\,Q$
Net inflow:	$+\$1.00\,Q$

The entries in Table 4.2 are obtained by applying the appropriate one of these two formulas to every Q, z combination in the table.   For example:

$$Q = 4, z = 2: (\$3 \times 2) - (\$2 \times 4) = -\$2,$$
$$Q = 2, z = 4: \$1 \times 2 = +\$2.$$

Table 4.2
Payoff Table

Demand z	Stock Q					
	0	1	2	3	4	5
0	$0	−$2	−$4	−$6	−$8	−$10
1	0	+ 1	− 1	− 3	− 5	− 7
2	0	+ 1	+ 2	0	− 2	− 4
3	0	+ 1	+ 2	+ 3	+ 1	− 1
4	0	+ 1	+ 2	+ 3	+ 4	+ 2
5	0	+ 1	+ 2	+ 3	+ 4	+ 5

The *expected* profit of any act (any value of Q) can now be computed by taking a weighted average of the corresponding column in Table 4.2,

Table 4.3
Expected Profit with Stock of 3

Demand z	P(z)	Conditional profit	Expected value
0	.05	−$6	−$ .30
1	.10	− 3	− .30
2	.25	0	+ 0
3	.30	+ 3	+ .90
4	.20	+ 3	+ .60
5	.10	+ 3	+ .30
	1.00		+$1.20

the probabilities of Table 4.1 being used as the weights.   The expected profit for a stock of 3 is computed in Table 4.3 by way of review; it is left to the student to verify the expected profits for the other stocks shown in Table 4.4.

Table 4.4
Expected Profits of All Acts

Act Q	Expected profit
0	$0
1	+ .85
2	+ 1.40
3	+ 1.20
4	+ .10
5	− 1.60

4.2 Definition of Opportunity Loss

Even though we choose the best possible decision in the light of the information available *before the fact*, this decision will often turn out "wrong" *after the fact*. To use the example discussed just above: the best decision we can make before the fact is to stock 2 units, but after the fact we may wish we had stocked some other number of units. This, of course, is no criticism of the rationality of the original decision: such things are bound to happen when a decision has to be made on the basis of less than perfect information. It does mean, however, that there is a particular interest attached to the *losses which may be incurred because of the imperfection of our information*, and such losses are the subject of the remainder of this chapter.

Losses of this kind will be called *opportunity losses* because they represent the difference between the profit we actually realize and the greater profit we had the opportunity of realizing; or if we measure the consequences of our chosen act in terms of cost, they represent the difference between the cost we actually incur and the lesser cost we had the opportunity of incurring. Formally, we define

> *Opportunity loss of a decision:* the *difference* between the cost or profit *actually* realized under that decision and the cost or profit which *would have been* realized if the decision had been the best one possible for the event which actually occurred.

Observe that an "opportunity loss" may be suffered even when the decision results in a profit rather than a loss in the ordinary sense of the word. Henceforth the word "loss" will be used only in the sense of "opportunity loss" as we have just defined this term, whether or not we repeat the word "opportunity" on every occasion. If a decision results in costs which exceed revenues, we shall call the difference a "negative profit"; we shall no longer call it a "loss."

The opportunity loss which is actually suffered as the result of some decision may be a subject of curiosity and regret, but the businessman will gain little practical advantage from its calculation.   What is really useful to the businessman is to look at the risk of loss *before* he makes his final decision, i.e. to compute the *expected* loss of the act which he is contemplating, since if this expected loss is great he may be able to reduce it either by postponing the final choice of an act until more information has been acquired or by finding some way of hedging the risk.   The real subject of the present chapter is therefore the computation of expected opportunity loss.

4.3 Computation of Expected Loss

4.3.1 The Loss Table

If we wish to compute the expected losses of all the possible acts in any decision problem our first step is very similar to the first step we take when we wish to compute the expected profits or costs of all possible acts: we lay out a table which shows the *conditional* loss which will be incurred as the result of each act given every possible event.   Such a table will be called a *loss table*.   Since the conditional opportunity loss of any act given a particular event is simply the difference between the resulting profit or cost and the profit or cost which would have resulted from the best possible act for that event, the most systematic way of computing a loss table for any problem is to start with the payoff table which shows all the profits or costs for that problem.

Although the very definition of opportunity loss makes it virtually obvious how the loss table is to be derived from the payoff table, it is well to follow a systematic procedure in carrying out the calculations and we shall explain this procedure by applying it to the inventory problem discussed at length in Section 4.1.   Table 4.5 is the payoff table for that problem and is identical to Table 4.2.   Table 4.6 is the corresponding loss table; it is derived from Table 4.5 in the following two steps:

1. The greatest possible profit for each *event* is identified by starring the greatest profit in each *row* of Table 4.5.
2. Table 4.6 is then constructed row by row, each entry in Table 4.6 being obtained by subtracting the corresponding entry in Table 4.5 from the starred entry *in the same row* of Table 4.5.

Thus the $1 *opportunity* loss attached to the event "demand for 4" under the act "stock 3" represents the fact that the corresponding profit is only $3 whereas with a stock of 4 (the best decision for a demand of 4) the profit would be $4—this is the starred entry in the row for $z = 4$ in

Table 4.5
Payoff Table

z	Q 0	1	2	3	4	5
0	$0*	−$2	−$4	−$6	−$8	−$10
1	0	+ 1*	− 1	− 3	− 5	− 7
2	0	+ 1	+ 2*	0	− 2	− 4
3	0	+ 1	+ 2	+ 3*	+ 1	− 1
4	0	+ 1	+ 2	+ 3	+ 4*	+ 2
5	0	+ 1	+ 2	+ 3	+ 4	+ 5*

Table 4.6
Loss Table

z	Q 0	1	2	3	4	5
0	$0	$2	$4	$6	$8	$10
1	1	0	2	4	6	8
2	2	1	0	2	4	6
3	3	2	1	0	2	4
4	4	3	2	1	0	2
5	5	4	3	2	1	0

Table 4.5. The $6 *opportunity* loss attached to "demand 2" under "stock 5" represents the fact that the corresponding profit is a *negative* $4 whereas with a stock of 2 (the best decision) the profit would be a *positive* $2.

The student should pay very careful attention to the following points concerning algebraic signs:

1. Care must be paid to algebraic signs in subtracting the profit for a given act-event combination from the greatest possible profit for that event, since one or both of these quantities may be negative.
2. Opportunity loss itself can never be negative. The loss of the best possible act for any event is 0, and all other acts necessarily involve positive losses.

Payoff Tables Showing Costs. With two obvious exceptions, the procedure for deriving a loss table from a payoff table which shows costs rather than profits is identical to the procedure described above:

1. The *lowest* cost in each row is starred.
2. The starred entry is *subtracted from* all the entries in the same row.

4.3.2 *Direct Computation of Conditional Losses*

While the conditional losses in *any* problem can always be computed by first constructing a payoff table and then deriving the loss table from it as we did in Section 4.3.1 above, the conditional losses in some problems can be easily computed by a more direct line of reasoning which we shall now explain by using our inventory problem as an example. It is obvious in this problem that if the stock Q chosen by the retailer proves to be exactly *equal* to the quantity actually demanded, the resulting loss is 0; we shall now consider separately the losses which a stock Q entails if it turns out to be *over* or *under* the quantity actually demanded.

Loss Due to Overage. If the retailer's stock is *over* the quantity actually demanded, he will have to salvage the excess units and each unit salvaged will entail a loss amounting to the $2.00 difference between the $2.50 cost of the unit and its $.50 salvage value. Consequently

Conditional loss of overage $= \$2(Q - z)$.

Loss Due to Underage. The retailer makes a profit of

$$\$3.70 - \$.20 - \$2.50 = \$1.00$$

on every unit stocked and sold. If, therefore, his stock is *under* the quantity actually demanded, he has an opportunity loss amounting to $1 for every unit of unsatisfied demand. Consequently

Conditional loss of underage $= \$1(z - Q)$.

The implications of these two formulas are illustrated graphically in Figure 4.1, which shows the conditional losses for stocks of $Q = 2$ and $Q = 3$. Notice that in both cases the graph forms an asymmetric V whose point shows that loss is 0 when $z = Q$; for all other z, *the height of either arm of the V is proportional to the difference* $(Q - z)$ *or* $(z - Q)$ as the case may be. Notice carefully that because we have defined an overage as an excess of *stock over demand*, it is the *left-hand* branch of each V which gives the conditional loss of overage while the right-hand branch gives the cost of underage. If $Q = 3$ and $z = 1$, the retailer will have 2 units left *over* and will suffer a loss of $2 \times \$2 = \$4$; if $Q = 2$ and $z = 5$, he will be *under* or short by 3 units and will suffer a loss of $3 \times \$1 = \$3$.

The student should make sure that he understands the meaning of Figure 4.1 and the underlying formulas by reading several figures from the "curves" and identifying them in Table 4.6. Even more important, he should remember that

In case of doubt, the only really safe way of computing conditional losses is to start by considering *total* cash flows and using them to construct a *payoff* table from which a loss table can then be systematically derived. The direct or short-cut method of evaluating conditional losses should be used only in very simple problems where there is no danger of confusion.

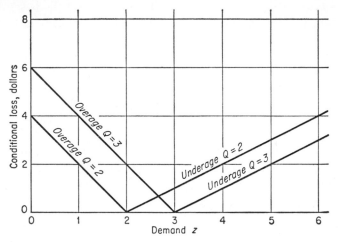

Figure 4.1

4.3.3   *Expected Loss*

The *expected* opportunity loss of any act is computed from the conditional losses in exactly the same way that its expected profit or cost is computed from conditional profits or costs. Thus in our example the expected opportunity loss of a decision to stock 3 units is computed as $1.60 in Table 4.7, where the conditional losses are taken from the proper

Table 4.7
Expected Loss with Stock of 3

z	$P(z)$	Conditional loss	Expected loss
0	.05	$6	$ .30
1	.10	4	.40
2	.25	2	.50
3	.30	0	0
4	.20	1	.20
5	.10	2	.20
	1.00		$1.60

column in Table 4.6 and the probabilities are taken from Table 4.1. In Table 4.8 we show the expected loss of every possible decision in our example computed by this same method; the last column of the table shows the corresponding expected *profits* (simply copied from Table 4.4) for a reason which will be made clear in a moment.

Table 4.8
Expected Losses and Profits of All Acts

Q	Expected loss	Expected profit
0	$2.80	$0
1	1.95	+ .85
2	1.40	+ 1.40
3	1.60	+ 1.20
4	2.70	+ .10
5	4.40	− 1.60

4.3.4 Comparison of Acts in Terms of Expected Loss

By the very definition of opportunity loss it seems obvious that the businessman who wishes to choose the act with the *highest* expected *profit* can accomplish his objective by choosing the act with the *lowest* expected *loss*, and it can be proved that this is in fact true. It can be proved, in other words, that *in any decision problem whatever*

The difference between the expected profits of any two acts is equal in magnitude but opposite in sign to the difference between their expected losses.

Thus Table 4.8 shows that in our example *profit* with a stock of 3 is *higher* than profit with a stock of 4 by $1.20 − $.10 = $1.10; *loss* with a stock of 3 is *lower* than loss with a stock of 4 by $2.70 − $1.60 = $1.10. The student can easily convince himself that when payoff tables are expressed in terms of cost rather than profit

The difference between the expected costs of any two acts is equal in magnitude and identical in sign to the difference between their expected losses.

4.4 The Cost of Uncertainty and the Cost of Irrationality

By Table 4.8, the best possible decision which the retailer can make under uncertainty has an expected opportunity loss of $1.40. This $1.40 can be considered to be the *inherent cost of uncertainty itself*, since it is the difference between the *best* that the decision maker can expect to do with the information he has available and what he could expect to do with perfect information. We define

> *Cost of uncertainty:* the expected opportunity loss of the *best possible* decision under a given probability distribution.

The cost of uncertainty in our example is the loss associated with a stock of 2 units. If instead of stocking 2 units the retailer stocks any other number, his expected loss will be greater than the $1.40 cost of uncertainty. Such an additional expected loss is completely unnecessary, and we define

> *Cost of irrationality:* the amount by which the expected opportunity loss of the chosen decision exceeds the cost of uncertainty under a given probability distribution.

4.5   The Principle of Minimax-Loss

In Section 1.1.2 we said that some writers on statistics had advocated use of the so-called minimax principle for making "objective" decisions under uncertainty—i.e., decisions which do not depend on the decision maker's "subjective" feelings about events; but when we examined the implications of this principle as applied to the simplest possible kind of decision problem, we found that it led to patently intolerable results. We shall now examine a second version of the minimax principle, one which has been even more widely advocated than the first as a way of making "objective" or "scientific" decisions under uncertainty.

According to the principle of minimax-loss,† the decision maker should choose the act such that the *worst* possible *opportunity loss* he can suffer is *least*. In the problem whose loss table is shown as Table 4.6, this principle tells the businessman to stock either 1 or 2 units, since the worst loss that he can incur if he does so is $4, whereas any other act *might* result in a greater loss.‡

† Many writers give the name "regret" to what we have called "opportunity loss" or simply "loss," and therefore this principle is often called the principle of minimax-regret.

‡ Strictly speaking, the principle says that the businessman should roll a die and then stock 1 unit if the die shows ace or deuce, 2 units if it shows any other face, since if this is done the businessman's worst *expected* loss (occurring if demand is for either 0 or 5 units) is

$$\tfrac{1}{3}\ \$2 + \tfrac{2}{3}\ \$4 = \tfrac{1}{3}\ \$4 + \tfrac{2}{3}\ \$3 = \$3\tfrac{1}{3}$$

and this is smaller than the $4 worst loss of definitely deciding to stock either 1 or 2 units. We would not bother the student with such curious ideas were it not for the fact that he will find great importance attached to them in books on "statistical inference."

Now since this "objective" principle says that the businessman should stock 1 or 2 units whether the article in question is an improved model sold at the same price as an article of which he has sold 5 units in every one of the past 1000 weeks or is an article priced at $100 but obviously worth no more than 10 cents, we could reject it without further ado as a principle which would quickly lead any businessman to bankruptcy. Just for fun, however, we shall point out one other curious feature of the principle. The student can readily verify that if the businessman has *space* for 9 units rather than just 5, so that his *possible* acts run from $Q = 0$ to 9 rather than just to 5, then the loss table for the stocking problem will be as shown in Table 4.9. From this table the

Table 4.9
Loss Table

z	Q									
	0	1	2	3	4	5	6	7	8	9
0	$0	$2	$4	$6	$8	$10	$12	$14	$16	$18
1	1	0	2	4	6	8	10	12	14	16
2	2	1	0	2	4	6	8	10	12	14
3	3	2	1	0	2	4	6	8	10	14
4	4	3	2	1	0	2	4	6	8	10
5	5	4	3	2	1	0	2	4	6	8
6	6	5	4	3	2	1	0	2	4	6
7	7	6	5	4	3	2	1	0	2	4
8	8	7	6	5	4	3	2	1	0	2
9	9	8	7	6	5	4	3	2	1	0

student can see that the minimax-loss principle now leads to a stock of 3 units, since the worst loss with this act is $6 whereas any other act *might* result in a still larger loss. In other words, the minimax-loss principle says that although a retailer could obviously stock 3 units if he has space for 5 units, he "should" not stock 3 units unless he has space for 9 units.

We are driven back once again to the conclusion that *there is no substitute for common sense and business judgment*. A businessman who wishes to act sensibly will base his stocking decisions on what *he* thinks about demand for the article in question, whether or not someone else may say that this is an "unobjective" way to act.

PROBLEMS

1. A manufacturer must decide whether to manufacture and market a new seasonal novelty which has just been developed to sell at $1.50 per unit. If he decides to manufacture it, he will have to purchase special machinery which will be scrapped after the season is over.   If a machine costing $1000 is bought, the variable cost of manufacturing will be $1 per unit; if a machine costing $5000 is bought, the variable manufacturing cost will be $.50 per unit.   In either case it will be possible to manufacture in small batches as sales actually occur and there will be no danger of having unsold merchandise left over at the end of the season.   The manufacturer's probability distribution for sales volume is shown in the table below.

Sales volume	Probability
1,000	½
5,000	¼
10,000	¼
	1

a. Draw up a *payoff* table, remembering that there are *three* possible acts.
b. Compute the expected profits of the three possible acts.
c. Draw up a *loss* table.
d. Compute the expected losses of the three possible acts.
e. What is the cost of uncertainty?

2. The Beacon Catering Corporation operated a cafeteria in a medium-sized industrial firm, serving about 50 of the firm's employees at lunchtime.   The ordinary check amounted to about 50 cents, and the gross margin was about 40 per cent.   After several years' operation, the management decided to offer its customers a special $1 hot lunch.   Gross margin on this item would also be about 40 per cent.

A question arose as to how much food to prepare for the special $1 lunch.   Any remaining at the end of the day would have to be thrown out; if the cafeteria ran short, on the other hand, the extra gross margin would be lost.   Any food remaining at the end of the day from the other items on the menu could be saved until the next day. The manager decided to experiment by preparing enough special lunches on each of the first 20 days to run a negligible risk of running short on any day.   Sales of the special lunch on these 20 days were as follows:

Day	Unit sales = demand	Day	Unit sales = demand
1	20	11	20
2	19	12	17
3	20	13	20
4	16	14	17
5	24	15	17
6	21	16	23
7	20	17	18
8	22	18	15
9	19	19	21
10	22	20	19

Assuming that all buyers of hot lunches would buy a cold lunch if the hot lunches were not available, *a.* Draw up a payoff table for stock levels from 17 through 22 and demands from 17 through 22.

b. Assuming that management assesses probabilities by simply equating them to historical relative frequencies, compute the expected profit of a decision to stock food for 20 hot lunches.

c. Draw up a loss table.

d. On the same assumption as in part *b*, compute the expected loss of a decision to stock food for 20 hot lunches.

CHAPTER 5

Incremental Analysis

Provided that expected monetary value is a valid guide to action in a given decision problem, the best act can always be found by computing and comparing the expected profits, costs, or opportunity losses of *all* the possible acts, but when the number of possible acts is large this method becomes extremely tedious. In many practical inventory problems the random variable "demand" will have hundreds or even thousands of possible values and consequently it will be necessary to choose among hundreds or thousands of acts (stock levels) none of which is *obviously* unreasonable. We would therefore like very much to find some way of selecting the best act without having to compute the expected profit, cost, or loss of *every* act, and in some kinds of problems this can be done very easily by the use of *incremental analysis*.

A decision on a stock level in an inventory problem of the kind we have been discussing can be analyzed incrementally by thinking of the decision as being the result, not of a direct choice among the acts $Q = 0$, 1, 2, and so forth, but as the result of *a whole sequence of decisions* each of which *increases* the stock level *by one unit*. In principle, we first decide whether a *first* unit should be stocked; if the answer is yes, we then decide whether a *second* unit should be stocked; and we continue in this way until we come to a point where we decide to increase the stock no further. In general, any decision which consists in selecting a *quantity* can be analyzed in this way, whether the quantity is a number stocked, a scrap allowance, or anything else:

> Instead of looking at the problem as one of making a *single* decision on a particular *number* of units, we can look at it as one of making a whole *sequence* of decisions, each one involving *one more* unit.

Just like the "single" decisions discussed in the last chapter, an incremental decision can be evaluated in terms of either (1) profit or cost or (2) opportunity loss. Only the analysis in terms of loss will be described in this chapter, but the student will not find it difficult to work out the corresponding analysis in terms of profit or cost. We shall take as an example the inventory problem discussed in the last chapter; for the student's convenience we repeat here the probability distribution originally given as Table 4.1 and add to it two columns of tail probabilities the need for which will appear in a moment.

Table 5.1

Demand z	$P(z)$	$P(\tilde{z} < z)$	$P(\tilde{z} \geq z)$
0	.05	0	1.00
1	.10	.05	.95
2	.25	.15	.85
3	.30	.40	.60
4	.20	.70	.30
5	.10	.90	.10
6+	0	1.00	0
	1.00		

5.1 Complete Analysis in Terms of Incremental Loss

The great advantage of the incremental method over the "direct" method which we have used previously lies in the fact that we can often identify the *last* unit which should be added without actually making any computations whatever concerning the earlier units in the sequence, but before showing how this can be done we shall explain the basic logic of the incremental method by analyzing a complete sequence of incremental decisions.

5.1.1 *The Decision Concerning a First Unit*

In deciding whether or not to stock a *first* unit (which is by no means the same as deciding whether or not to stock *exactly one* unit), there are just two possible *acts:* "stock" and "do not stock"; and there are just two *events* of interest: "no demand for a first unit" and "demand for a first unit." If the first unit is *not* stocked, the retailer's *profit* will obviously be 0 regardless of the event. If the first unit *is* stocked, the profit depends on the event: if the unit is demanded, the retailer's profit will be $3.70 - \$.20 - \$2.50 = \$1.00$; if it is not demanded, he will have a negative profit of $-\$2.50 + \$.50 = -\$2.00$. The *payoff* table for the decision concerning the first unit is shown as Table 5.2a.

The corresponding *loss* table is shown as Table 5.2b. It is derived from the payoff table in exactly the same way that Table 4.6 was derived from Table 4.5, but it could also have been derived directly by the reasoning in Section 4.3.2. If the retailer *stocks* a unit which is *not*

Table 5.2a Payoff Table for the First Unit			Table 5.2b Loss Table for the First Unit		
		Act			**Act**
Event	Do not stock	Stock	**Event**	Do not stock	Stock
No demand for first unit	$0*	−$2	No demand for first unit	$0	$2
Demand for first unit	0	+ 1*	Demand for first unit	1	0

demanded he will have to salvage it, and this will entail a loss amounting to the $2.00 difference between the $2.50 cost of the unit and its $.50 salvage value. If he *does not stock* a unit which *is demanded,* he loses the opportunity of making a profit of $1.00 corresponding to the difference between the $3.70 retail price of the unit and the $2.50 + $.20 = $2.70 which it would have cost him to buy and wrap the unit.

To find the *expected* opportunity losses of the acts "do not stock a first unit" and "stock a first unit," *probabilities* must be assigned to the events "no demand for first unit" and "demand for first unit" which appear in Table 5.2b. Now there will be *no* demand for a *first* unit if and only if the *total* quantity demanded is *less than one* unit, i.e. if $\tilde{z} < 1$, and the probability which the retailer has assigned to this event is .05 by Table 5.1. Similarly the probability that there *will* be a demand for a *first* unit is the same thing as the probability that the *total* quantity demanded will be *one or more* units, and $P(\tilde{z} \geq 1) = .95$ by Table 5.1. Given these two probabilities, the expected losses of the two possible acts are as shown in Table 5.3, and it is clear that *a first* unit *should* be stocked.

Table 5.3
Expected Losses of Stocking and Not Stocking a First Unit

Event	Probability	Loss of not stocking		Loss of stocking	
		Conditional	Expected	Conditional	Expected
$\tilde{z} < 1$; no demand for first unit	.05	$0	$0	$2	$ .10
$\tilde{z} \geq 1$; demand for first unit	.95	1	.95	0	0
	1.00		$ .95		$ .10

5.1.2 The Decision Concerning a Second Unit

Having decided to stock a first unit, we now proceed to consider stocking a *second* unit. The possible acts are again "stock" and "do not stock"; the relevant events are "no demand for a *second* unit" and "demand for a *second* unit." In making the entries in the payoff table we must remember that *a final decision has already been made concerning the first unit,* so that we are interested only in the consequences of a decision to stock or not to stock a *second* unit and not in the consequences of a decision to stock *two* units. If the retailer chooses not to stock the second unit, the *incremental* profit of *this* decision will be 0 regardless of the event, i.e. whether or not there is a demand for a second unit; *all the cash flows which occur will be due to the previous decision to stock the first unit.* If the retailer does decide to stock the second unit, his profit will be *increased* by \$3.70 − \$.20 − \$2.50 = \$1.00 if the *second* unit is demanded and can be sold at full price; it will be *decreased* by \$2.50 − \$.50 = \$2.00 if the *second* unit is not demanded and has to be salvaged. Accordingly the *payoff* table for the second unit has the entries shown in Table 5.4*a*.

Table 5.4a Payoff Table for the Second Unit			Table 5.4b Loss Table for the Second Unit		
	Act			Act	
Event	Do not stock	Stock	Event	Do not stock	Stock
No demand for second unit	0*	−\$2	No demand for second unit	\$0	\$2
Demand for second unit	0	+ 1*	Demand for second unit	1	0

The corresponding *loss* table is shown as Table 5.4*b*. Again, it was derived from Table 5.4*a* exactly as Table 4.6 was derived from Table 4.5, but again, it could have been derived directly by the reasoning in Section 4.3.2. Stocking an unsold second unit results in the loss of the \$2 difference between the cost and the salvage value *of that unit;* failure to stock a second unit which could have been sold results in loss of the opportunity to *add* \$1 to the retailer's total profit.

As in the case of the first unit, probabilities must be assigned to the two events in Table 5.4*b* before the *expected* losses of the two possible acts can be computed; and these probabilities are found by exactly the same kind of argument that we used in connection with the first unit. If the *total* quantity demanded is *less than two* units, there will be *no* demand for a *second* unit; if the total quantity demanded is *two or more* units, there *will* be a demand for a *second* unit.   From Table 5.1 we have $P(\tilde{z} < 2) = .15$ and $P(\tilde{z} \geq 2) = .85$, and we can then find that the expected losses of the two possible acts are as shown in Table 5.5.   The retailer should clearly stock a *second* unit as well as a *first;* the *total* stock should be *at least two* units.

Table 5.5
Expected Losses of Stocking and Not Stocking a Second Unit

Event	Probability	Loss of not stocking		Loss of stocking	
		Conditional	Expected	Conditional	Expected
$\tilde{z} < 2$; no demand for second unit	.15	\$0	\$0	\$2	\$ .30
$\tilde{z} \geq 2$; demand for second unit	.85	1	.85	0	0
	1.00		\$ .85		\$ .30

5.1.3   The Decision Concerning the jth Unit

The general pattern of the analysis should now be clear.   Letting j denote the "serial number" of *any* incremental decision, be it number 1, number 2, or any other number, the payoff and loss tables will be exactly like Tables 5.2 and 5.4 except that the word "first" or "second" is replaced by the word "*j*th," and the *expected* losses of the two possible acts will be as shown in Table 5.6.

Table 5.6
Expected Losses of Stocking and Not Stocking the jth Unit

Event	Probability	Loss of not stocking		Loss of stocking	
		Conditional	Expected	Conditional	Expected
No demand for jth unit	$P(\tilde{z} < j)$	\$0	\$0	\$2	$\$2\,P(\tilde{z} < j)$
Demand for jth unit	$P(\tilde{z} \geq j)$	1	$1\,P(\tilde{z} \geq j)$	0	0
	1		$\$1\,P(\tilde{z} \geq j)$		$\$2\,P(\tilde{z} < j)$

5.1.4   Complete Incremental Analysis

Applying the tail probabilities in Table 5.1 to the formulas shown as totals in Table 5.6, we obtain the results shown in Table 5.7.   From this

Table 5.7
Complete Incremental Analysis

Serial number of Unit j	$P(\tilde{z} \geq j)$	Expected loss of not stocking $1\ P(\tilde{z} \geq j)$	$P(\tilde{z} < j)$	Expected loss of stocking $2\ P(\tilde{z} < j)$
1	.95	$ .95	.05	$ .10
2	.85	.85	.15	.30
3	.60	.60	.40	.80
4	.30	.30	.70	1.40
5	.10	.10	.90	1.80
6+	0	0	1.00	2.00

table we can obtain the *total* expected loss of a decision to stock any particular *number of units* by simply adding up the *incremental* losses of (1) stocking the units which are stocked, and (2) not stocking those which are not stocked. Thus the expected loss of a decision to stock *three units* is $(.10 + .30 + .80) + $(.30 + .10 + 0) = $1.60, in exact agreement with the result obtained by direct analysis of the act "stock 3" in Table 4.7 of the previous chapter.

5.2   Selection of the Best Number to Stock

Looking back now at the incremental expected losses in the third and fifth columns of Table 5.7, we observe that:

1. Each successive loss of *not* stocking is *smaller* than the preceding one;
2. Each successive loss of *stocking* is *greater* than the preceding one.

This suggests that if all we were looking for had been the best number to stock, we could have stopped computing and settled on a total stock of *two units* as soon as we found that the incremental loss of stocking a *third unit* exceeded the incremental loss of not stocking that unit.

It is easy to prove that this guess is correct in *any* decision problem of the kind typified by our example. To do so let us define

k_u: the loss of *underage* which results from failure to stock one unit which could have been sold;

k_o: the loss of *overage* which results from stocking one unit which cannot be sold.

Then going back to Table 5.6 and substituting k_u for the particular value $1 which it had in our example and k_o for the particular value $2, we obtain the general result shown in Table 5.8:

Table 5.8
Expected Losses Associated with the jth Unit

Event	Probability	Loss of not stocking Conditional	Loss of not stocking Expected	Loss of stocking Conditional	Loss of stocking Expected
No demand for jth unit	$P(\tilde{z} < j)$	0	0	k_o	$k_o\, P(\tilde{z} < j)$
Demand for jth unit	$P(\tilde{z} \geq j)$	k_u	$k_u\, P(\tilde{z} \geq j)$	0	0
	1		$k_u\, P(\tilde{z} \geq j)$		$k_o\, P(\tilde{z} < j)$

and we see that, in general,

●●

Expected loss of not stocking the jth unit $= k_u\, P(\tilde{z} \geq j)$
Expected loss of stocking the jth unit $= k_o\, P(\tilde{z} < j)$

●●

Since $P(\tilde{z} < j)$ obviously cannot *decrease* as j increases, the incremental loss of stocking must either remain the same or *increase* as j increases.   Since on the other hand $P(\tilde{z} > j)$ cannot *increase* as j increases, the incremental loss of not stocking must either remain the same or *decrease* as j increases.   We can therefore be sure that:

1. If the incremental loss of stocking is *less* than the incremental loss of not stocking for any particular value of j, it is less for *all lower* values.
2. If the incremental loss of stocking is *greater* than the incremental loss of not stocking for any particular value of j, it is greater for *all higher* values.

Since we want to stock those units and only those units for which the loss of stocking is less than the loss of not stocking, it follows that

All that we need to do to find the best stock level Q^* in any problem of this sort is to find the highest value of j for which the incremental expected loss of stocking is less than the incremental expected loss of not stocking.

5.2.1 *Practical Location of the Last Profitable Unit*

In algebraic notation, the best number to stock is the highest j for which

$$k_o\, P(\tilde{z} < j) < k_u\, P(\tilde{z} \geq j).$$

It will be easier to find this highest value if we have to deal with only one cumulative probability rather than two, and therefore making use of the fact that the two tails of any distribution must add to 1 we replace $P(\tilde{z} \geq j)$ by $1 - P(\tilde{z} < j)$ and write the condition in the form

$$k_o\, P(\tilde{z} < j) < k_u[1 - P(\tilde{z} < j)].$$

By the use of a little elementary algebra this can be put into the more convenient form

$$P(\tilde{z} < j) < \frac{k_u}{k_u + k_o}$$

The best act in any problem of this sort can thus be found by the following steps:

1. Determine (1) the loss k_o which results from stocking one unsold unit and (2) the loss k_u which results from failure to stock one unit which could have been sold.

2. Compute the *"critical ratio"* $k_u/(k_u + k_o)$.

3. From the values already assigned to $P(z)$, compute $P(\tilde{z} < j)$ for $j = 1, 2, 3$, etc., until the last value of j has been found for which $P(\tilde{z} < j)$ is less than the critical ratio.

In our example, the critical ratio is

$$\frac{k_u}{k_u + k_o} = \frac{\$1}{\$1 + \$2} = .33.$$

Looking at the list of values of $P(\tilde{z} < j)$ in Table 5.1 we see at once that 2 is the highest value of j for which this probability is less than .33; the best stock level is therefore $Q^* = 2$.

PROBLEMS

1. In the problem of the Beacon Catering Corporation (Chapter 4, Problem 2):

a. Draw up a payoff table for an incremental decision concerning the jth hot lunch.

b. Draw up the corresponding loss table.

c. For how many hot lunches should management provide food?

d. What is the expected *profit* of the optimal decision?

e. What is the expected *loss* of the optimal decision?

f. How much could management afford to pay for a perfect forecast of demand?

g. What is the cost of irrationality of a decision to stock food for 20 hot lunches?

2. A newsstand operator buys the *Daily Racing Form* for 30 cents per copy and sells it for 50 cents. Any copies remaining unsold after the races are valueless. The operator believes that it is very important to avoid running short, since he is afraid that he will lose customers permanently if they find him an unreliable source of supply, and in order to minimize this risk he has adopted the policy of ordering 30 copies a

day. The distribution of daily requests for the journal over the last 100 days has been as follows:

Number requested	Relative frequency	Number requested	Relative frequency
Less than 20	0	27	.12
20	.01	28	.10
21	.04	29	.08
22	.07	30	.05
23	.10	31	.02
24	.12	32	.01
25	.14	Over 32	0
26	.14		

a. Assuming that running short would actually have *no* effect on any customer's tendency to return, draw up the *loss* table for a decision on stocking the *j*th copy.

b. On the assumption of part *a*, how many copies should be stocked?

c. What are the per-unit losses of underage and overage k_u and k_o if the operator believes that failure to satisfy any one customer's request for a journal will lead to *future* lost profits amounting to \$1 *in addition* to the lost profit on the immediate sale? This is an example of good-will cost, which we define as follows:

Good-will cost: the loss *over and above* immediate loss of profit which is incurred for *each unit* of unsatisfied demand.

d. How many units should the operator stock under the condition of *c*?

e. What is the smallest good-will cost which will justify the operator's actual stock of 30 copies?

CHAPTER 6

Measures of Location:
Fractiles and Expectations;
Linear Profits and Costs

In many situations we do not really need all the detailed information contained in a probability distribution or frequency distribution. In order to compute the total number of defectives in 100 lots of parts, we do not need to know the frequency with which each possible number of defectives occurred. All we need to know is a single number: the average or mean number of defectives per lot. Similarly we have seen in the previous chapter that in one kind of inventory problem we do not need the entire probability distribution of tomorrow's demand in order to decide on the best number of units to stock. All we need to know is a single number: the greatest number Q for which $P(\tilde{z} < Q)$ is less than a certain "critical ratio."

Numbers such as these are known as *measures of location* of a frequency or probability distribution. If we think of the distribution as represented by a histogram, we can think of such a number as specifying the *location* of the histogram on the horizontal axis without specifying anything about the *shape* of the histogram. We shall study two quite different kinds of measures of location in this chapter. The first kind consists of *fractiles*, of which the median is the best known example; the second consists of *expectations*, of which the ordinary arithmetic mean is the best-known example.

Our interest in measures of location is due only in small part to the fact that the amount of arithmetic required to solve a problem is often reduced by their use. Their real importance lies in the fact that when correctly used a measure of location *focuses our attention on the particular aspect of the probability distribution which is really critical for the problem at hand* and keeps us from being distracted by those aspects of the distribution which are irrelevant for that particular problem. On the other hand, the use of measures of location is attended by considerable danger. To cite a single example, one of the most common errors made by both students and businessmen is to assume that the best quantity to stock can be determined by looking only at average demand in situations where in fact the best decision *cannot* be found in this way. *In studying this chapter the student must therefore pay as close attention to what* cannot *be done with a given measure of location as he pays to what* can *be done with it.*

6.1 Fractiles

6.1.1 The Median

Before defining fractiles in general, let us consider the best known of the fractiles, the median.   Given a set of values (which may or may not be values of a random variable),

> Any value which is *both* (1) equal to or greater than half the values in the set *and* (2) equal to or less than half the values in the set is a *median* of the set.

In order to apply this definition to a given set of values we must:
1. List the values *in order of increasing size;*
2. Split the arrayed set in half.

To find the median of the values 5, 3, 2, 4, we first array them in the order 2, 3, 4, 5.   We then observe that since there are four values in the whole set, there must be two in each half.   The largest value in the lower half is therefore 3, the smallest value in the upper half is 4, and any value from 3 to 4 inclusive is a median of the set.   Notice that a value such as 3.2 is a median of this set even though the value 3.2 is not itself a *member* of the set.

Table 6.1

Serial number of lot	Number of defectives
1	2
2	4
3	0
4	2
5	4
6	3
7	3
8	1
9	3
10	5
	27

In many cases a set can be divided in half only by assigning some of the members with a certain value to the lower half and other members with this same value to the upper half. Thus in order to divide the set 2, 3, 3, 4 in half, we must assign one of the 3's to the lower half and one to the upper half. The only median of this set is 3. In other cases— whenever the number of members in the set is odd—one of the individual members must be "split" in order to divide the set into halves. The only median of the values 2, 3, 4 is 3: we may think of the member with value 3 as going half in the lower half of the set, half in the upper half.

Suppose now that 10 successive lots of purchased parts have been 100 per cent inspected, that the number of defectives found in each lot is as shown in Table 6.1, and that we wish to find the median or medians of these 10 values of the random variable "number of defectives." We first array the values in order of size: 0, 1, 2, 2, 3, 3, 3, 4, 4, 5. Since there are 10 values in the set, 5 must go in the lower half and 5 in the upper. The fifth value from the bottom is 3 and so is the sixth, so that the median is 3.

6.1.2 Fractiles in General

As we have said, the median is simply a special case of a *fractile*. The median of a set of values is known as the .5 fractile (read: point 5 fractile) and will be denoted by $F_{.5}$ because it is equal to or greater than *half* the values in the set. We now generalize this idea to define the "point f" fractile, where $.f$ is *any* fraction between 0 and 1. Given any set of values,

> Any value which is *both* (1) equal to or greater than a fraction $.f$ of the values in the set *and* (2) equal to or less than a fraction $(1 - .f)$ of the values in the set is a $.f$ *fractile* of the set.

To find the .25 fractile or $F_{.25}$ of the values 5, 3, 2, 4, we first array them in the order 2, 3, 4, 5 and then split this set of four values into two parts, a lower part containing $.25 \times 4 = 1$ value and an upper part containing the remaining three values. The largest value in the lower part of the set is 2, the smallest value in the upper part is 3, and therefore any value from 2 to 3 inclusive is a .25 fractile of this set. Similarly any value from 4 to 5 inclusive is a .75 fractile of the set.

In many cases a set can be divided into a lower part containing $.f$ of the members and an upper part containing the remainder only by assigning some of the members with a certain value to the lower part and other members with this same value to the upper part. The only .2 fractile of the values 2, 2, 3, 4, 5 is 2: one of the 2's in the set is assigned to the lower .2 of the set and the other to the upper .8. In other cases one of the individual members must be "split" in order to divide the set in the specified manner. The only .3 fractile of the values 1, 2, 3, 4 is 2: we need 1.2 members to make up the lower .3 of this set of four values, and we may think of the value 2 as going partly in this lower .3 of the set and partly in the upper .7.

6.1.3 *Computation of Fractiles from Relative Frequencies or Probabilities*

Now that we have seen how to compute fractiles from a *complete list* of the values taken on by a random variable we are ready to learn how to compute them when the values taken on by the variable have been put into the form of a *frequency distribution*. As an example we show in Table 6.2 a frequency distribution of the values of the random variable "number of defectives" which are listed in Table 6.1 in their historical order, and in Figure 6.1 we show a graph of the cumulative frequencies of Table 6.2.

Table 6.2

Value z of the random variable	Relative frequency of z	Cumulative frequency of z or less
0	.1	.1
1	.1	.2
2	.2	.4
3	.3	.7
4	.2	.9
5	.1	1.0
	1.0	

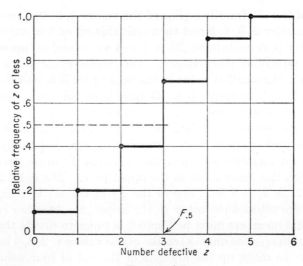

Figure 6.1

Suppose now that we wish to find the .5 fractile of the distribution of Table 6.2. Recalling the rules for reading graphs of cumulative distributions as given in Section 3.4.2, we can see from Figure 6.1 that .4 of the frequency belongs to values of the variable *less than* 3 while .7 of the frequency belongs to values of 3 *or less*. In order to divide the whole set of values into a lower .5 and an upper .5, we must split the 3's and assign some of them to the lower group and some to the upper. Accordingly the .5 fractile or median of this distribution is 3.

The horizontal dashed line in Figure 6.1 shows how any fractile can be located immediately by use of a graph of a cumulative distribution. If we are looking for the .5 fractile, the line is drawn at height .5 on the *vertical* axis; the .5 fractile is then the value on the *horizontal* axis directly below the point where the dashed line cuts the graph of the distribution. In general,

> To find the .f fractile of any frequency distribution, plot the cumulative distribution, read across from the value .f on the vertical axis to the curve, and read down from this point on the curve to the horizontal axis.

Thus we can immediately read from Figure 6.1 that $F_{.3} = 2$, that $F_{.8} = 4$, and so forth.

We have already seen that in some cases a fractile has a range of values rather a single, unique value. In terms of a graph of the cumulative distribution, these are the fractiles whose broken lines coincide with a "flat" in the graph rather than cutting a "riser." If we look for the .4 fractile of the distribution of Figure 6.1, the fact that a line drawn at height .4 would coincide with the top of the jump above the value 2 on the horizontal axis shows that *all* the 2's in the set must go in the lower .4; the fact that the same dashed line would coincide with the bottom of the jump above the value 3 shows that *all* the 3's must go in the upper .6; accordingly any value in the interval 2 to 3 inclusive is a .4 fractile of this distribution. Similarly any value from 1 to 2 is a .2 fractile, any value from 3 to 4 is a .7 fractile, and so forth.

No new problems arise when we wish to compute the fractiles of a *probability* distribution:

> The fractiles of a probability distribution are computed by using the probabilities in exactly the same way that relative frequencies are used in computing the fractiles of a frequency distribution.

6.1.4 An Example of the Use of Fractiles

In Chapter 5 we saw that in a certain class of inventory problems the best stock level was the highest number Q for which

$$P(\tilde{z} < Q) < \frac{k_u}{k_u + k_o}$$

and we discussed in detail an example in which the "critical ratio" $k_u/(k_u + k_o)$ had the value .33.   The probability distribution assigned to "demand" in that example is reproduced in Table 6.3 and the cumulative

Table 6.3

Demand z	Probability $P(z)$	Cumulative $P(\tilde{z} \leq z)$
0	.05	.05
1	.10	.15
2	.25	.40
3	.30	.70
4	.20	.90
5	.10	1.00
	1.00	

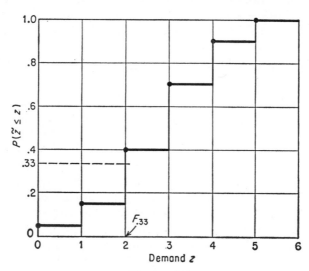

Figure 6.2

probabilities are graphed in Figure 6.2.   If now we draw in a dashed line to locate the .33 fractile of this distribution, we can make the following observations

1. $F_{.33} = 2$.
2. $P(\tilde{z} < 2) < .33$ but $P(\tilde{z} < 3) > .33$.

In other words:

The optimum stock level in problems of this sort is simply the $k_u/(k_u + k_o)$ fractile of the distribution of the random variable "demand."

Henceforth we shall refer to this fractile as the "critical fractile" in problems of this kind.†

6.2 Expectations

6.2.1 The Arithmetic Mean

The arithmetic mean of a set of values is simply their everyday "average," defined as follows:

Arithmetic mean: the sum of a set of values divided by the number of values in the set.

The mean of the values in Table 6.1 is

$$\frac{1}{10}(2 + 4 + 0 + 2 + 4 + 3 + 3 + 1 + 3 + 5) = \frac{27}{10} = 2.7.$$

6.2.2 Computation of the Arithmetic Mean from Relative Frequencies or Probabilities

When we computed fractiles from original data, all we did was arrange the individual values in order of size and then count off from the left; when we computed them from relative frequencies, all we did was arrange the values in this same way and then cumulate their relative frequencies. There was no need for arithmetical operations. The mean, on the contrary, rests on an *averaging* operation; and if we replace the original data by a frequency distribution *we must use the frequencies as weights in this averaging.*

Table 6.4

Value of the random variable
0
1
2
2
3
3
3
4
4
5
$\overline{27}$

Table 6.5

Value of the random variable	Number of occurrences	Product
0	1	0
1	1	1
2	2	4
3	3	9
4	2	8
5	1	5
	$\overline{10}$	$\overline{27}$

† It is left to the student to show that when the critical fractile has a range of values rather than a single value, total expected profit is the same whichever one of these values is selected for the stock level. If the critical fractile had been .40 instead of .33 in our example, then total expected profit would have been the same with a stock of 3 units as with a stock of 2 units.

Let us reexamine the computation of the mean of the distribution of Table 6.1 as we carried it out above. If we rearrange the data in order of increasing value of the variable we have Table 6.4; the mean is still the total divided by the number of items, or $27/10 = 2.7$. Now instead of writing down two identical rows for the value 2, three rows for 3, and two rows for 4, we can get the same total, 27, by writing each value of the variable once and multiplying it by the number of times that the value occurs. This is done in Table 6.5. To get the mean we *divide the sum of the products by the sum of the weights;* this divisor, of course, is simply the total number of occurrences as before.

Again we will get exactly the same result if, instead of adding the products and then dividing their sum by 10, we divide each of the individual products by 10 before adding; and instead of doing that, we can divide each of the numbers of occurrences by 10 before computing the products. The last two columns of Table 6.5 would then be as shown in Table 6.6. *Since the sum of the weights is now 1, the mean is simply the total in the last column.*

Table 6.6

Value of the random variable	Number of occurrences divided by 10	Product
0	.1	0
1	.1	.1
2	.2	.4
3	.3	.9
4	.2	.8
5	.1	.5
	1.0	2.7

The weights of this last table are actually relative frequencies, and in general

> The mean of a frequency distribution is a *weighted average* of the values of the variable, each value being weighted by its relative frequency. Since relative frequencies always add to 1, the sum of the weights is 1 and there is no need to divide by it to get the average.

No new problems arise when we wish to compute the mean of a *probability* distribution:

> The mean of a probability distribution is computed by using the probabilities in exactly the same way that relative frequencies are used in computing the mean of a frequency distribution.

6.2.3　*The Expected Value of a Random Variable*

Recall now that to compute the *expected value* of the various profits which might result from a given act, we multiplied each possible profit by the probability that it would be made and added these products. But *"profit" in such a computation is just a special case of a random variable, i.e., a variable which has a definite "conditional" value for every possible event;* and when we compute the mean of the probability distribution of *any* random variable we are computing the expected value of that variable. In general, we define for any random variable

> *Expected value or expectation:* the quantity obtained by multiplying each possible value of a random variable by the probability of that value and adding the products.

The expected value of the random variable "demand" under the probability distribution of Table 4.1 is computed in Table 6.7 by way of example.

Table 6.7

z	$P(z)$	$z\,P(z)$
0	.05	0
1	.10	.10
2	.25	.50
3	.30	.90
4	.20	.80
5	.10	.50
6+	0	0
	1.00	2.80

We shall uniformly denote the expected value of a random variable by the symbol E (for expectation) followed by the "name" of the variable in parentheses. Thus if the random variable is called $\tilde{z}$, the expected value of $\tilde{z}$ or mean of the distribution of $\tilde{z}$ will be denoted by $E(\tilde{z})$.

6.3　Straight-line Conditional Profits and Costs; Applications of Expectations

The great majority of the decision problems which we shall study in this course will involve conditional profits or costs which are *linear functions* of some basic random variable, and in all such problems the burden of analysis can be lessened and clarity increased by the use of expectations of the basic random variable.

6.3.1   *Linear Conditional Profit or Cost*

Let us start by considering a simple artificial problem which will illustrate the meaning and importance of linear or straight-line conditional profits. Suppose that a lottery is to be conducted by rolling an irregular die with faces serially numbered from 0 to 5 rather than 1 to 6, that we are given a ticket which entitles us to receive $2 times the number which comes up plus an additional $5 regardless of the result of the roll, and that after inspection of the die we assign the probability distribution shown in Table 6.8 to the basic random variable "number which comes up."   If we use z to denote the value actually taken on by this basic random variable, the conditional profit of holding the ticket can be written

Conditional profit = \$5 + \$2 z.

In Table 6.8 our usual method of computation is used to show that the *expected* profit of holding this ticket is $10.40, but we shall now see

Table 6.8

z	$P(z)$	Conditional profit	Expected profit
0	.1	\$5 + 0 × \$2 = \$ 5	\$ .50
1	.1	\$5 + 1 × \$2 = 7	.70
2	.2	\$5 + 2 × \$2 = 9	1.80
3	.3	\$5 + 3 × \$2 = 11	3.30
4	.2	\$5 + 4 × \$2 = 13	2.60
5	.1	\$5 + 5 × \$2 = 15	1.50
	1.0		\$10.40

that *this expected profit can be calculated from the expected value of the basic random variable $\bar{z}$ without the use of any other information concerning the distribution of $\bar{z}$.*   Instead of computing the net conditional profit for each value of the basic random variable and then multiplying this net by the probability of that value as we did in Table 6.8, we could have made each entry as the sum of two parts, as we shall show by taking the entries for $\bar{z} = 3$ as an example.   The $11 conditional profit for $\bar{z} = 3$ is made up of the two parts,

$5 + (3 × \$2),

and instead of entering .3 × \$11 = \$3.30 in the last column of Table 6.8 we could have multiplied .3 into each of the two parts separately and entered

(.3)\$5 + .3(3 × \$2).

Furthermore it is obviously legitimate to regroup the term .3(3 × $2) and write it as (.3 × 3)$2, so that for $\bar{z} = 3$ the complete entry in the last column could have been written as

$$(.3)\$5 + (.3 \times 3)\$2.$$

Table 6.9 is identical to Table 6.8 except that all the entries in the last column have been made in this new form; to obtain the total of

Table 6.9

z	P(z)	Conditional profit	Expected profit
0	.1	$5 + 0 × $2	(.1)$5 + (.1 × 0)$2
1	.1	$5 + 1 × $2	(.1)$5 + (.1 × 1)$2
2	.2	$5 + 2 × $2	(.2)$5 + (.2 × 2)$2
3	.3	$5 + 3 × $2	(.3)$5 + (.3 × 3)$2
4	.2	$5 + 4 × $2	(.2)$5 + (.2 × 4)$2
5	.1	$5 + 5 × $2	(.1)$5 + (.1 × 5)$2
	1.0		(1.0)$5 + (2.7)$2

this column, which will give us the expected profit, we now make two observations.

1. The first term in each line consists of P(z) multiplied by the constant factor $5. Instead of multiplying out each of these terms and then adding, we can add the values of P(z) and then multiply by the constant $5. But since the total probability of all possible values of any random variable is 1, the result of this calculation is simply 1 times the constant $5.

2. The second term in each line consists of the product z P(z) (in parentheses) multiplied by the constant factor $2. Instead of multiplying out each of these terms and then adding, we can multiply out only the portion z P(z) within the parentheses, add *these* products to get the total 2.7, and then multiply this total by the constant $2. This 2.7, however, is simply the expected value of the basic random variable $\bar{z}$, since it is computed by multiplying every possible value of $\bar{z}$ by its probability and adding the products, and therefore in this example

Expected profit $= \$5 + \$2 \, E(\bar{z})$.

The important thing to notice is that *this formula for the* expected *profit is identical to the formula given previously for the* conditional *profit except that z is replaced by* E($\bar{z}$). This result can be generalized as follows:

Whenever the conditional profits or costs for *all possible values* of the basic random variable are given by a formula of the type

Conditional profit or cost $= K + kz$,

where K and k are *constants*, the expected profit or cost is given by the formula

Expected profit or cost $= K + k\,\mathrm{E}(\bar{z})$.

The student must pay particular attention to the words "all possible values" in this rule: *it is only because we summed the products $z\,\mathrm{P}(z)$ for all possible values of $\bar{z}$ in Table 6.9 that the quantity $\mathrm{E}(\bar{z})$ appeared in our result.*

Graphic Representation of Linear Conditional Profits. Conditional profits or costs given by formulas of the type $K + kz$ are called straight-line or *linear* because when the conditional profit or cost is plotted against the value of the basic random variable the graph is a straight line. The principle is illustrated in Figure 6.3 for the example just discussed.

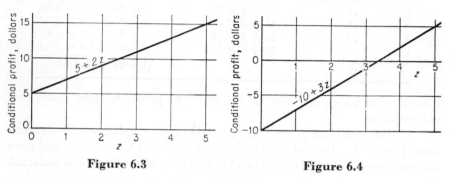

Figure 6.3   Figure 6.4

Application to an Inventory Problem. Let us now reconsider the computation of expected profit with a stock $Q = 5$ in the inventory problem discussed at length in Chapter 4. In Section 4.1 we saw that when the demand z was no greater than the stock Q, the conditional profit was given by the formula

Conditional profit $= -\$2\,Q + \$3\,z = -\$10 + \$3\,z$.

Since values of $\bar{z}$ greater than 5 are impossible by Table 4.1, this formula applies to *all possible* values of $\bar{z}$ when $Q = 5$; the conditional profit for this case has the graph shown in Figure 6.4.

The fact that this graph of conditional profit is a straight line over the whole range of possible values of $\bar{z}$ entitles us to apply the formula

Expected profit $= K + k\,\mathrm{E}(\bar{z})$.

It was shown in Table 6.7 that $\mathrm{E}(\bar{z}) = 2.8$ for the probability distribution assigned by the retailer; noticing that in our present problem K has a *negative* value,

$K = -\$10,$

we obtain

$$\text{Expected profit} = -\$10 + \$3\ E(\tilde{z}) = -\$10 + \$8.40 = -\$1.60$$

in agreement with Table 4.4.

6.3.2   Broken-line Conditional Profit or Cost

Suppose now that we wish to compute expected profit in this same inventory problem but with a stock of 2 rather than with a stock of 5. In this case, as shown in Section 4.1, we have two different formulas for the conditional profit, one of which applies when $z \leq 2$, the other when $z > 2$:

$$\text{Conditional profit} = \begin{cases} -\$4 + \$3\ z & \text{if } z \leq 2, \\ +\$2 & \text{if } z > 2. \end{cases}$$

This conditional profit is graphed in Figure 6.5, where it appears as a *broken* straight line.

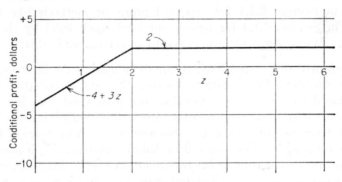

Figure 6.5

The expected profit for this case is computed in Table 6.10 by a method similar to the one used in Table 6.9 except that two *subtotals* are

Table 6.10

z	$P(z)$	Conditional profit	Expected profit
0	.05	$-\$4 + 0 \times \$3 = -\$4$	$.05(-\$4) + (.05 \times 0)\ \$3 = -\$\ .20$
1	.10	$-\$4 + 1 \times \$3 = -\ 1$	$.10(-\$4) + (.10 \times 1)\ \$3 = -\ \ .10$
2	.25	$-\$4 + 2 \times \$3 = +\ 2$	$.25(-\$4) + (.25 \times 2)\ \$3 = +\ \ .50$
Subtotal	.40		$.40(-\$4) + \quad 60 \times \$3 \qquad = +\$\ .20$
3	.30	$\$2$	$.30 \times \$2 = +\ \ .60$
4	.20	$\$2$	$.20 \times \$2 = +\ \ .40$
5	.10	$\$2$	$.10 \times \$2 = +\ \ .20$
Subtotal	.60		$.60 \times \$2 = +\$1.20$
Total	1.00		$+\$1.40$

brought out, one for the values of $\bar{z}$ to which the first formula for conditional profit applies and one for the values to which the second formula applies.   It takes only a brief examination of the last column of this table to realize that in this case the mean of the distribution of $\bar{z}$ can *not* be factored out of the total profit in the way in which the mean was factored out of the total of the last column of Table 6.9.

It is *only* when the conditional profits or costs for *all* possible values of the basic random variable are given by a *single* formula of the type $K + kz$ that the expected profit or cost can be found by use of the mean of the distribution.   *In all other cases we must use the complete distribution.*

6.4   The Choice and Use of a Measure of Location

The student is not expected to memorize formulas like the one derived in Section 6.3.1 for expected profit or methods like the one derived in Section 6.1.4 for finding the best stock level by the use of fractiles.   What the student *is* expected to remember is this:

When probability distributions are to be used as the basis for a business decision, the question whether the full distribution can be replaced by a measure of location, and if so which one, is not to be answered by some kind of vague discussion concerning the "representativeness" of various possible measures.   A measure of location may be used in place of a full probability distribution if and only if it can be *proved* that *in the particular problem at hand* the expected costs can be correctly calculated or the best decision can be correctly identified by use of the particular measure under consideration.

One of the commonest errors in dealing with problems involving uncertainty is to assume incorrectly that the full distribution can be replaced by some "measure of central tendency" such as the mean or median.   When the full distribution can be replaced by some measure of location, the correct measure is usually *not* a "measure of central tendency."   In inventory problems of the kind we have been studying, the best decision can be found by use of the median only when the critical ratio $k_u/(k_u + k_o)$ has the value .5; the cost of a decision can be evaluated by use of the mean only when the decision is to carry so much stock that there is absolutely no chance that it will fail to meet the demand.

Even more important, it is not to be assumed that *every* problem can be solved by the use of *some* measure of location and that the only problem is choosing the correct measure.   *Most problems require the full distribution; it is only exceptionally that we can replace it by a measure of location or by any other single number.*

PROBLEMS

1. Considering the distribution given in Chapter 5, Problem 2, as a probability distribution rather than a frequency distribution:

a. Graph $P(\tilde{z} \leq z)$ against z.

b. Show that $F_{.1} = 22$, $F_{.2} = 23$, $F_{.5} = 26$, and that $F_{.74}$ is any value from 27 to 28 inclusive.

c. Using $\tilde{z}$ to denote the random variable "number requested," show that $E(\tilde{z}) = 25.70$.

d. Compute the critical ratio from the cost data in the original problem, use your answer to (a) to find the optimum stock by the method of Section 6.1.4, and check against your answer to the original problem.

2. Assuming that in the situation of Chapter 4, Problem 2, management assesses probabilities by equating them to historical relative frequencies, and using $\tilde{z}$ to denote the random variable "demand":

a. Graph $P(\tilde{z} \leq z)$ against z.

b. Compute the critical ratio from the data of the original problem, use your answer to (a) to find the optimum stock by the method of Section 6.1.4, and check against your answer to the original problem.

3. A store sells for $4 an item costing $3. Selling expenses amount to 10 per cent of sales. If the item is out of stock, customers demanding it will simply go next door, where it is displayed in the window. At the end of 1 day, the manager notices that there are only 5 units left in stock. Under the following assumptions what is the expected loss due to the manager's failure to reorder earlier?

a. It always takes exactly 1 day to place an order with the supplier and to get delivery. Demand for the item over the past 1000 days has been as follows:

Number demanded	Number of occurrences		Number demanded	Number of occurrences
5	3		12	148
6	21		13	59
7	45		14	34
8	75		15	22
9	130		16	12
10	186		17	2
11	263			

b. Sales of the item have been regularly 10 units every day, but the time to place an order and get delivery is irregular: it usually takes 3 business days, but 25 per cent of the time it takes 4 days and 10 per cent of the time it takes 5.

c. Daily sales are distributed as in part a and delivery time is distributed as in part b. [HINT: Take "lead time" as the basic random variable and use your answer to (a) to get the conditional losses.]

CHAPTER 7

Assessment of Probabilities
by Smoothing Historical Frequencies†

Our object in the last three chapters has been to learn how to use probabilities once they have been assessed rather than to learn how to assess them, and accordingly we have simply equated probabilities to historical relative frequencies in various exercises without stopping to worry about the arguments given in Section 1.6 to show that when *all* the available information is considered such a procedure will often appear to be clearly unreasonable, particularly when the historical frequencies rest on only a small number of trials. In this chapter we shall study one group of methods by which observed relative frequencies may be modified or adjusted in order to make more reasonable assessments of probabilities.

7.1 The Historical Record Considered as a Sample

Consider the historical frequency distribution of daily demand shown in Table 7.1 and graphed in Figure 7.1*a*. There is a "dip" in the relative

Table 7.1

Demand z	Number of occurrences	Relative frequency
2	1	.063
3	3	.187
4	2	.125
5	4	.250
6	3	.187
7	2	.125
8	0	.000
9	1	.063
10+	0	.000
	16	1.000

† The contents of this chapter are not required in any subsequent chapter.

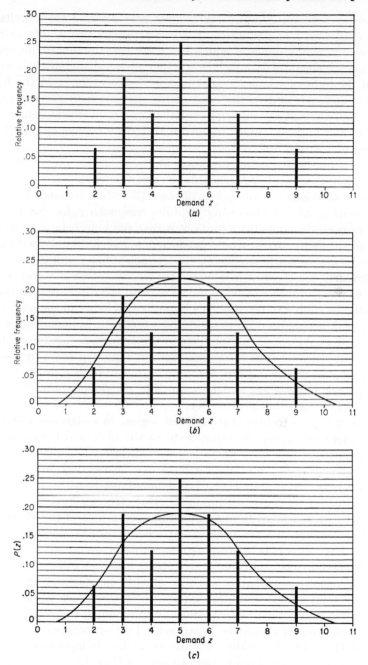

Figure 7.1

frequencies between demand for 3 units and demand for 5 units and another between 7 and 9 units. Before adopting a probability distribution for tomorrow's demand which is a mere copy of this frequency distribution, we should ask ourselves whether such a distribution is reasonable in the light of whatever general knowledge we have of the factors affecting demand; and in the light of the discussion in Section 1.6 this means that we must ask ourselves whether we would expect demand on a large number of days "like" tomorrow to have a frequency distribution like that of Figure 7.1*a*.

Under most circumstances almost any sensible person would answer immediately that it is *not* reasonable to expect demands for 7 and 9 units to occur with relative frequencies .125 and .063 while demands for 8 units never occur at all. Unless some definite, *assignable cause* can be found which *prevents* demands for 8 units, it is reasonable to believe that a long run of days like tomorrow would produce demands for 8 units with a relative frequency somewhere *between* the frequencies of 7 and 9 units.

Similarly for the dip in relative frequency between 3 and 5 units: unless a specific cause can be found to explain the dip, a reasonable person would be willing to bet that in a hypothetical long run the relative frequency of demands for 4 units would be *between* the frequencies for 3 and 5 units and would assign probabilities to tomorrow's demand accordingly.

Finally, the fact that no demand for less than 2 or more than 9 units has occurred in the 16 days in the record is not in itself a proof that such demands are impossible; and a reasonable person might well want to assign them some small probability.

This intuitive feeling that it is not logical to assign probabilities in this problem by simply equating them to the historical frequencies can be rationalized as follows. Certain factors affecting demand on any given day can be identified and their effects can be isolated and measured. Thus we may know that Saturday demand tends to be greater than Friday demand by a certain amount. But after we have identified all the factors we can identify and thus explained a part of the variation in historical demand, we are usually left with a certain amount of unexplained variation. It is because we are unable to *explain* all the variation in *past* demand that we are *uncertain* about *tomorrow's* demand.

It is usually reasonable to think of this unexplained variation as being the joint effect of a large number of factors each of which individually has only a small effect, since any individual factor which has a large effect can and should be identified. Furthermore we may usually think of these small, residual factors as acting independently of each other—if several small factors tend to act together, the group as a whole will produce large effects and therefore can and should be identified. Consequently *it is reasonable under most circumstances to think of demand on any one day as being equal to some "basic" amount determined by the identified factors plus or minus a "deviation" which is really the sum of a large number of small, independent deviations due to the unidentified factors.*

Let us now simplify the problem for a moment by imagining that although some deviations will be positive while others will be negative, all the deviations are of equal absolute size. If this were true, the variation in demand would be something like the variation in the number of heads turning up when 100 coins are tossed repeatedly. Even though some or all of these coins may be badly bent, so that the probability of heads for any one coin may be far from $\frac{1}{2}$, intuition tells us immediately that in the long run:

1. There will be some one most common number of heads;
2. The relative frequencies of other numbers of heads will be smaller the farther the numbers are from this most common number.

If, therefore, a very short series of tosses showed, say, that 54 heads had occurred twice, 56 heads once, and 55 heads not at all, we would nevertheless insist that *in the long run* 55 heads would occur with a relative frequency somewhere between the frequency of 54 heads and the frequency of 56. In other words, irregularities in the long-run frequency distribution of number of heads would seem inconsistent with our intuitive ideas concerning the nature of the chance mechanism or random process generating this number. We would say that the irregularities in the record are due to the fact that these tosses are only a "sample" of the behavior of the random process and that the absence of 55 heads from the record reflected "sampling error" rather than the true long-run behavior of the process.

We do not, of course, really think that the total deviation of demand from its most common value is the sum of deviations which are exactly of equal size, but this part of the analogy is not essential. A closer analogy would be a sequence of rolls of 1000 deformed dice, all different, and here again intuition tells us (and it can be proved) that in any really long sequence of rolls of the 1000 dice:

1. There will be some one most common total number of spots showing,
2. The relative frequencies of other numbers will be smaller the farther the numbers are from this most common number.

This analogy is close enough to our notions of the mechanism generating demand to justify the proposition that the *long-run frequency distribution and therefore the probability distribution of demand should fall away* smoothly *on either side of a* single *most probable value.*

7.2 Smoothing a Frequency Distribution

In a great many situations the *only* available evidence on the behavior of the random process generating values of some random variable is (1) a frequency distribution of values actually generated by the process in the past and (2) the knowledge that we have eliminated from this distribution the effect of every assignable cause which we are able to identify. In such cases the only reasonable way of estimating the long-run behavior of the process and thus assessing a probability distribution for the next value which will be generated by the process is to smooth this historical frequency distribution.

This has been done for the data of Table 7.1 in Figure 7.1c (not *b*). A smooth curve has been drawn in such a way that the *total amount added to the frequencies of certain demands equals the total amount subtracted from the frequencies of all other demands.* Like the type of graph shown in Figure 3.2, the curve has no meaning except at the points corresponding to integral values of the sales volume.

Table 7.2

Demand	Ordinate of Figure 7.1b	Probability
0	0	0
1	.01	.009
2	.07	.060
3	.16	.138
4	.21	.181
5	.22	.190
6	.21	.181
7	.15	.129
8	.08	.069
9	.04	.034
10	.01	.009
11+	0	0
	1.16	1.000

Fitting the Curve.   It is difficult in a single operation to fit a smooth curve to an irregular graph like Figure 7.1a and make it come out in such a way that it both has the right shape and leads to probabilities which add up exactly to 1.   In practice it is easier to break the fitting procedure down into two steps.

1. Fit by eye a smooth curve which has the right general *shape*.
2. Adjust the curve so that the probabilities will add to 1 by reading

the curve at each possible value of the variable, adding the readings, and then increasing or decreasing every point on the curve by the same proportional amount.

The curve shown in Figure 7.1c was actually derived from the curve in Figure 7.1b. This latter curve was fitted by eye and the ordinates listed in column 2 of Table 7.2 were read from it. Each figure in column 2 was then divided by the total of the column (1.16) to obtain a set of *probabilities* which would add to 1. Once these probabilities were listed in column 3 of the table, the smoothing was really complete; the only reason for plotting the probabilities in Figure 7.1c and drawing a smooth curve through the plotted points was to obtain a visual check on the reasonableness of the final results.

7.2.1 Assignable Causes

Now that the student has learned how to smooth out all the irregularities in a frequency distribution, let him beware of doing this indiscriminately. *Assignable causes for irregularities often exist:* if we make the effort, we *are* often able to find reasons for dips in a historical frequency distribution. In the case of daily demand, this means that we can often explain why the frequencies bunch in two or more ranges by looking for factors which were present on the days (or months or other periods) showing high demand and which were absent on the days showing low demand or vice versa.

It has already been pointed out that if the data in the record apply to all days in the week, we may find that demand was usually higher on Saturday than on other days. Unless our general knowledge of consumer behavior leads us to a strong belief that there is no real reason for this phenomenon, we should *not* reject it as an accident of chance, which is what we are doing implicitly if we assess a probability distribution by smoothing a frequency distribution containing data on both Saturdays and other days. Rather, we should use only Saturday data to arrive at a probability distribution for next Saturday's demand, and so forth. If demand in summer was higher than demand in winter and it is reasonable to believe that there is a real cause for this phenomenon, summer and winter data should not be lumped in arriving at a probability distribution.

The help which even a professional statistician can derive from probability theory in deciding whether irregularities in a historical frequency distribution are to be attributed to an assignable cause or to chance is usually very slight. *Basically, the problem is one to be decided by the use of judgment, and judgment must be based more on a general understanding of the real phenomena under study than on statistical theory.*

7.3   Smoothing of Extremely Sparse Data

Consider next the historical frequency distribution of demand shown in Table 7.3 and graphed in Figure 7.2.   As can be seen in the figure, the

Table 7.3

Demand z	Number of occurrences	Relative frequency
9	1	.1
11	1	.1
15	1	.1
16	1	.1
17	1	.1
20	1	.1
22	1	.1
24	1	.1
29	1	.1
35	1	.1
	10	1.0

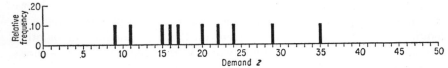

Figure 7.2

demands "bunch" in the range 15 to 24 and suggest that the probability distribution should be of the same general shape as the curve in Figure 7.1c; but because all the individual bars in the figure are of the same height it is impossible to fit a smooth curve by the method used to produce Figure 7.1c.   When the historical data are as sparse as those of Table 7.3, it is much more effective to make a smoothed assessment of the *cumulative* probability distribution than it is to use the method described in Section 7.2.

When we smoothed the frequency distribution of Figure 7.1a, what we did in effect was:

1. Take the historical relative frequency of each recorded demand as a *preliminary estimate* of the long-run relative frequency of that demand;
2. *Adjust* these preliminary estimates so that the whole distribution would be smooth and of reasonable shape.

In our present problem we shall use an analogous procedure:

1. Make a *preliminary estimate* of the long-run *cumulative* relative frequency corresponding to each recorded demand;
2. *Adjust* these preliminary estimates so that the whole distribution will be smooth and of reasonable shape.

7.3.1   *Estimates of Fractiles*

The first point to observe when we set out to estimate a long-run *cumulative* frequency is this: *when the record contains only a very few observations, it is contrary to common sense to use the historical cumulative frequency of any value of a random variable as an estimate of the long-run cumulative frequency of that value.* The truth of this assertion can easily be seen by considering the values 35 and 9 of the random variable "demand" in our example.

As can be seen from Table 7.3, the historical cumulative frequency of 35 or less is 1. We know, however, that it is extremely unlikely that a "sample" of only 10 demands includes the *highest possible* demand; and therefore 1 is not a sensible estimate of the long-run cumulative frequency of 35 or less. Similarly, the historical cumulative frequency of less than 9 is 0; but it is not at all likely that 9 is the *lowest possible* demand and therefore 0 is not a sensible estimate of the long-run cumulative frequency of less than 9.

In order to find a way of making more reasonable preliminary estimates of long-run cumulative frequencies, let us think of what would happen if the random process generating tomorrow's demand were to operate on each of a very large number of days "like" tomorrow, and to make the discussion concrete let us think of 11,000 days. Further, let us think of these 11,000 days as having been arrayed in order of quantity demanded and then given a *rank number*. The day with the smallest demand will have rank 1; the day with the largest demand will have rank 11,000; days with identical demands are ranked arbitrarily among themselves. Then it can be proved that if a sample of 10 days is drawn from these 11,000 days, the expected rank number of the lowest-ranking day in the sample is 1000, the rank number of the $\frac{1}{11}$, *not* the $\frac{1}{10}$, fractile of the 11,000 demands. The expected rank of the second-lowest day in the sample is 2000, the rank of the $\frac{2}{11}$ fractile of the 11,000 demands; and so forth. The expected rank of the highest-ranking day in the sample is 10,000, *not* 11,000, and this is the rank of the $\frac{10}{11}$ fractile of the 11,000 demands.

Consequently the smallest demand in a sample of 10 demands is a reasonable estimate of the $\frac{1}{11}$ fractile of the distribution of demands from which the sample is drawn; the largest demand in the sample is a reasonable estimate of the $\frac{10}{11}$ fractile of the distribution; and so forth. More generally,

If a sample of *n* observations is drawn from some distribution and arrayed in order of size, the *k*th observation is a reasonable estimate of the $k/(n + 1)$ fractile of the distribution.

If there are 25 observations in the sample, the third smallest is a reasonable estimate of the $\frac{3}{26} = .115$ fractile of the distribution from which the sample is drawn, and so forth.

7.3.2 *Fitting and Reading the Cumulative Probability Distribution*

Let us now proceed to assess a probability distribution for tomorrow's demand by using the 10 demands in the record of Table 7.3 as estimates of the fractiles of the long-run frequency distribution of demand. In Figure 7.3 we plot the smallest of the 10 demands at a cumulative probability of $\frac{1}{11}$ rather than $\frac{1}{10}$, the second smallest at a cumulative prob-

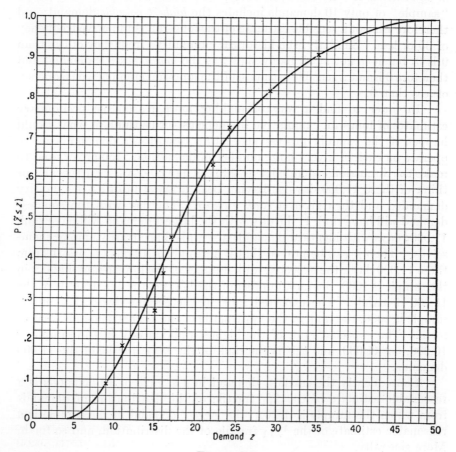

Figure 7.3

ability of $\frac{2}{11}$, and so forth, and we then adjust these preliminary estimates and assess the complete cumulative probability distribution by fitting a smooth curve to the 10 plotted points.

7.3.3   The Relation between the Shapes of Noncumulative and Cumulative Distributions

Because it is easier to visualize the shape of the frequency distribution which would tend to be generated by a given random process than it is to visualize the shape of the corresponding cumulative distribution, we shall point out some simple relations between the two. These relations should be kept clearly in mind when assessing a probability distribution by smoothing fractile estimates.

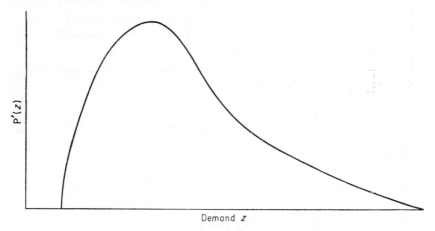

Figure 7.4

The basic relation is simply this: when a cumulative distribution is accurately represented by a stepped graph, each *jump* in the cumulative distribution is equal to the *height* of the corresponding bar in the frequency distribution. This means that when both distributions are smoothed, the *slope* of the cumulative distribution at any value of the variable is proportional to the *height* of the frequency distribution at that value.

Consequently a *one-humped frequency distribution* corresponds to an *S-shaped cumulative distribution*. It can be shown that the frequency distribution corresponding to the cumulative distribution of Figure 7.3 has the shape depicted in Figure 7.4, and comparing these two figures we see that as the value of the variable increases, the *height* of the frequency distribution at first increases and therefore the *slope* of the cumulative distribution increases. Beyond the point corresponding to the peak of the frequency distribution, the height of that distribution decreases and with it the slope of the cumulative distribution.

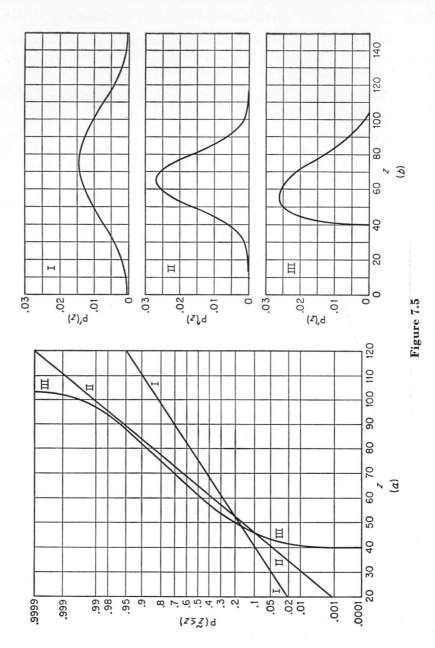

Figure 7.5

A *two-humped* frequency distribution would correspond to a cumulative distribution in which the slope at first increased, then decreased, then increased again, and then decreased again.   If the dip in the frequency distribution went down to 0, the cumulative distribution would become absolutely flat at the corresponding value of the variable.   It is such irregularities which we will ordinarily want to smooth out in assessing a probability distribution; but as we have already said, this must be done only after we have asked ourselves whether the observed flattening may represent a genuine *assignable cause*.

Normal-probability Paper.   Even when we are aware of these relations between the shapes of noncumulative distributions and cumulative distributions it is usually very difficult to say whether a graph of cumulative probabilities like Figure 7.3 is reasonable—i.e., expresses our considered judgment about the workings of the underlying mechanism or process.   For the reasons explained in Section 7.1 we will usually be of the opinion that our noncumulative probability distribution should be smooth and single-humped; and when this is true it will usually be easier to sketch the corresponding cumulative distribution on graph paper with a special grid known as "Normal-probability paper."

The statistical theory underlying this special grid will not be discussed until later in the course; for the moment we shall justify its use solely by example.   The lines labeled I, II, and III in Figure 7.5a represent three hypothetical cumulative distributions; the corresponding noncumulative distributions are shown as Figure 7.5b.   The points to notice are the following:

1. A perfectly straight line on Normal-probability paper corresponds to a symmetrical, one-humped probability distribution, the tails of which never quite fall to zero.   It is impossible to plot the cumulative probabilities 0 or 1 on this paper, although we can plot .0001 and .9999.

2. Most reasonable one-humped probability distributions will correspond to *nearly* straight lines on this paper *except at the two tails;* if the "ends" of the distribution are to be represented, this must be done by turning the ends of the graph parallel to the vertical axis.   The point at which the ends turn vertical will necessarily be largely arbitrary, but fortunately this is rarely of any practical importance whatever.   *The small probabilities in the extreme tails usually have little effect on expected costs and even less or none at all on the actual decision.*

PROBLEMS

1. The fractile estimates shown as X's in Figure 7.3 have been replotted on Normal-probability paper as Figure 7.6.

   a. Fit a smooth curve to these points, turning the left end vertical just to the

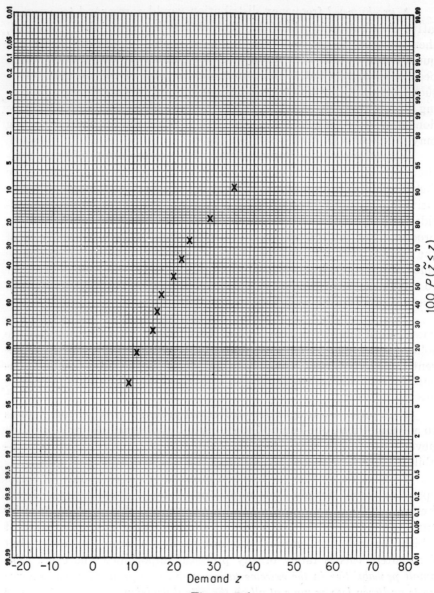

Figure 7.6

left of what you believe to be the lowest possible demand and turning the right end
vertical just to the right of what you believe to be the highest possible demand.

   b. Assuming that the item in question costs \$.60, sells for \$2, and is a total loss
if it is not sold by the end of the day on which it is stocked, decide how many units to
stock.

2. A certain product is stocked daily and spoils if it is not sold by the end of the day. The retailer pays $1.37 per unit for the product; he prices it at $6.50 on the day it is stocked; leftover stock is worthless. The retailer believes that he knows at least approximately the effect which a variety of factors such as season, weather, advertising, etc., exert on demand for this product; and because no one combination of "values" of these factors is ever repeated exactly, he believes that it is impossible to build up a historical frequency distribution of demand on a number of "identical" days. Instead, therefore, of looking at such a distribution before deciding how many units to order, he has based each order on a forecast of the next day's demand. The table below shows the record for the past 19 days of his forecast of demand and the demand which actually occurred; his forecast of tomorrow's demand is 100 units.

Day	Forecast	Demand	Day	Forecast	Demand
1	75	92	11	110	101
2	100	107	12	95	100
3	120	98	13	100	107
4	85	78	14	125	118
5	110	104	15	70	61
6	130	140	16	100	105
7	90	90	17	105	91
8	80	85	18	80	86
9	75	93	19	120	108
10	120	127			

a. Compute the *discrepancies* between actual demand and forecast demand, defining the discrepancy as *actual minus forecast,* and array them in order from the most negative to the most positive.

b. Assess a probability distribution for tomorrow's *discrepancy* by treating the recorded discrepancies as fractile estimates. Use Normal-probability paper and choose the horizontal scale such that the extreme left of the axis represents −50, the extreme right +50. In plotting the estimates, observe that a discrepancy of −9 is the estimate of *two successive* fractiles and that therefore you must plot *two X's* above −9.

c. Making use of the fact that

Demand = forecast + discrepancy,

convert your answer to (*b*) into a probability distribution for tomorrow's *demand* by simply relabeling the horizontal axis.

d. Determine the best number of units to stock.

3. In the situation of Problem 2:

a. Compute the *ratio* of actual demand to forecast demand on the 19 days in the historical record, *dividing actual by forecast.*

b. Assess a probability distribution for tomorrow's *ratio* by treating the recorded ratios as fractile estimates. Use Normal-probability paper and choose the horizontal scale such that the extreme left of the axis represents .50, the extreme right 1.50.

c. Making use of the fact that

Demand = forecast × ratio,

convert your answer to (*b*) into a probability distribution for tomorrow's *demand* by simply relabeling the horizontal axis.

d. Determine the best number of units to stock.

4. Discuss the merits of the alternative procedures used in Problems 2 and 3. Considering the retailer as a forecasting mechanism or process, what implicit assumptions were made about the behavior of this process in Problem 2? In Problem 3? How in practice would you try to determine which assumptions were closer to the truth?

5. A retailer with costs and prices identical to those of Problem 2 also bases his orders on forecasts of demand but has kept no record of the accuracy of previous forecasts. After reviewing the reports he has received on the state of the market for his product he decides that he would be willing to bet at the following odds on tomorrow's demand:

1 to 99 (1 chance in 100) that $\bar{z} < 100$.
1 to 9 that $\bar{z} < 115$.
1 to 1 that $\bar{z} < 130$.
1 to 9 that $\bar{z} > 145$.
1 to 99 that $\bar{z} > 160$.

How many units should he stock?

PART TWO

Binomial Sampling

CHAPTER 8

Conditional, Joint, and Marginal Probability

8.1 Introduction to Part Two of the Course

The probabilities which we have assigned to events have hitherto all been directly assessed on the basis of experience with the events themselves. The only way in which we have used the mathematical theory of probability was to compute the probability of events such as $\tilde{z} \leq 2$ by adding the probabilities of the events $\tilde{z} = 0$, 1, and 2. In some cases, however, we have refused to assess probabilities by simply *equating* them to relative frequencies experienced in the past. Thus our general knowledge of the nature of the factors affecting demand led us in Chapter 7 to the conclusions that the probabilities assigned to certain values of the basic random variable should be between those assigned to other values and that the whole distribution should be smooth.

We now begin our study of problems involving *sampling*, and in these problems our general knowledge of (or beliefs concerning) the factors affecting certain random variables can be shown to lead to conclusions much more specific than the mere proposition that the probability distribution should be smooth. In the present chapter we shall examine the basic concepts which underlie the indirect assessment of probabilities; and in order to make these concepts as clear as possible our examples will be simple and artificial ones involving urns and dice. Every general proposition we make will be stated both in terms of probabilities and in terms of frequencies; it is up to the student to remember that the two concepts are entirely different and that great caution must be exercised before a probability is equated to a relative frequency *however* the relative frequency has been determined.

8.2 Joint and Conditional Probability

When probabilities are assigned directly to a single set of mutually exclusive events, our meaning is perfectly clear when we speak of "the" probability of an event. When probabilities are assessed indirectly, the situation becomes more complex. If two pieces are to be produced on some machine and we wish to assign a probability to the event "two defectives," we may do so by first assigning probabilities to the events "first piece defective" and "second piece defective." If we do so, it is obvious that we are no longer dealing with a single set of mutually exclusive events: all three of the events just named may occur on a single two-piece run. A moment's reflection will also show that we may have to deal with more than one probability for the same event: the probability which a reasonable man assigns to the event "second piece defective" may well depend on the quality of the first piece. In order to avoid confusion in discussing such situations we must introduce the concepts of "joint" and "conditional" probability and with them the concepts of joint and conditional relative frequency.

8.2.1   Joint Probability

The probability that two or more events will *all* occur will be called the *joint* probability of these events. Thus we may talk about the joint probability of "first piece defective" *and* "second piece defective," or about the joint probability of "rain tomorrow" *and* "demand for 17 pairs of rubbers."

It is important to observe that joint probability is in no sense a new "kind" of probability; it is simply a new way of looking at certain probabilities. The joint probability of "first piece defective" *and* "second piece defective" is exactly the same thing as the ordinary probability of "two defectives"; the new name simply reflects the new way in which we look at this probability when we try to assess it indirectly rather than directly.

In terms of frequencies rather than probabilities, the *joint relative frequency* of several events is the ratio of the number of trials on which *all the events in question* occur to the total number of trials.

8.2.2   Conditional Probability

The probability which is assigned to an event A when it is known that another event B has occurred, or which *would* be assigned to A *if* it were known that B had occurred, will be called the *conditional* probability of A given B. Thus we may talk about the conditional probability of the event "second piece defective" *given* the event "first piece defective" or about the conditional probability of the event "demand for 17 pairs of rubbers" *given* that the event "rain tomorrow" occurs.

To see how conditional probability is related to ordinary or unconditional probability, suppose that someone is thinking of betting on one roll of a deformed die with faces 1, 2, and 3 colored red and faces 4, 5, and 6 colored green. The roll can result in any one of the six *elementary* events described by the numbers 1 through 6 and in either of the *com-*

pound events "red" or "green"; we shall suppose that before the die is rolled this person assigns the probabilities shown in Table 8.1 to the six elementary events and computes the corresponding probabilities of the two compound events also shown in that table. These are the "ordinary," "simple," or *unconditional* probabilities of this problem.

Table 8.1

Elementary event	Compound event	Probability	
1		.10	
2		.10	
3		.20	
	Red		.40
4		.15	
5		.20	
6		.25	
	Green		.60
			1.00

Suppose now that *after* the die has been rolled this same person is told that the event "red" has occurred but is *not* told which particular one of the three elementary events 1, 2, or 3 has occurred; and suppose that this person now wishes to assign new probabilities taking account of this limited additional information. Clearly any reasonable man placed in this situation will assign probability 0 to the three elementary events 4, 5, and 6, since these events are impossible given the new information, and will assign a total probability of 1 to the three elementary events 1, 2, and 3, since he knows that some one of these events has occurred.

The only question concerns the sharing of the total probability 1 among the three events 1, 2, and 3, and we answer this question by assuming that any reasonable man will do this in such a way that the probabilities which he originally assigned to these events are *all increased in the same proportion*. Since the total probability originally assigned to events 1, 2, and 3 was .4, this assumption implies that the probability assigned to each one of these events must be multiplied by 1/.4; the results are shown in Table 8.2.

The justification for our assumption can now be seen by comparing Tables 8.1 and 8.2. When our hypothetical person originally assigned the same probability .10 to event 1 that he assigned to event 2, he said in effect that he was indifferent between a chance at a prize conditional on event 1 and a chance at the same prize conditional on event 2. Since the information that the event was in fact 1, 2, or 3 in no way favors

Table 8.2

Elementary event	Probability
1	$\dfrac{1}{.4} \times .10 = .25$
2	$\dfrac{1}{.4} \times .10 = .25$
<u>3</u>	$\dfrac{1}{.4} \times .20 = \underline{.50}$
Total ("red")	$\dfrac{1}{.4} \times .40 = 1.00$

event 1 over event 2 or vice versa, a person who held this attitude of indifference before this information was received should continue to hold it after the information is received; and this is what he shows by assigning the same probability to events 1 and 2 in Table 8.2. Similarly the original assignments in Table 8.1 showed indifference between the right to receive a certain prize if event 3 occurred and the right to receive the same prize if *either* event 1 or 2 occurred: the .20 probability assigned to event 3 in Table 8.1 equals the total probability of events 1 and 2. Again the new information had no relevance for the *relative* values of these two chances, and again the probabilities of Table 8.2 agree with this fact: the probability .50 assigned to event 3 equals the total probability assigned to events 1 and 2.

Although our discussion has involved the actual effect of information which has already been received, it is obvious that exactly the same arguments hold for the potential effect of information which might be received. The reasonable man we have been discussing would say that *if* he learned that the event "red" had occurred, he *would* then assign to event 1 a probability computed according to the formula

$$\frac{\text{Unconditional probability of elementary event 1}}{\text{Unconditional probability of compound event "red"}} = \frac{.10}{.40} = .25$$

and so forth.   Generalizing from this example we may assert that

<u>If *e* is an elementary event which is contained in a compound event *A*, the only conditional probability which it is reasonable to assign to *e* given *A* is the unconditional probability of *e* divided by the unconditional probability of *A*.</u>

In our example, *e* was the event 1 and *A* was the event "red."

The *conditional relative frequency* of an elementary event is related to its unconditional relative frequency in exactly the same way that conditional probability is related to unconditional probability. Suppose, for example, that the die we have been discussing had in fact been rolled 200 times with the results shown in Table 8.3.   By the conditional rela-

Table 8.3

Elementary event	Compound event	Occurrences	Relative frequency
1		20	.10
2		20	.10
3		40	.20
	Red	80	.40
4		30	.15
5		40	.20
6		50	.25
		120	.60
	Green	200	1.00

tive frequency of event 1 *given* the event "red" we mean the ratio

$$\frac{\text{Number of occurrences of elementary event 1}}{\text{Number of occurrences of compound event ``red''}}$$

Using the actual numbers of occurrences given in the third column of Table 8.3 we can compute this ratio directly as $20/80 = .25$, but we can obtain exactly the same result by using the relative frequencies in the third column: $.10/.40 = .25$.   The latter calculation is formally identical to the calculation used in computing conditional probability.

8.3   The Conditional Probability of Compound Events

The example discussed just above shows how a reasonable person will compute the conditional probability of an *elementary* event given that a particular compound event has occurred.   We shall now use a simple urn example to show how the same principle can be used to calculate the conditional probability of a *compound* event given that some other compound event has occurred.

One ball is to be drawn from an urn containing 10 serially numbered balls each of which is colored either red or green and in addition is either dotted or striped; the detailed description of the balls is presented in Table 8.4.   The elementary events of this trial are the 10 numbers 1 through 10, but we shall be primarily interested in the compound events "red," "green," "dotted," and "striped."   Drawing a dotted red ball will be considered as the *joint* occurrence of the events "red" and "dotted" or as the occurrence of the *joint event* "red *and* dotted"; and similarly for the other combinations shown in Table 8.4. We shall assume that before any knowledge concerning the outcome of this trial is available we have assigned equal probability to all 10 elementary events. The probabilities of the four joint events of Table 8.4 and the probabilities of "red" and "green" can then be computed as in Table 8.5, and by similar logic we can show that the probability of the event "dotted" is .3 + .2 = .5; these are the unconditional probabilities of this problem.

Table 8.4

Serial number	Description
1–3	Red and dotted
4	Red and striped
5–6	Green and dotted
7–10	Green and striped

Table 8.5

Elementary event	Probability	Joint event	Probability	Compound event	Probability
1	.1				
2	.1	Red and dotted	.3		
3	.1			Red	.4
4	.1	Red and striped	.1		
5	.1				
6	.1	Green and dotted	.2		
7	.1			Green	.6
8	.1				
9	.1	Green and striped	.4		
10	.1				
	1.0		1.0		1.0

Suppose now that the ball is actually drawn from the urn, that we are told that the ball is *red*, and that we wish to revise the .5 probability which we originally assigned to *dotted* in such a way as to take proper account of this information. We observe immediately that since we know that "red" has occurred, the probability of "dotted" is now the same thing as the probability of "dotted and red"—"dotted and green" is impossible given the new information. The reasoning of Section 8.2.2 then tells us that we must multiply the probability of every elementary event contained in the event "red" by $1/P(red)$, and this means that the total probability of all the three elementary events contained in "red and

dotted" will be multiplied by 1/P(red).   We conclude that the conditional probability of "dotted" given "red" is

$$\frac{\text{Unconditional probability of ``dotted and red''}}{\text{Unconditional probability of ``red''}} = \frac{.3}{.4} = .75$$

Geometrically, this reasoning can be visualized as follows.   The
original or unconditional probabilities of the various compound and joint
events of the problem are represented by areas in Figure 8.1.   As soon as
we know that "red" has occurred, the area of the "green" bar in this
figure must be reduced to 0 and the area of the "red" bar increased to 1;
the altered diagram is shown as Figure 8.2.   We must, however, leave the

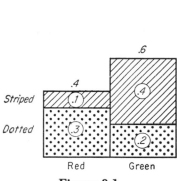

Figure 8.1

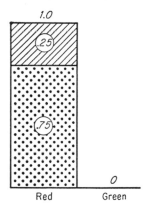

Figure 8.2

proportions within the "red" bar unchanged when we change its total
area in this way, since our new information gives us no justification for
changing these proportions.   Then since the area within the "red" bar
corresponding to "dotted" was .3/.4 = .75 of the original area *of the
"red" bar*, it becomes .75 of the entire diagram when the "red" bar is
enlarged to become the entire diagram as in Figure 8.2.

Before we generalize this example, let us introduce some new notation which will simplify the statement of our results.   In addition to the
symbol

   P(A): the ordinary, simple, or *unconditional* probability of the
        event A

we shall henceforth use

   P(A|B): the *conditional* probability of the event A *given* the event B;
        the probability assigned to A when it is known that B has
        occurred, or which *would* be assigned to A *if* it were known
        that B had occurred.

P(*A,B*): the *joint* probability of the events *A* and *B*; the probability that *both A* and *B* will occur.

In the *mathematical theory* of probability, conditional probability is *defined* by the formula

$$P(A|B) = \frac{P(A,B)}{P(B)} \qquad \textit{Mathematical definition of conditional probability}$$

In talking about probabilities assigned to real events in the real world, we defined $P(A|B)$ quite differently, as the probability which a person *would in fact assign* to *A* if he knew that *B* had occurred. Our urn example shows, however, that a reasonable man will always assign conditional probabilities in accordance with the mathematical definition, and therefore *we may use the mathematical definition of conditional probability as a "formula" for assigning conditional probabilities in a real problem.* Thus when we calculated the conditional probability of "dotted" given "red" we set

$$P(\text{dotted}|\text{red}) = \frac{P(\text{dotted, red})}{P(\text{red})} = \frac{.3}{.4} = .75.$$

Similarly, we would have for the conditional probability of "striped" given "red"

$$P(\text{striped}|\text{red}) = \frac{P(\text{striped, red})}{P(\text{red})} = \frac{.1}{.4} = .25.$$

Geometrically, this is the ratio of the area representing "striped *and* red" in Figure 8.1 to the area representing "red." If we had wanted the conditional probability of "red" given "dotted," i.e., if we had wanted to know what probability should be assigned to "red" after being told that the ball was dotted, we would first have used Table 8.5 or Figure 8.1 to calculate the unconditional probability of "dotted" as $.3 + .2 = .5$. We would then have had

$$P(\text{red}|\text{dotted}) = \frac{P(\text{red, dotted})}{P(\text{dotted})} = \frac{.3}{.5} = .60;$$

This is the ratio of the area representing "dotted *and* red" in Figure 8.1 to the area representing "dotted."

The distinction between unconditional and conditional *relative frequencies* is shown by the following definitions:

The ordinary or unconditional relative frequency of the event *A* is the ratio of the number of occurrences of *A* to the *total number of trials*.

The conditional relative frequency of A given B is the ratio of the number of occurrences of *both A and B* to the *number of occurrences of B*.

If balls are drawn repeatedly from an urn, the ordinary relative frequency of "dotted" is the ratio of the number of times a dotted ball is drawn to the total number of draws. The conditional relative frequency of "dotted" given "red" is the ratio of the number of times the ball is *both* dotted and red to the number of times the ball is red.

Table 8.6

Event	Number of occurrences		Relative frequency	
Red and dotted	60		.3	
Red and striped	20		.1	
Red		80		.4
Green and dotted	40		.2	
Green and striped	80		.4	
Green		120		.6
		200		1.0

To see how conditional relative frequencies of compound events are actually computed, suppose that 200 draws from an urn have actually been made with the results shown in Table 8.6. We can then compute the conditional relative frequency of "dotted" given "red" directly from the numbers of occurrences as $^{60}/_{80} = .75$, but we can equally well use the ratio of the corresponding relative frequencies: $.3/.4 = .75$. Formally, the latter computation is identical to the computation of conditional probability; again we see that the mathematical "theory of probability" can be used *either* to compute probabilities from other probabilities or to compute frequencies from other frequencies.

8.4   The Multiplication Rule

Although we shall have very frequent occasion to compute conditional probabilities from joint probabilities in many applied problems, in others we shall want to use the definition of conditional probability in reverse—we shall want to start with conditional probabilities which have been directly assigned to certain events and from these to calculate the unconditional probabilities of certain joint events. The so-called multiplication rule for performing such calculations is obtained by applying elementary algebra to the mathematical definition of conditional probability given in the previous section:

$$P(A,B) = P(B)\,P(A|B) \qquad \textit{Multiplication rule}$$

To see how this rule works, suppose that instead of starting with probabilities assigned to joint events in our urn example we had started by assigning the following unconditional and conditional probabilities:

$$
\begin{aligned}
P(\text{red}) &= .4;\\
P(\text{green}) &= .6;\\
P(\text{dotted}|\text{red}) &= \tfrac{3}{4};\\
P(\text{dotted}|\text{green}) &= \tfrac{1}{3}.
\end{aligned}
$$

We could then have applied the multiplication rule to *compute* such joint probabilities as

$$P(\text{red } \textit{and} \text{ dotted}) = P(\text{red})\,P(\text{dotted}|\text{red}) = .4 \times \tfrac{3}{4} = .3.$$

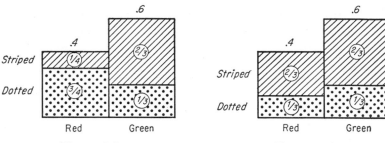

Figure 8.3   **Figure 8.4**

The operation of the rule is depicted geometrically in Figure 8.3, which is identical to Figure 8.1 except for the labeling.   The bars for "red" and "green" constitute respectively .4 and .6 of the total area of the figure. The area representing "dotted *and* red" is ¾ *of the area representing red;* the area representing "dotted *and* green" is ⅓ *of the area representing green.*   The calculation of P(red *and* dotted) which was carried out just above amounts simply to saying that the lower left-hand area in Figure 8.3 constitutes ¾ × .4 = .3 of the total area of the diagram.

In terms of *frequencies:* if a red ball is drawn on .4 of *all* draws, and if ¾ *of the red balls* are dotted, then the ball will be *both* red and dotted on ¾ × .4 = .3 of all draws.   We have thus computed a joint relative frequency from an unconditional and a conditional relative frequency.

8.5   Statistical Independence

Suppose now that the mix of balls in an urn were such that we assigned the probabilities depicted in Figure 8.4: the unconditional probabilities assigned to "red" and "green" are still .4 and .6 respectively, but the conditional probability of "dotted" given "red" is now ⅓ and identical to the conditional probability of "dotted" given "green." It is obvious that if the dotted area *in each bar* is ⅓ of the area of that bar, then the *total* dotted area is ⅓ of the area of the entire figure. In other words, the *conditional probability of "dotted" given "red" is exactly the same as the unconditional probability of "dotted."*

In such a situation we shall say that the events "dotted" and "red" are *statistically independent.* More generally, we say that events A and B are statistically independent if

$$P(A|B) = P(A) \qquad \textit{Condition of statistical independence}$$

By considering ratios of areas in Figure 8.4 the student can easily convince himself that if A is independent of B, then necessarily B is independent of A. The area representing "red" constitutes .4 of the entire diagram and at the same time "red, dotted" constitutes .4 of the total "dotted" area; $P(red) = P(red|dotted)$.

When A is independent of B, the multiplication rule reduces to

$$P(A,B) = P(B) P(A) \qquad \textit{Multiplication rule for independent events}$$

The student is warned that one of the most common errors in the use of the theory of probability is the application of this form of the multiplication rule to events which are not independent.

8.6 Marginal Probability

We have already in this chapter encountered and solved problems in which we knew the probabilities of certain *joint* events and wished to compute from them the probabilities of certain *compound* events, but we shall find it useful later on to have a systematic method for performing these computations and a standard name for the results. Suppose, therefore, that a ball drawn from an urn may be (1) red, green, or blue, *and* (2) striped or dotted; and suppose that the probabilities shown in Table 8.7 have been assigned to the various possible joint events.

If now we wish to compute the probability of an event such as "red" or "striped," all that we have to do is lay out the data of Table 8.7 in the form of Table 8.8 and then add across the proper row or down the proper column: because the *joint* events are *mutually exclusive* (cf. Section 1.2.2), the third basic rule of probability given in Section 1.3 applies.

Table 8.7

Joint event	Probability
Red and dotted	.12
Red and striped	.18
Green and dotted	.15
Green and striped	.21
Blue and dotted	.20
Blue and striped	.14
	1.00

Thus the probabilities of "striped" and "dotted" are respectively .53 and .47; the probabilities of "red," "green," and "blue" are respectively .30, .36, and .34.

Table 8.8
Joint and Marginal Probabilities

		Color			Total
		Red	Green	Blue	
Marking {	Striped	.18	.21	.14	.53
	Dotted	.12	.15	.20	.47
Total		.30	.36	.34	1.00

Because the probabilities of these compound events appear in the margins of Table 8.8, they are known as *marginal* probabilities. More generally,

The probability of any event A can always be computed by adding the probabilities of *all* joint events in which A is involved; and if the probability of A *is* computed in this particular way, it is called the marginal probability of A.

PROBLEMS

In addition to studying Chapter 8, the student should review the discussion of the third basic rule of probability in Section 1.3 before attempting to solve these problems.

1. An urn contains four kinds of balls in the mix shown in the following table; you yourself have stirred the contents of the urn thoroughly and will make certain drawings from the urn in such a way that you cannot see the color of the ball before it is drawn.

Description	Number of balls
Red and dotted	2
Red and striped	3
Green and dotted	4
Green and striped	1
	10

a. If you draw one ball from the urn and without looking at it show it to someone who tells you that it is red, what probability would you then assign to the event "red *and* dotted"?   To the event "dotted"?   To the event "red *or* dotted"?

b. If after drawing a ball from the urn and seeing that it is red you are to draw a second ball without replacing the first one, what probability would you assign to the event "second ball green"?

c. Same as (*b*) except that you have *not* seen that the first ball is red.

d. Same as (*b*) except that after the first ball is drawn and inspected you replace it in the urn and stir the contents before making the second draw.

e. Give a frequency justification for your answers to parts *a* through *d*.

f. If you are to draw two balls from the urn replacing the first ball and stirring the urn before the second is drawn, what probability would you assign to the event "red followed by green"?   To the event "green followed by red"?   To the event "one red and one green ball"?

g. Same as (*f*) except that the first ball is *not* to be replaced before the second ball is drawn.

(2.) One thousand people are asked whether they listen to classical music on the radio.   Each person is also asked whether he has reached his thirtieth birthday and whether he did or did not graduate from high school.   The results of the survey are tabulated below.   Compute the following relative frequencies of the event "listens to classical music":

a. Unconditional.

b. Conditional given "under 30," given "30 or over," given "graduated," given "not graduated."

c. Conditional given "under 30 *and* graduated," given "30 or over *and* graduated."

Age	High school	Listens	Number
Under 30	Yes	Yes	110
		No	190
	No	Yes	10
		No	90
30 or over	Yes	Yes	55
		No	195
	No	Yes	125
		No	225
			1000

d. Would knowledge of age be useful in predicting whether a person listens to classical music?

(3.) The tolerances for balls used in ball bearings are so tight that the balls cannot be ground exactly to specified size. Instead, they are ground to approximate size, sorted into size groups, and then 100 per cent inspected for correct sizing. Even this process does not always result in adequately accurate classification owing to "inspection fatigue," a well-known phenomenon in 100 per cent inspection.

A manufacturer of ball bearings has determneid by extensive investigations that the first inspection of a lot of 10,000 balls removes about 200 incorrectly sorted balls but that about 50 incorrectly sorted balls remain in the lot. He is thinking of using 200 or 300 per cent inspection (a common practice in this industry) instead of 100 per cent. What improvement in quality do you believe he will obtain if he does this?

(4.) *a.* A very carefully made die is to be rolled twice. What expected value would you assign to the right to receive $1 if one or both throws result in an ace? (HINT: Compare Problem 1*f.*)

b. A very carefully made coin is to be tossed three times. What expected value would you assign to the right to receive $1 if heads occurs on at least one of the three tosses? (HINT: Write out all the elementary events and compute the probability of the only one which is *not* contained in the compound event in which you are interested.)

c. Two very carefully made coins are tossed together three times. What is the probability that both coins will fall heads on at least one throw?

(5.) The XYZ Company manufactures a small cylindrical part used in a precision assembly. The part will be rejected if it does not meet specifications as regards out-of-roundness, taper, and average diameter. The fraction of all parts not meeting these specifications has been:

Out-of-roundness: .03,
Taper: .04,
Average diameter: .05.

a. What probability would you assign to the rejection of any particular part if you knew that the three kinds of defects are independent? (HINT: Compare Problem 4*b.*)

b. When XYZ has manufactured a lot of these parts, a sample is drawn from the lot and the lot is screened (100 per cent inspected) at a cost of $10 if there is a single defective in the sample. What is the expected cost of screening per lot if the sample consists of a single piece? Of three pieces?

c. How would you in practice determine whether the three kinds of defects are independent?

(6.) A retailer stocks a product which deteriorates rapidly on the shelf. The product costs the retailer $2; he prices it at $5 on the day it is stocked but reduces the price to $1 on the following day. Product which has not been sold by the end of the second day is scrapped at a total loss. The retailer assigns the probability distributions shown in the following table to demand for the fresh product and demand for the day-old product, and he asserts that because the fresh and day-old products are put to different uses the demand for one is unrelated to the demand for the other. How many units should he stock? (HINT: The events in the payoff table for this problem are of the type "demand for 2 units of fresh *and* demand for 1 unit of day-old.")

Fresh product		Day-old product	
Demand	Probability	Demand	Probability
0	0	0	.1
1	.3	1	.2
2	.4	2	.3
3	.3	3	.3
4+	0	4	.1
		5+	0
	1.0		1.0

CHAPTER 9

The Binomial Distribution

The output of a great many random processes encountered in practical business problems can be described in terms of a number of *distinct trials* each of which has one or the other of *just two possible results*. Thus an automatic screw machine turns out a number of separate parts which may be classified simply as either good or defective, or the process of drawing a sample of United States housewives yields a number of separate respondents each of whom may be classified simply as a user or a nonuser of instant coffee. In order to have a standard terminology to use in discussing all processes of this kind, we shall call one of the two possible results of each trial a *success* and the other a *failure*. These names are of course completely arbitrary—we can use either name for a defective or for a housewife who uses instant coffee provided that we are consistent in any one problem.

The simplest processes of this kind are those in which

There is absolutely *no pattern* to the occurrences of successes and failures; successes tend to occur with exactly the same frequency in the first as in the last part of a long run; successes tend to be followed by failures exactly as frequently as failures are followed by failures, and so forth.

A process which meets this condition is known as a *Bernoulli* process and the long-run fraction of successes which characterizes a Bernoulli process is called the *parameter* of the process. The present part of the course will be devoted to the study of the use of samples generated by Bernoulli processes or by processes which for practical purposes can be treated as if they were Bernoulli processes.

9.1 A Numerical Example

To make the initial discussion concrete, assume that we wish to assess the probability that exactly two aces will occur in five rolls of a die when the probability of ace on any roll is *and will be* assessed at $\frac{1}{6}$ *regardless of the outcomes of any of these five rolls*. Equivalently, we wish to compute the long-run relative frequency with which two aces will occur in five rolls of a die when aces and non-aces occur *in no predictable pattern* and it is *known* that aces will occur on $\frac{1}{6}$ of the individual rolls in the long run: the die behaves as a Bernoulli process with parameter $\frac{1}{6}$.

We first compute the probability of rolling exactly two aces (A) and three non-aces (N) *in the specified order AANNN*. Since the probability of an ace on any roll is the same regardless of the results of previous rolls, the events are *independent* by definition; and by the multiplication rule for independent events we have

$$P = \tfrac{1}{6}\ \tfrac{1}{6}\ \tfrac{5}{6}\ \tfrac{5}{6}\ \tfrac{5}{6} = {}^{125}\!/_{7776}.$$

If we divide an infinite sequence of rolls into groups of 5 consecutive rolls, ${}^{125}\!/_{7776}$ of these groups will show the pattern $AANNN$.

We next observe that the probability or relative frequency is the same for *any other specified order*. For example, the probability of $NANNA$ is

$$P = \tfrac{5}{6}\ \tfrac{1}{6}\ \tfrac{5}{6}\ \tfrac{5}{6}\ \tfrac{1}{6} = {}^{125}\!/_{7776}.$$

Since the occurrence of two aces and three non-aces in any specified order and their occurrence in any other specified order are *mutually exclusive* events, we can get the probability of two aces and three non-aces *regardless* of order by adding the probabilities of all the possible orders. The possible orders are

$$AANNN \quad NAANN \quad NNAAN \quad NNNAA$$
$$ANANN \quad NANAN \quad NNANA$$
$$ANNAN \quad NANNA$$
$$ANNNA$$

or 10 in all. The probability of two aces in five trials is thus

$$P = 10 \times {}^{125}\!/_{7776} = {}^{1250}\!/_{7776}.$$

If we divide an infinite sequence of rolls into groups of five consecutive rolls, ${}^{1250}\!/_{7776}$ of the groups will contain exactly two aces.

9.2 The Binomial Distribution

Let us now generalize this example by considering the probability of r successes in n trials where the probability of a success is p on any trial. The symbol q will denote the probability of a failure: $q = 1 - p$. *We repeat that we assume that p will remain the same for every one of these n trials regardless of the outcomes of any of them.*

1. The probability of r successes and $(n - r)$ failures *in a specified order* is

$$(p \times p \times p \times \cdots \times p) \times (q \times q \times q \cdots \times q) = p^r q^{n-r}.$$
$$\underset{(r \text{ factors})}{} \qquad \underset{(n-r \text{ factors})}{}$$

2. If we use the symbol C_r^n to denote the *number of possible orders* in which r successes can occur in n trials, then it can be shown that

$$C_r^n = \frac{n!}{r!(n-r)!},$$

where by definition

$$n! = 1 \times 2 \times 3 \times 4 \times \cdots \times n$$

and is read "n factorial." To cover the cases $r = 0$ and $r = n$, we define

$$0! = 1.$$

3. Since the orders are mutually exclusive, the probability of *exactly* r successes in n trials, *regardless of order*, is

$$P_b(r) = C_r^n p^r q^{n-r} \qquad \textit{Binomial probability}$$

Example. In the problem of the probability of two aces in five rolls of a die, $n = 5$, $r = 2$, and $p = \frac{1}{6}$. Substituting these values in the binomial probability formula we have

$$P_b(2) = C_2^5 (\tfrac{1}{6})^2 (\tfrac{5}{6})^3$$
$$= \frac{5!}{2!3!} \left(\frac{1}{6}\right)^2 \left(\frac{5}{6}\right)^3$$
$$= 10(\tfrac{1}{6})^2 (\tfrac{5}{6})^3$$
$$= 10 \times {}^{125}\!/_{7776}$$

as before.

9.2.1 The Random Variable $\tilde{r}$ and the Binomial Distribution

Although for purposes of analysis we have broken down the output of a random process into a number n of distinct trials, our real interest is not in these individual trials as such but in the "experiment" which consists of all n individual trials taken as a whole. Using S to denote a success and F a failure, we can describe an *elementary* event of such an experiment by a sequence of n symbols of the form $SSFSFS \cdots$, but we are assuming in this chapter that we are interested only in the number r of S's in this sequence and not in the order in which the S's and F's occur. Every conceivable outcome of the experiment will have a definite *value r*, and therefore we may consider any r as a value of a *random variable $\tilde{r}$*.

Provided that the process which generates the successes and failures meets the condition stated on the first page of this chapter and can therefore

be said to behave as a Bernoulli process, the probability of each r can therefore be computed by the binomial formula given above; we then say that
$\tilde{r}$ is a *binomial* random variable.   By using the binomial formula to compute the probability of every possible number of successes (from 0 to n),
we arrive at the complete *binomial probability distribution*.   The distribution for $n = 5$, $p = .5$ is shown in Figure 9.1 and can be taken as

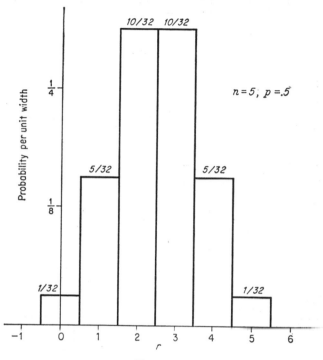

Figure 9.1

representing the probabilities of various numbers of heads when a "fair"
coin is tossed five times.   The distribution for $n = 5$, $p = \frac{1}{6}$ is shown in
Figure 9.2 and can be taken as representing the probabilities of various
numbers of aces when a "fair" die is rolled five times.

Parameters.   The formula $P_b(r) = C_r^n p^r q^{n-r}$ thus defines, not just one
distribution of $\tilde{r}$, but a whole *family* of distributions, one for every possible
combination of values of n and p.   We shall call n and p the *parameters* of
the binomial distribution.   It is only after definite numerical values have
been assigned to the parameters that the binomial formula defines a
specific distribution of the random variable $\tilde{r}$.   To show the dependence
of the probabilities on the parameters n and p we shall often write
$P_b(r|n,p)$, which should be read "the binomial probability of r *given* n
and p."

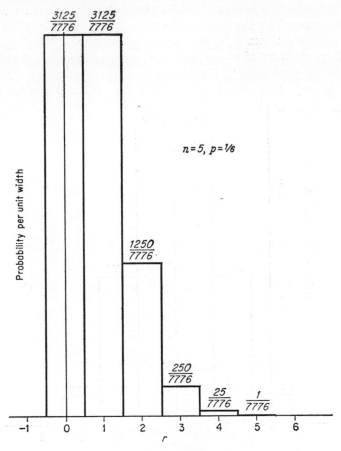

Figure 9.2

9.2.2   *The Mean of the Binomial Distribution*

In many applications all that we need to know about a binomial random variable $\tilde{r}$ is its *mean* or *expected value*. It can be proved by algebra that this information is given by the very simple formula

$$E(\tilde{r}) = np \qquad \textit{Expected number of successes, binomial distribution}$$

This formula agrees in an obvious way with common sense. In terms of frequencies rather than probabilities: if on the average $p = \frac{1}{2}$ of all trials are successes, then in a series of experiments each of which consists of $n = 10$ trials there will be on the average $\frac{1}{2} \times 10 = 5$ successes, and so forth.

9.3   Cumulative Probabilities; Tables of the Binomial Distribution

In many applications we need the probability, not of exactly r successes, but of r *or less* successes or of *more than r* successes or of something of the sort. Graphically, such probabilities are represented by the *area of a tail of the distribution*. The probability of three or more successes when $n = 15$, $p = .33$, or $P_b(\tilde{r} \geq 3 | n = 15, p = .33)$, is represented by the shaded area in Figure 9.3.

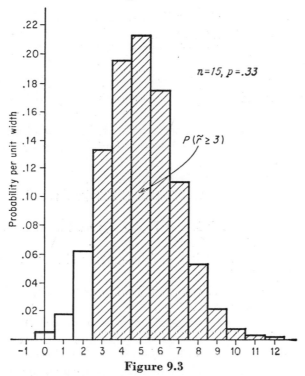

Figure 9.3

Cumulative probabilities can be computed exactly only by computing all the included individual probabilities and adding, and the task becomes very laborious when n is large and the r in "r or more," etc., is not close to either 0 or n. For this reason tables have been published giving the tail areas directly for certain values of n and p and all the possible values of r; and these tables can also be used to obtain individual probabilities $P_b(\tilde{r} = r)$. A short set of tables of cumulative binomial probabilities is given as Table I at the end of this book.†

† For very complete tables, see "Tables of the Cumulative Binomial Probability Distribution," Annals of the Computation Laboratory of Harvard University, vol. XXXV, Harvard University Press, Cambridge, Mass., 1955.

9.3.1   The Use of Probability Tables

Before using *any* table or chart of cumulative probabilities, the student must examine it to be clear on two points.

1. *Which tail is shown?*   Tables may show the area of either the left or the right tail, but they never show both.   Recall that the total area of any probability distribution is 1, so that the area of one tail is 1 minus the area of the other tail.   The white area in Figure 9.3 is 1 minus the shaded area.

2. *How far does the tail extend?*   Tables may show the probability of *r or more* successes, $P(\tilde{r} \geq r)$, or they may show the probability of *more than r* successes, $P(\tilde{r} > \tilde{r})$; and similarly if it is the left tail which is shown.

Table I of the binomial distribution shows $P_b(\tilde{r} \geq r)$, in other words the area of the right tail of the distribution *including* the probability of r itself. The value .9167 given opposite $r = 3$ in the table for $n = 15$, $p = .33$ is $P_b(r \geq 3 | n = 15,\ p = .33)$ and corresponds to the shaded area in Figure 9.3.   Other cumulative probabilities and individual probabilities can be very simply obtained as is shown in the following examples for $n = 15$, $p = .33$, the distribution graphed in Figure 9.3.

To find $P_b(\tilde{r} > 3)$: this is the same as $P_b(\tilde{r} \geq 4)$; read .7829 opposite $r = 4$.

To find $P_b(\tilde{r} < 3)$: this is $1 - P_b(\tilde{r} \geq 3)$; read .9167 opposite $r = 3$, and compute $1 - .9167 = .0833$.

To find $P_b(\tilde{r} \leq 3)$: this is $1 - P_b(r \geq 4)$; read .7829 opposite $r = 4$ and compute $1 - .7829 = .2171$.

To find $P_b(\tilde{r} = 3)$: this is $P_b(\tilde{r} \geq 3) - P(\tilde{r} \geq 4)$; read these two probabilities and compute $.9167 - .7829 = .1338$.

To use the tables when $p > .50$, rephrase the problem in terms of $q = 1 - p$.   For example, to find the probability that a machine will produce 12 or more defectives in a lot of 15 when the probability is .67 that any individual piece will be defective: look up instead the probability that there will be three or less good pieces when the probability is .33 that any individual piece will be good.   This probability is .2171 as shown above.

9.4   Simple Sampling

9.4.1   Sampling from a Bernoulli Process

Although the binomial distribution which we have just derived has a great many practical business applications—e.g., in determining the best number of pieces to allow for scrap in scheduling a production run on a machine which behaves like a Bernoulli process—there is only one which we shall have time to study in this course: the problem of using a *sample* from a Bernoulli process to reach decisions in situations where the costs or losses of the various possible acts depend on the unknown value of the process parameter p. As an example of such a problem, consider an automatic machine which requires a tool change and new setup at periodic intervals. It may be known that after any one setup the machine behaves as a Bernoulli process with *some* fixed long-run fraction defective p, but the actual value of p may depend on the individual setup. Since the losses due to manufacture of defective product will be high if p is high, it is common practice in situations of this sort to take the first n pieces produced after each setup as a *sample* of the output which the machine will produce in the long run, and then to spend the amount of time and money required to readjust the setup if the number of defectives in the sample equals or exceeds some predetermined number c. In the next chapters we shall see how the probability theory we have now learned can be used to determine the *best* values for the sample size n and the "rejection number" c; for the moment, we merely remark that if the machine really behaves as a Bernoulli process, then the *conditional* distribution of the number $\tilde{r}$ of defectives in a sample of size n, *given* (or assuming) any particular value p of the long-run fraction defective, is binomial with parameters n and p.

9.4.2 *Sampling from a Finite Population*

The binomial distribution is also of great practical importance as a tool for obtaining good approximate solutions to problems involving samples drawn from a *finite population* rather than from a Bernoulli process. The simplest possible business example is acceptance sampling. A lot of purchased parts contains N pieces, an unknown fraction p of which are defective. Each defective which is installed in an assembly must later be removed and replaced by a good part, so that if p were high it would be preferable to spend the time and money required to "screen" the lot (i.e., inspect every piece in it) and thus to remove the defectives before sending the lot to the assembly department. In such a situation it is common practice to draw a *sample* of n pieces from the lot and then to screen the whole lot if the number of defectives $\tilde{r}$ equals or exceeds some predetermined number c.

Now in order to find the best values of n and c in a situation like this, we shall need to know the *conditional* distribution of the number $\tilde{r}$ of defectives in a sample of size n *given* various values of the *lot* fraction defective p, just as we need to know the corresponding distribution of $\tilde{r}$ given n and the *process* fraction defective p when we are sampling from a Bernoulli process. We have already seen that, when the sample is drawn

from a Bernoulli process, the distribution of $\tilde{r}$ is binomial; we now ask
what will be the distribution of $\tilde{r}$ when the sample is drawn from a lot.
What we have to say will apply much more generally to any problem of
sampling from a *finite population* every member of which can be classified as a "success" or a "failure."   It will apply, for example, when
information on the fraction of all United States citizens using a certain
product is obtained from a sample of the population of all United States
citizens, or when a mail-order company deciding how many to stock of a
certain item uses an advance mailing to get information on the proportion of customers on the mailing list for its regular catalogue who will
order the item.

In discussing sampling from a Bernoulli process, we assumed that
the sample items would be taken from the process *in the order in which
they were produced*.   The probability distribution for the value of each
observation was therefore given directly by the characteristics of the
process in terms of the parameter of the process.   When, on the contrary, a sample is drawn from an already existing finite population, it is
the *process by which the sample is drawn* that determines the probability
distribution for the value of each observation.   We shall consider here
only the drawing process known as *simple sampling without replacement*.
Sampling is said to be of this type when the sample items are drawn from
the population one by one and:

1. After each item is drawn, it is kept aside so that it cannot be
   drawn again;
2. As each successive draw is made, every member of the population
   which has *not* been drawn previously has an *equal* chance of entering the sample.

It is easy to see that this drawing process will *not* give rise to a distribution of $\tilde{r}$ which is strictly binomial.   The basic assumption from
which we derived the binomial distribution in Section 9.2 above was the
assumption that the probability of a success remains *absolutely constant
from one trial to the next*, whereas in simple sampling without replacement
this probability changes from one draw to the next because the fact that
the sample items are removed from the population as they are drawn
means that the proportion of successes in the *remaining* population
changes from one draw to the next.   If the whole population contains N
members, R of which are successes, the probability of a success on the
first draw is $p = R/N$; but the probability of a success on the *second* draw
is $(R - 1)/(N - 1)$ if the first draw was a success, $R/(N - 1)$ if the
first draw was a failure, and so forth.

The probability distribution of $\tilde{r}$ to which this kind of drawing process gives rise is known as the *hypergeometric* distribution, discussions of

which can be found in most longer books on statistics. In this course, however, we shall not study the hypergeometric distribution as such because the examples which occur in the great majority of practical applications are nearly identical to binomial distributions and for all practical purposes can be treated as if they *were* binomial.

To get some feeling for the circumstances under which it is or is not legitimate to treat a hypergeometric distribution *as if* it were binomial, suppose first that we draw a sample of 10 from a population of 16 containing 8 successes, $p = .5$. The probability of a success on the first draw is .5, just as it would be if we were drawing from a Bernoulli process with $p = .5$. If, however, the first sample item is a success, the probability of a success on the second draw is only $\frac{7}{15} = .467$; if the first two items are successes, the probability of a success on the third draw is only $\frac{6}{14} = .429$; and if the first eight items are all successes the probability of a success on the ninth draw is 0. Exactly the same argument would apply if we considered a sample with an unduly large number of failures rather than successes, and we see that

> If a sample drawn without replacement from a finite population starts to go "out of line" in either direction, the proportion of successes in the remaining population changes in such a way as to tend to bring the sample back into line.

Suppose, however, that a sample of 10 is drawn from a population of 1000 rather than a population of 16, the fraction of successes in the population still being .5. Even if the first nine sample items are all successes, the probability of a success on the tenth draw is still $\frac{491}{991} = .495$, or only a little different from the value .5 which it had on the first draw or the value $\frac{500}{991} = .505$ which it would have on the tenth draw if the first nine items had all been failures.

The effect of the finiteness of the population in this second example is thus far smaller than in our first example, and a little thought will show that the magnitude of the effect of the finite population depends essentially on the *ratio* of sample size to population size. If the first 90 draws from a population of 10,000 with $p = .5$ are all successes, the probability of a success on the next draw is $\frac{4910}{9910} = .495$, the same as after nine successes have been taken from a population of 1000. Generalizing from this discussion we see that

> As the ratio of sample to population decreases, the extent to which the probability of a success changes from draw to draw becomes smaller and smaller, approaching 0 as the ratio approaches 0.

Now we know that if the probabilities did not change at all from draw to draw, the reasoning which led to the hypergeometric distribution

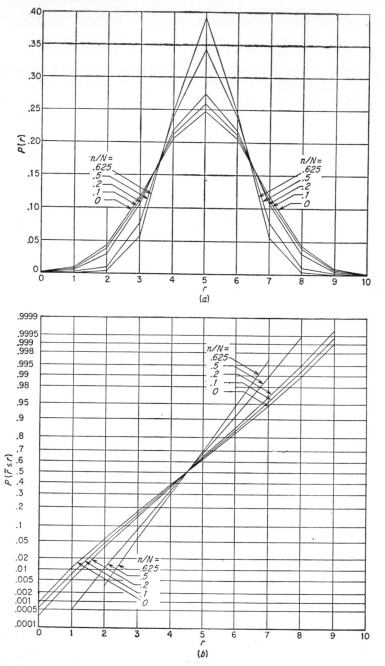

Figure 9.4. Hypergeometric distributions with binomial limit, $n = 10$, $p = .5$.

would have led to the binomial distribution. We thus reach the very important conclusion:

> As the size of the sample decreases relative to the size of the popula-
> tion, the hypergeometric distribution approaches the binomial dis-
> tribution with the same n and p.

This is shown graphically in Figure 9.4 for samples from populations with $p = .5$. The figure applies to a single sample size $n = 10$ but a variety of population sizes. The exact hypergeometric distributions are shown for populations ranging from 16 (sampling ratio $n/N = .625$) to 100 $(n/N = .1)$; the corresponding binomial distribution is labeled $n/N = 0$. The figure makes it clear that the effect of the finiteness of the population is already quite small for n/N as large as .2 and very small indeed for $n/N = .1$. To sum up:

> It is only when a sample drawn without replacement takes in a really
> substantial fraction of the total population that any attention need
> be paid to the finiteness of the population.

Percentage Samples. One of the most common "vulgar errors" concerning sampling is the belief that the reliability of a sample depends upon its *percentage* relationship to the population. Many businessmen operate sampling inspection plans which call for inspection of a certain percentage of each lot—usually 10 per cent. Sampling surveys to determine the current value of properties of a utility such as poles, transformers, etc., are often based on a percentage—again usually 10 per cent because public service commissions seem to have accepted this as the proper size. Our discussion of the behavior of the finite-population correction shows, however, that this policy is completely misguided: *unless the sample takes in a really substantial fraction of the population, its reliability depends on its absolute rather than its relative size.*

The Importance of Simple Sampling. Although the finiteness of the population is only rarely of importance in dealing with samples taken from a finite population, it *is* always of the greatest importance to remember that sampling is *simple* and that the hypergeometric distribution *or* its binomial approximation applies *only* if the sample items are selected in such a way that the probability which it is reasonable to assign to a success on any draw is equal to the proportion of successes among all items not yet drawn at that time. Such an assignment will be reasonable only if we are firmly convinced that the selection of the items in the sample has not been influenced, *either consciously or unconsciously,* by any information which may bear on their values. If we know *or suspect* that such information has been used, sampling is not simple and *the results of this chapter do not apply.*

In the urn model, sampling is not simple if some of the balls are rougher than others, the person drawing the balls tends to choose either rough or smooth balls by preference, and we either know or suspect that roughness may be associated with color.   In a consumer survey carried out to get information on the usage of a certain product, sampling is not simple if interviewers call only once at each household and we suspect that use of the product in question is associated with a tendency to stay at home.   In inspection of incoming lots, sampling is not simple if the sample is drawn from the top of the container and we suspect that the parts on top are of different average quality from those on the bottom.

PROBLEMS

1. A coin is to be tossed seven times.   What probability should be assigned to the following numbers of heads by a person who is firmly convinced that the coin is "fair"?

    a. Exactly 3.   *b.* 3 or more.

    c. More than 3.   *d.* 3 or less.

    e. Less than 3.   *f.* Between 3 and 5 inclusive.

2. The chief inspector of the ABC Company is about to take a sample of 10 pieces from the output of an automatic machine.   He is convinced that the machine always behaves as a Bernoulli process, but because the setup has just been changed, he does not know the long-run fraction defective p which characterizes the present state of the machine.   What *conditional* probability should he assign to the appearance of *three or more* defectives in the sample, *given* (i.e., assuming) that

    a. $p = .02$?   *b.* $p = .05c$

    c. $p = .10$?   *d.* $p = .20$?

    e. $p = .30$?   *f.* $p = .40$?

    g. $p = .50$?   *h.* $p = .60$?

3. Using your answer to Problem 2, graph the conditional probability of *less than three* defectives (vertical axis) against the long-run fraction defective (horizontal axis).

4. From Figure 9.4 find the probability of drawing three or less users of instant coffee in a sample of 10 taken by simple sampling without replacement from a population containing 50 per cent users if the entire population consists of

    a. 20 individuals.   *b.* 50 individuals.

    c. 100 individuals.   *d.* 10,000 individuals.

5. The XYZ Company purchases a certain part in lots of size N, draws a sample of 10 pieces from each lot, and accepts the lot if there are less than three defectives in the sample.   Does your answer to Problem 3 show the conditional probability that the lot will be accepted

    a. If $N = 20$?   *b.* If $N = 50$?

    c. If $N = 100$?   *d.* If $N = 1000$?

6. *Using the same vertical and horizontal scales in both cases,* sketch a smooth curve approximating the histogram of the probability distribution for number defective r in lots produced by a Bernoulli process with $p = .4$

    a. When the lot size $n = 10$.   *b.* When the lot size $n = 100$.

The heights of all the bars in the histogram for $n = 10$ should be computed and plotted before the curve is fitted, but in fitting the curve for $n = 100$ it will suffice to compute and plot the heights for every other value of $\bar{r}$ from 30 to 50.

7. *a*. Same as Problem 6 but use *fraction* defective r/n as the horizontal scale rather than number defective r.   Remember that the vertical scale of a histogram shows probability *per unit width* and that it is the *area* of the bar which corresponds to probability itself.   Thus $P_b(\bar{r} = 3 | p = .4, n = 10) = .2150$ gives the *area* of the bar for $r/n = \frac{3}{10} = .3$.   Since the adjacent values of r/n are .2 and .4, the edges of the bar for .3 are at .25 and .35 and the bar has *width* .1.   Then since the area of the bar is .215 and its width is .1, its *height P'* is $.215/.1 = 2.15$.   Similarly the height of the bar for $r/n = .3$ when $n = 100$ is $.0100/.01 = 1.0$.

b. Can you approximate the binomial distribution for $n = 200$, $p = .3$, by using the distribution for $n = 100$, $p = .3$, and multiplying all values of r by 2?

CHAPTER 10

Statistical Decision Rules and
Their Error Characteristics

We now begin our study of situations in which a sample may be taken as an aid to choice among a number of possible acts. In principle, there may be any number of possible acts, but in this introductory course we shall restrict ourselves to the simplest possible case, where only *two acts* are under consideration. The theory will be developed in terms of two very simple but typical business problems.

10.1 An Example from Quality Control

A manufacturer has used a particular automatic machine for production of a particular part over a considerable period of time. At the beginning of each production run, the machine is taken down for replacement of worn tools, etc., and then is readjusted by the operator. Experience has convinced the manufacturer that during any one production run the machine behaves as a Bernoulli process, and he knows that when properly adjusted the machine will have a process average fraction defective $p = .01$—it is not within the machine's capability to do better than this, but there is no mechanical reason why it should do worse. It sometimes turns out, however, that the adjustments made by the operator in charge of the machine are not correct and that the machine produces a fraction defective considerably higher than .01.

The entire output of this machine goes directly to the assembly department and the entire output is actually used in the final product, but a defective requires special hand fitting which costs $.40 per piece. Since a single production run amounts to 500 pieces, this means that a really bad setup leads to a fairly heavy "cost of accepting defective product"; specifically, the expected number of defective pieces is $500p$, and therefore

Cost if operator's setup is accepted = $.40 \times 500p = \$200\,p$.

The cost of accepting defective product can be reduced almost to nothing by having the operator's setup checked and if necessary readjusted by an expert mechanic, since if this is done the process average is always brought down to its minimum value, $p = .01$. The time of the expert mechanic costs \$6, however, and if the machine operator has made a setup which would produce a fraction defective .01, this extra cost would be a complete loss. Even if the operator's setup is slightly worse than .01, the saving in cost of defectives would still not amount to enough to cover the cost of having the adjustment checked and corrected; it is only if the operator's setup is really bad that the \$6 expenditure will pay for itself.

10.1.1   The Conditional Losses

It is easy to calculate how bad the operator's setup must be to justify the employment of the expert mechanic. The *total* cost which the manufacturer can expect to incur if the expert mechanic is employed is the sum of the \$6 he receives as wages plus the cost of the defectives which will be produced with even the best setup. The expected number of defectives when $p = .01$ is $500 \times .01 = 5$, and therefore

Cost if operator's setup is rejected $= \$6 + (\$.40 \times 5) = \$8$.

If we let p_b denote the *break-even value* of p, i.e., the value for which the two possible acts are *equally* costly, then we can use our two cost formulas to assert algebraically that the costs of the two acts are equal when $p = p_b$,

$$\$200 \; p_b = \$8,$$

and solve this equation to calculate

$$p_b = .04.$$

Thus if the manufacturer *knew* that $p < .04$, he would accept the operator's setup; if he *knew* that $p > .04$, he would reject the operator's setup. Unfortunately, however, he must choose between the two possible acts *without* knowing the true value of p, and therefore he runs a risk of making the wrong choice and thereby incurring an *opportunity loss*. Suppose for example that he accepts: then if p actually turns out to be .04 or less, he will incur no loss; but if p turns out to be greater than .04, he has spent \$200 p when he need have spent only \$8, and so he has lost $\$200 \; p - \$8 = \$200(p - .04)$:

$$\text{Loss of acceptance} = \begin{cases} \$0 & \text{if } p \leq .04 \\ \$200(p - .04) & \text{if } p > .04 \end{cases}$$

Similarly we can calculate

$$\text{Loss of rejection} = \begin{cases} \$200(.04 - p) & \text{if } p < .04 \\ \$0 & \text{if } p \geq .04 \end{cases}$$

These opportunity losses are graphed against p in Figure 10.1.

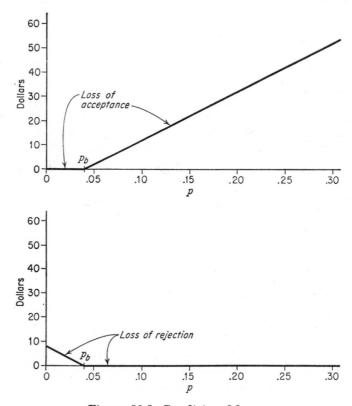

Figure 10.1. Conditional losses.

10.1.2   *The Possibility of Sampling*

Rather than make an *immediate* choice between the two possible acts, the manufacturer can, if he wishes, take a *sample* consisting of the first several pieces produced by the machine as set up by the operator and then base his final decision on the number of defectives in the sample. Sampling is not free, however.   An inspector who is paid $3.00 per hour can inspect 150 sample pieces per hour, so that an inspection cost of $.02 would be incurred for each piece in the sample; and in addition it would take 5 minutes of the inspector's time simply to go to the machine to take the sample, carry it to the inspection point, and report the results to the operator, so that taking any sample at all would involve a fixed cost of $.25 in addition to the $.02 per piece in the sample.

10.2 Statistical Decision Rules; Producer's and Consumer's Risks

10.2.1 *The Form of the Appropriate Decision Rule*

Suppose that the manufacturer does decide to take a sample, and denote by n the *size* of the sample and by $\tilde{r}$ the as yet unknown *number of defectives* that will be found in the sample. If the manufacturer's final decision to accept or reject (readjust) the operator's setup is to depend on the value of $\tilde{r}$ in a sample of some particular size n, then clearly a *small* value of $\tilde{r}$ should lead him to act as if p is small and *accept* the setup, while a *large* value of $\tilde{r}$ should lead him to act as if p is large and *reject* the setup. In other words, the manufacturer will want to adopt (or to act as if he had adopted) a "statistical decision rule" of the general *form*

Take a sample of size n and observe the number of defectives r. Then accept the operator's setup if r is less than some predetermined number c; reject the operator's setup if r is equal to or greater than c.

This much can be established by mere common sense, but the next step is much more difficult. What the manufacturer wants to do, of course, is to find the *best* rule of this general form—i.e., to find the best values for the sample size n and the "rejection number" c.

10.2.2 *Producer's and Consumer's Risks*

In trying to select a best decision rule, the manufacturer will be concerned with two kinds of consideration: (1) the cost of taking the sample and (2) the danger that, even though he does take a sample before choosing whether to accept or reject, he may end up by making the wrong decision anyway: he may accept even though $p > .04$, or reject even though $p < .04$. Since there is no great difficulty about evaluating the cost of sampling, we shall next devote our attention to the evaluation of the risks of a wrong decision; and to make the discussion as clear as possible, we shall separate these risks into two categories:

1. *Producer's risks*, arising from the possibility that a *good* ($p \leq .04$) setup will be *rejected;*
2. *Consumer's risks*, arising from the possibility that a *bad* ($p > .04$) setup will be *accepted*.

These names have their origin in acceptance sampling problems where a "consumer" purchases lots of raw material or manufactured parts from a "producer" and samples each lot to help guard against both the consumer's risk of accepting a bad lot and the producer's risk of rejecting a good lot. They are universally applied, however, even in problems like the present one, where the same manufacturer is both producer and consumer.

10.2.3 The Error Characteristic of a Statistical Decision Rule

Our first task is to see how these two kinds of risks can be systematically *described* for any one given decision rule, and we arbitrarily take as an example the rule ($n = 20$, $c = 2$), or more briefly, (20,2)—i.e., the rule "take a sample of 20 pieces and then accept if less than 2 of the 20 are defective; otherwise reject." Provided that the manufacturer is convinced that the machine behaves as a Bernoulli process with *some* fixed p, the number $\tilde{r}$ of defectives in a sample of size n will have a binomial distribution with parameters n and p and we can use Table I to evaluate *for any given p* either (1) the probability that there will be less than $c = 2$ defectives in the sample of $n = 20$ pieces and that the operator's setup will therefore be *accepted* under the rule (20,2),

$$P(\text{accept}|p) = P_b(\tilde{r} < 2|n = 20, p),$$

or (2) the probability that there will be $c = 2$ or more defectives in the sample of $n = 20$ and that the operator's setup will therefore be *rejected* under the rule (20,2),

$$P(\text{reject}|p) = P_b(\tilde{r} \geq 2|n = 20, p).$$

An expression such as $P(\text{accept}|p)$ should be read "the *conditional* probability of acceptance *given some particular p*," just as $P_b(\tilde{r} < 2|n = 20, p)$ should be read "the *conditional* probability that there will be less than 2 defectives in a sample of size 20 *given some particular p*." We cannot emphasize too strongly that *these probabilities will in general have a different value for every different p;* an expression such as $P(\text{accept})$ or $P(\tilde{r} < 2)$ without the "$|p$" would have *no meaning whatever* in our present discussion.

Having found formulas for the probabilities that the rule (20,2) will lead to either acceptance or rejection *if* the operator's setup has any *particular* fraction defective p, we can easily obtain a formula for the probability that the rule will lead to a *wrong* decision *if* the operator's setup has any *particular* fraction defective p. Remembering that rejection is a *wrong decision* if $p < .04$ while acceptance is a wrong decision if $p > .04$, we have at once

$$P(\text{wrong decision}|p) = \begin{cases} P_b(\tilde{r} \geq 2|20, p) & \text{if } p < .04 & \textit{Producer's} \\ & & \textit{risk} \\ P_b(\tilde{r} < 2|20, p) & \text{if } p > .04 & \textit{Consumer's} \\ & & \textit{risk} \end{cases}$$

In Figure 10.2 the producer's and consumer's risks are graphed against p for the rule (20,2) which we are taking as our first example; observe once more that

The probability of a wrong decision *depends on the unknown true p.*

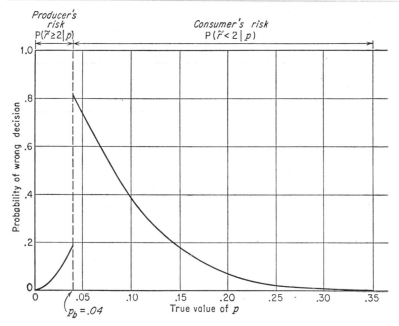

Figure 10.2. **Error characteristic of the decision rule (20,2).**

A broken curve like the one in Figure 10.2, showing the *probability of wrong decision* under a particular decision rule as a function of the (unknown) *true value of p*, is known as the *error characteristic* of the decision rule.

10.3   Effect on the Risks of Changes in *c* and *n*

Now that we have seen how the producer's and consumer's risks under any one decision rule or (*n,c*) pair can be adequately described *as functions of the unknown true p*, we are ready to examine the effect on these risks of changes in n and c. We shall examine these effects one at a time, starting with the effect of changing the rejection number c while holding the sample size n fixed.

10.3.1   *Effect of Changes in c*

The effect of *changing c with n held fixed* can be seen in Figure 10.3, which shows the error characteristics of the rules (20,1), (20,2), and (20,3). What we observe in this figure agrees with common sense.   As *c increases* from 1 to 3—i.e., as it takes more and more defectives to lead to rejec-

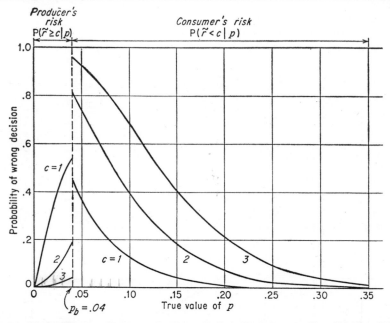

Figure 10.3. Error characteristics of the decision rules (20,1), (20,2), (20,3).

tion—the probability of rejection decreases for all values of p and therefore (1) the producer's risk of *erroneous* rejection *decreases* for all values of p which make rejection an error ($p < .04$), while (2) the consumer's risk of *erroneous* acceptance *increases* for all values of p which make acceptance an error ($p > .04$).   We conclude immediately that

By changing c with n fixed, the manufacturer can reduce his producer's risks at the cost of increasing his consumer's risks or vice versa, but he *cannot* reduce both kinds of risks together.

10.3.2   *Effect of Changes in n*

We next look at the effect on the error characteristic of changes in the sample size n.   At first glance it might seem sensible to hold c fixed while we do this, just as we held n fixed while we looked at changes in c, but it will be more instructive to proceed somewhat differently: we shall choose a different c for each n in such a way that the probability of accepting a setup of *break-even* quality ($p = .04$) is as nearly as possible the same under all the rules.

Figure 10.4 shows the error characteristics of the decision rules (20,1), (50,2), and (100,4), and we observe at once that—with minor exceptions very near to $p = .04$ which are due to the fact that r must be a whole number—

By increasing n and changing c appropriately, the manufacturer can reduce *both* his producer's *and* his consumer's risks.

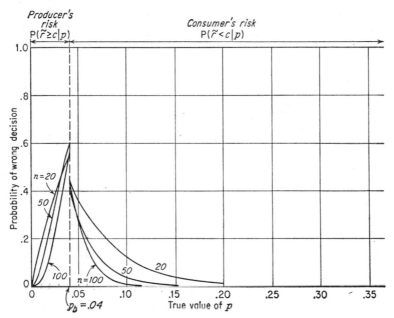

Figure 10.4. Error characteristics of the decision rules (20,1), (50,2), and (100,4).

In common sense, a large sample will give a more reliable "indication" of the true p than a small sample will. The only trouble is, of course, that a large sample costs more money.

10.4 Choice of a Decision Rule by Specification of Producer's and Consumer's Risks

It should now be clear that in order to choose among all possible decision rules or (n,c) pairs, the manufacturer must simultaneously balance off (1) risks of wrong decision against cost of sampling, the balance being controlled primarily by the sample size n, and (2) producer's risks against consumer's risks, the balance being controlled by the rejection number c.   In the present section we present the approach to solution of this problem most commonly recommended in the more traditional expositions of statistics; newer methods will be presented in the next chapter.

Figures 10.2, 10.3, and 10.4 make it clear that under any given decision rule there are *not* just *one* producer's risk and just *one* consumer's risk: *both risks depend on the true value of the unknown p.*   Since, however, it is obviously impossible to keep in mind an infinite number of risk values for each of all the possible decision rules or (n,c) pairs among which a choice must be made, it has often been proposed that a rule be chosen by looking at the producer's risk for just one p which is below the break-even value p_b and at the consumer's risk for just one p which is above p_b.   More specifically, the advice of this school goes as follows.

1*a*. Remembering that a *producer's loss* will be incurred if a setup with $p < p_b$ is rejected, and remembering that this loss is larger the farther p is *below* p_b, decide what value p_1 of p is just far enough below p_b to make the producer's loss "serious."

1*b*. Decide just how large a *producer's risk* or conditional probability of rejection you are willing to tolerate *if $p = p_1$*.   This specified value of the producer's risk is usually called α (alpha).

2*a*. Remembering that a *consumer's loss* will be incurred if a setup with $p > p_b$ is accepted, and remembering that this loss is larger the farther p is *above* p_b, decide what value p_2 of p is just far enough above p_b to make the consumer's loss "serious."

2*b*. Decide just how large a *consumer's risk* or conditional probability of acceptance you are willing to tolerate *if $p = p_2$*.   This specified value of the consumer's risk is usually called β (beta).

3. Use the decision rule—i.e., the (n,c) pair—which comes as close as possible to having a producer's risk equal to the specified α for $p = p_1$ and a consumer's risk equal to the specified β for $p = p_2$.

Thus, in our example, the advocates of this procedure believe that the manufacturer may be able to convince himself that any loss of less than \$4 (say) is "negligible," but that \$4 is "serious."   He will incur a \$4 loss if he rejects a setup with $p = .02$, as we can see by substituting .02 for p in the appropriate formula in Section 10.1.1:

Loss of rejection $= \$200(.04 - .02) = \$4$.

He will also incur a \$4 loss if he accepts a setup with $p = .06$, since this gives

Loss of acceptance $= \$200(.06 - .04) = \$4$.

The manufacturer has thus specified $p_1 = .02$ and $p_2 = .06$; he must next specify the producer's risk or conditional *probability* of rejection α which he is just willing to tolerate *if* $p = p_1$ and the consumer's risk or conditional probability of acceptance β which he is just willing to tolerate *if* $p = p_2$. The advocates of this procedure believe that the manufacturer may be able to specify these values and set $\alpha = \beta = .05$ (say).

If the manufacturer does in fact give these specifications of p_1, p_2, α, and β, then a statistician equipped with a complete set of binomial tables can easily show that he should use the decision rule (240,9): take a sample of 240 pieces and accept if there are less than 9 defectives in the sample; otherwise reject. The rule does not quite meet the specifications exactly, since

$$P(\text{reject}|p = .02) = P_b(\tilde{r} \geq 9|n = 240, p = .02) = .054,$$
$$P(\text{accept}|p = .06) = P_b(\tilde{r} < 9|n = 240, p = .06) = .046,$$

but it is impossible to come closer because of the fact that n and r must be whole numbers.

At this point, however, the manufacturer may observe that if he takes a sample of the recommended size he will incur

$$\text{Sampling cost} = \$.25 + (\$.02 \times 240) = \$5.05,$$

and this may seem a rather large amount in view of the fact that, since the operator's setup *cannot* have a p less than .01, the *greatest* loss he could incur by not sampling at all and simply having the setup checked by the expert mechanic would be \$6. If he does make this observation, a statistician would traditionally recommend that he consider taking somewhat larger producer's and consumer's risks, setting $\alpha = \beta = .10$ (say) at $p_1 = .02$ and $p_2 = .06$. With these risks, he would need to take a sample of only $n = 154$ rather than 240 pieces; the rejection number would be $c = 9$. If the

$$\text{Sampling cost} = \$.25 + (\$.02 \times 154) = \$3.33$$

still seems high, the manufacturer could try still higher values of α and β; it is for him, not the statistician, to decide what *is* a proper balance between risks of wrong decision and cost of sampling.

10.5   An Example from Marketing

As a second example of the use of samples as an aid to decision under uncertainty, we take a problem facing the president of a book club which sells paperback reprints of scientific books by direct mail only. Immediately after learning that he could obtain the rights to a certain book, the president calculated that production would involve a fixed cost of $3000 (payment for the rights and the original plates, setup of the presses, etc.) plus a variable cost of $.45 per book produced (paper, ink, labor), etc. The club's regular pricing policy called for pricing the book at $1.95 plus cost of mailing, so that there would be a gross margin of $1.50 on each book produced and sold.

If the book were to be produced, the actual press run would not be made until after it had been offered to the members and time had been allowed for all orders to be received. There was thus no problem of over- or underproduction; the only problem was whether the number of orders would at least equal the $3000/$1.50 = 2000 required to cover the fixed costs and break even. Since there were 50,000 names on the club's membership list and it was virtually certain that no member would buy more than one copy, this was equivalent to asking whether at least 2000/50,000 = .04 of the members would buy a copy. Serious risks were involved in either possible decision, publishing or not publishing; for letting p denote the unknown fraction of the members who would actually buy a copy, it was easy to calculate the potential opportunity losses as

$$\text{Loss of publishing} = \begin{cases} \$75{,}000(.04 - p) & \text{if } p < .04 \\ \$0 & \text{if } p \geq .04 \end{cases}$$

$$\text{Loss of not publishing} = \begin{cases} \$0 & \text{if } p \leq .04 \\ \$75{,}000(p - .04) & \text{if } p > .04 \end{cases}$$

These losses are graphed in Figure 10.5.

Not wishing to make so important a decision purely by guesswork, the president designed the mailing piece which he would ultimately use if he did publish and then drew 100 names at random from his list of 50,000 names and sent them copies of the mailing piece as if he had actually decided to publish the book. Five orders were received from this mailing and were filled with hard-cover copies of the original edition bought in a book store for $9.45 each.

The fact that $5/100 = .05$ of the members in the sample mailing had ordered the book encouraged the president to think that at least .04 of the members on his complete list would buy if offered the chance, but at the same time he felt that his sample of 100 was perhaps too small to constitute a really adequate basis for so important a decision. The original publisher now informed him, however, that unless he actually bought the reprint rights without further delay they would be sold to

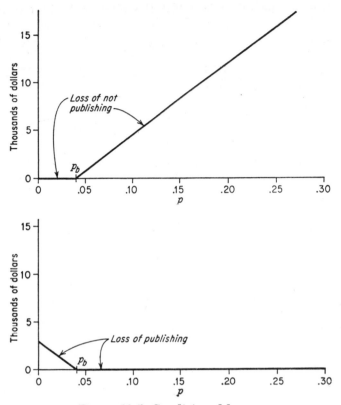

Figure 10.5. Conditional losses.

someone else, so that a decision one way or the other had to be reached immediately.

10.6 Null Hypotheses and Errors of the First and Second Kind

Although this problem is obviously quite similar in essence to the quality-control problem which we discussed just before, problems like this one are traditionally discussed in a special language which the student must learn if he is to understand the great majority of studies in which statistics are used.

First, the problem facing the president of the book club would not usually be expressed as one of choosing directly between the two possible *acts* "publish" and "do not publish."   Rather, it would be said that the president must draw an *inference* about the true value of p by choosing between two *hypotheses* about this value, one hypothesis asserting that $p \leq .04$, the other that $p > .04$.   In problems like the present one, the hypothesis which leads to inaction or the *status quo* is usually called the *null* hypothesis; the other is called the *alternate.*† In our example, the president would like to refuse to publish and thus preserve the *status quo* if $p \leq .04$, and therefore most practicing statisticians would define

Null hypothesis: $p \leq .04$;
Alternate: $p > .04$.

Second, it is standard practice to focus the discussion on the null hypothesis exclusively, i.e., to say that the problem is one of choosing between *acceptance* and *rejection* of the *null* hypothesis, with rejection of the null hypothesis being tacitly understood to imply acceptance of the alternate.

Third, there are standard names for the two "kinds" of mistakes or errors which can be made in choosing between acceptance and rejection of the null hypothesis. It is customary to define:

1. Error of the first kind (or of Type I): the mistake of *rejecting* the null hypothesis when it is *true.*
2. Error of the second kind (or of Type II): the mistake of *accepting* the null hypothesis when it is *false.*

With this vocabulary learned, we are ready to examine the analysis of the book-club problem which would traditionally be proposed.

10.7 Decision Rules and the Risks of Error

Traditionally, a statistician would analyze the book-club problem in exactly the same way that he would analyze our earlier example from quality control; the *only* difference would be in the choice of vocabulary. The statistician would probably start by saying that the president really should have thought more carefully about his problem *before* he took his sample. If he had done so, he would have seen that he should adopt a *decision rule* of the general form

Send a sample mailing to n members and count the number r of orders which are received. Then if r is *less* than some predetermined number c, *accept* the *null hypothesis* that $p \leq .04$ (and do not publish the book); if r is *equal to or greater than c, reject* the *null hypothesis* (and publish the book).

† In problems where one of the two acts can result in much more serious losses than the other, the hypothesis which leads to the *less risky* act is called the null hypothesis. Thus, in testing drugs, where sale of a poisonous batch will have enormously serious consequences, the hypothesis that the batch *is* poisonous (and should therefore *not* be sold) would be called the null hypothesis.

Having seen that the rule should be of this form, the president should then have gone on to pick a specific (n,c) pair, after which all that would have remained to do would have been actually to take the sample of size n and then to reach a final decision by comparing the number r of orders received with the predetermined rejection number c.

Turning now to the situation the president is actually in, with a sample of $n = 100$ already taken and $r_o = 5$ orders already received, the statistician would traditionally say that the president should still solve his problem by choosing a decision rule of exactly this same general form. In the traditional view, the *only* difference between the situation in which the president actually is and the situation in which he ought to have been is that he is no longer free to choose the n of the decision rule which he will ultimately use. He *is* free, however, to use any rule of the type

Sample $n = 100$ and reject the null hypothesis if $r \geq c$; accept if $r < c$;

and the choice of c should be made *as if the sample had not yet been taken*— i.e., without paying any attention to the fact that $r_o = 5$ orders have actually been received. *After* c has been chosen, the final decision can be reached by bringing in this observed value r_o, comparing it with the chosen value of c, and following the rule.

10.7.1   Error Characteristics

Now the rules among which the club president must choose in this marketing problem are identical in *form* to the rules of our earlier quality-control problem except that the words "null hypothesis" have been substituted for the words "operator's setup"; and although the fact that the sample in the present problem is taken from a finite population means that the distribution of $\tilde{r}$ is not strictly binomial, it is binomial for all practical purposes when the sample takes in only $100/50,000 = .002$ of the total population. It follows that before the sample outcome $\tilde{r}$ was known we could have calculated for any rule of the form $(n = 100, c)$ and any given value of p

$$P(\text{accept}|p) = P_b(\tilde{r} < c|n = 100, p),$$
$$P(\text{reject}|p) = P_b(\tilde{r} \geq c|n = 100, p).$$

Recalling that the null hypothesis asserts that $p \leq .04$, we would thus have had for the risks of errors of the first and second kind

$$P(\text{error}|p) = \begin{cases} P_b(\tilde{r} \geq c|n = 100, p) & \text{if } p \leq .04 \quad \text{Type I} \\ P_b(\tilde{r} < c|n = 100, p) & \text{if } p > .04 \quad \text{Type II} \end{cases}$$

In Figure 10.6 the risks of the two kinds of error are graphed for selected values of c, and we see exactly what we saw in Figure 10.3 in the quality-control problem: as the rejection number c *increases*, the conditional probability of rejection decreases for all values of p and therefore (1) the conditional probability of an error of the *first* kind *decreases* for all values of p which make the null hypothesis true ($p \leq .04$) and thus make an error of the first kind possible, while (2) the conditional probabil-

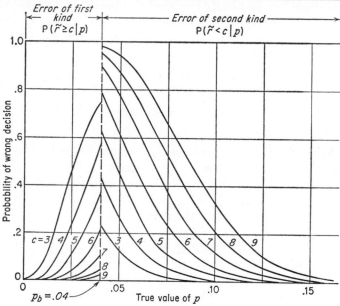

Figure 10.6. Error characteristics of decision rules $(100,c)$ for $c = 3$, 4, . . . , 9.

ity of an error of the *second* kind *increases* for all values of p which make the null hypothesis false ($p > .04$) and thus make an error of the second kind possible.   We conclude as before that

> By suitably adjusting c with n fixed, the president can decrease the risks of one kind of error at the cost of increasing the risks of the other kind of error; he cannot reduce the risks of both kinds of error together.

10.7.2   *Choice of a Decision Rule by Limitation of the Risks of Type I Error*

Although statisticians of the traditional school usually say that the decision maker in a situation like this one *ought* actually to construct a set of error characteristics like Figure 10.6 and then to choose c by comparing these curves for *all* values of p, a great many of these statisticians concede that this is very difficult to do in practice. Apparently because they believe that disturbing the *status quo* unnecessarily is more serious than failure to disturb it when it should be disturbed,† many statisticians suggest that the decision maker may focus primarily on errors of the first kind and choose c in one of the following two ways.

1. If the president would be badly upset by *any* out-of-pocket loss due to publishing when in fact $p < .04$, he should specify the greatest chance α which he is willing to take of publishing *if $p < .04$* and then choose a decision rule (value of c) which (*a*) satisfies this specification about the risks of Type I error while (*b*) reducing the risks of Type II error as far as possible. Thus if the president wants the chance of *any* out-of-pocket loss limited to $\alpha = .05$, Figure 10.6 shows immediately that he should choose $c = 8$: *lower* values of c all have risks of Type I error which are greater than $\alpha = .05$ for some p's to the left of .04, while *higher* values of c increase the risks of Type II error for all p's to the right of .04.

2. If the president would not be too badly upset by a *small* out-of-pocket loss due to publishing when in fact $p < .04$, he should first determine just what value p_o of p is far enough below .04 to make the out-of-pocket loss "serious." He can then specify the greatest chance α which he is willing to take of publishing *if $p \leq p_o$* and choose a decision rule which (*a*) satisfies this specification about the risks of Type I error while (*b*) reducing the risks of Type II error as far as possible. Thus if the president says that out-of-pocket losses of $999.99 or less are "not serious" but that a loss of $1000.00 or more is "serious," we can calculate that his p_o is .0267 because $\$75,000(.0400 - .0267) = \$1000$. Then if he wants the chance of incurring an out-of-pocket loss of $1000 or more limited to $\alpha = .05$, Figure 10.6 shows immediately that he should choose $c = 7$: *lower* values of c all have risks greater than $\alpha = .05$ for some p's equal to or less than .0267, while *higher* values of c increase the risk of Type II error for all p's greater than the break-even value .04.

Now *if* the president wants to choose a decision rule (value of c) in either of these two ways, *then* he can actually solve his problem just as well without the trouble of actually drawing out the operating characteristic for any value of c. To see how, suppose that the president has said that he does not want a risk of Type I error greater than $\alpha = .05$ for *any* p below the break-even value .04.

First, it is clear from Figure 10.6 that for any given c the risk of Type I error increases as p increases from 0 to .04, so that if we want to limit *all* such risks to $\alpha = .05$ or less the only one we really have to worry about is the risk for $p = .04$ itself. Second, it is also clear from Figure 10.6 that for any given p the risk of Type I error increases with c. Thus all that he needs to do is to look in the binomial tables (or have his

† Cf. footnote in Section 10.6.

statistician look) to find the *smallest c* such that

P(Type I error$|p = .04$) = $P_b(\tilde{r} \geq c|n = 100, p = .04) \leq .05 = \alpha$.

The student should verify from Table I that this procedure leads to exactly the same $c = 8$ which we obtained earlier by examining Figure 10.6. He should also modify the reasoning of the last paragraph to prove that if the president wants an $\alpha = .05$ limit on risks of Type I error for only those p's at which the error implies a loss of \$1000 or more ($p \leq .0267$), then all he has to do is find the *smallest c* such that

P(Type I error$|p = .0267$)

$$= P_b(\tilde{r} \geq c|n = 100, p = .0267) \leq .05 = \alpha;$$

and he should then verify by interpolation in Table I that this procedure leads to exactly the same $c = 7$ which we obtained earlier by examining Figure 10.6.

10.7.3   *Tests of Significance*

We have assumed in the last section that the president *might* want to choose the decision rule which (1) reduces the risks of Type II error as far as possible, subject to the overriding requirement that (2) the risk of Type I error shall not exceed some specified α for any p either (*a*) for which a Type I error is possible or (*b*) for which a Type I error would result in a "serious" loss. Letting p_o denote the highest p for which the risk of Type I error is to be limited to α, whether this is the break-even value or some lower value, we saw that *if* this is the president's intention, *then* all that he has to do is choose the *smallest c* such that

$P_b(\tilde{r} \geq c|n = 100, p = p_o) \leq \alpha$.

Actually, the president does not even have to determine the c of his decision rule if all that he wants is *to act in accordance with* a rule which meets these requirements. Letting r_o denote the number of orders that he has *actually observed* in his sample, all that he has to do is to use the following *equivalent* decision rule:

Compute $P_b(\tilde{r} \geq r_o|n = 100; p = p_o)$ and then *reject* the null hypothesis if this probability is *less than or equal to* α, *accept* the null hypothesis if this probability is *greater* than α.

To prove that this rule is in fact exactly equivalent to the rule the president wants to follow, remember that $P_b(\tilde{r} \geq r|n,p_o)$ increases as r decreases and suppose that he *did* find the smallest integer c such that $P_b(\tilde{r} \geq c|n,p_o) \leq \alpha$. Then if the observed number r_o is *less than c*, $P_b(\tilde{r} \geq r_o|n,p_o)$ will be *greater than* α and both rules will lead to acceptance; if r_o is equal to or greater than c, $P_b(\tilde{r} \geq r_o|n,p_o)$ will be equal to or less than α and both rules will lead to rejection.

When the decision rule is expressed in the equivalent rather than the original form, the whole procedure is called a test of significance at level α. If $P_b(\tilde{r} \geq r_o|n,p_o) \leq \alpha$, the *evidence* against the null hypothesis is said to be *significant at level* α; if $P_b(\tilde{r} \geq r_o|n,p_o) > \alpha$, the *evidence* r_o is said to be *not significant at level* α. The exact numerical value of $P_b(\tilde{r} \geq r_o|n,p_o)$ is called either the *statistical significance* of the *evidence* r_o or the *level at which* r_o *is just significant*.

In our example, the statistical significance of $r_o = 5$ successes in a sample of $n = 100$ computed at the break-even value $p_b = .04$ is $P_b(\tilde{r} \geq 5|n = 100, p = .04) \doteq .371$. The statistical significance of the same sample computed at the "point of serious loss" $p_o = .0267$ is $P_b(\tilde{r} \geq 5|n = 100, p = .0267) \doteq .138$. In either case the sample is "not significant" at the level $\alpha = .05$, which is most commonly used in practice. *If* the president wants to test at this traditional level, he should *accept the null hypothesis* $p \leq .04$ and therefore *refuse to publish*.

Null Hypotheses of the Form $p \geq p_b$. We leave it to the student to show by simply reversing the appropriate statements in this section that if the null hypothesis asserts that p is equal to or *greater* than some break-even value p_b, then:

1. The appropriate decision rule will call for rejection of the null hypothesis if $\tilde{r}$ is equal to or *less* than some predetermined number c, so that

$$P(\text{error}|p) = \begin{cases} P_b(\tilde{r} \leq c|n,p) & \text{if } p \geq p_b & \text{Type I,} \\ P_b(\tilde{r} > c|n,p) & \text{if } p < p_b & \text{Type II.} \end{cases}$$

2. The level of significance of r_o "successes" in a sample of size n is $P_b(\tilde{r} \leq r_o|n,p_o)$, where p_o is either p_b itself or some value of p far enough *above* p_b to make the loss of Type I error "serious."

PROBLEMS

1. Read from Figures 10.3 and 10.4 and also compute from the binomial tables the producer's risk at $p_1 = .02$ and the consumer's risk at $p_2 = .06$ under the following decision rules:

a. $n = 20, c = 1.$	b. $n = 20, c = 2.$
c. $n = 20, c = 3.$	d. $n = 50, c = 2.$
e. $n = 100, c = 4.$	

2. If the manufacturer of the quality-control example wants to put the *same* limit on the producer's risk at $p = .02$ that he puts on the consumer's risk at $p = .06$, what is the *lowest* value of $\alpha = \beta$ that he can attain with a sample costing

   a. \$2.25?   b. \$.65?

(HINT: The answers can be read from the graphs in the text; there is no need to use tables.)

3. If you were the president of the book club and had to reach a decision on the basis of the five orders received from the sample of 100 members,

    a. What c would you choose for a rule of the (n,c) form and why?

    b. What level of significance α would you specify for a test of significance and why?

    c. What action would you finally take and why?

4. An advertising agency which wishes to persuade its client to use four-color advertising rather than black-and-white draws 100 people at random, shows a dummy of both advertisements to each of them, and asks which one is preferred. Of the 100 people interviewed, 67 prefer the colored advertisement, 33 the black-and-white. The agency reports to its client that the evidence is "very highly significant" against the null hypothesis that the colored advertisement was no better (and possibly actually worse) than the black-and-white; upon being questioned by the client regarding the meaning of the words "very highly significant," the agency explains that this is a term frequently used by statisticians to mean "significant at the .001 level."

    a. What is the exact statistical significance of the data against the null hypothesis formulated by the agency?

    b. Supposing that the client had decided before the test was made that colored advertisements would be used if the data from a sample of 100 respondents came out significant at the .01 level (often called "highly significant"), compute the c of the implied (n,c) decision rule and graph its error characteristic.

    c. Discuss the relevance of the agency's test of significance to the client's decision problems.

5. In the literature on quality control, a *sampling plan* is a decision rule of the form

Take a sample of size n from the process (or lot); accept the process (or lot) if and only if the number r of defectives in the sample is less than c.

Such rules are usually described by *operating characteristics* which show for every value of p the conditional probability of *accepting* the process (or lot). Sketch the *operating* characteristics of the sampling plans whose *error* characteristics are graphed in Figures 10.3 and 10.4.

6. In the literature on hypothesis testing, decision rules are usually described by *performance characteristics* or *power curves* which show the conditional probability of *rejecting* the null hypothesis for every value of p rather than by curves which show the probability of making *whatever decision is wrong* for every value of p. Sketch performance characteristics for the rules $(100,3)$ and $(100,6)$ in the book-club example.

CHAPTER 11

Evaluation of Statistical Decision Rules in Terms of Expected Loss

11.1 Description of Decision Rules in Terms of Conditional Expected Terminal Loss

One of the reasons why we feel so helpless when asked to choose a decision rule by looking at curves like those shown in Figures 10.3, 10.4, and 10.6 is that these curves do not give anything like an adequate representation of the risks to which the businessman is exposed given a particular value of p. If the producer's loss or the penalty for making an error of the first kind were some *fixed amount* and the consumer's loss or the penalty for an error of the second kind were another *fixed amount*, then curves showing the conditional probabilities of errors of the two kinds would be directly relevant to a comparison of decision rules. In problems of the kind studied in the last chapter, however, the loss which will result from an error of either kind depends on the value of the unknown parameter p in such a way that *an error of either kind is more serious the farther the true value of p is from the break-even value p_b.* The curves of Figures 10.3, 10.4, and 10.6 show that the *conditional probability* of an error of either kind will be greatest if p has a value very near the break-even value; but if the parameter *is* near the break-even value, choice of the wrong act will lose the businessman virtually nothing. They show relatively small conditional probabilities of error for values of p well away from the break-even value, but if the parameter *is* quite far from the break-even value a wrong decision will entail a very severe loss.

This means that the true measure of the risk to which a given decision rule will expose the manufacturer if p has any given value is not the conditional *probability* that the rule will lead to a wrong decision if p has that value but the *expected value of the loss* to which the rule may lead if p has that value. By computing and graphing these *conditional losses* we can get a much more useful picture of the way in which a rule will operate given all possible values of the parameter p than we can get by looking at conditional probabilities of error; but before doing so we must introduce one new technical term.

169

Definition of "Terminal."　　Henceforth we shall use the adjective *terminal* to describe the act or decision which *finally* disposes of a problem, as opposed to a decision to take a sample (and hence to postpone a "terminal" decision).　　The opportunity loss which results from a wrong *terminal* act or decision will be called *terminal opportunity loss,* and it is terminal opportunity loss under a decision rule which we are about to examine.　　The need for the adjective "terminal" will become clear a little later on, when we start asking questions about the expected opportunity loss of a *decision to take a sample.*

11.1.1　*Computation of Conditional Expected Terminal Loss under a Decision Rule*

To see how the conditional expected terminal loss of a particular decision rule is computed for any given value of p, let us take the quality-control problem described in Section 10.1 and the decision rule ($n = 20$, $c = 2$) as an example and compute this loss for the two values $p = .02$ and $p = .06$.

Conditional Expected Terminal Loss When $p = .02$.　　It was shown in our original discussion of this problem that if the manufacturer *rejects* (readjusts) the operator's setup when $p = .02$, he will suffer a loss of $200(.04 - .02) = \$4$; if he *accepts* the setup, he has made the right decision and suffered no terminal loss.　　Looking at Figure 10.2 or Table I we can see that there is probability .0599 that the rule (20,2) will lead to *rejection* if $p = .02$; the probability that it will lead to *acceptance* is accordingly $1 - .0599 = .9401$.　　We can then compute the expected value of the terminal loss to be \$.24, as shown in Table 11.1.　　This is the *conditional expected* terminal loss of the rule (20,2) *given $p = .02$* because it is conditional as regards p but expected as regards $\tilde{r}$.

Table 11.1
Conditional Expected Terminal Loss of Rule (20,2) Given $p = .02$

Sample outcome	Resulting decision	Probability	Terminal loss	
			Conditional	Expected
$r < 2$	Accept	.9401	\$0	\$0
$r \geq 2$	Reject	.0599	4	.24
		1.0000		\$ .24

Conditional Expected Terminal Loss When $p = .06$.　　In this case the manufacturer will suffer no terminal loss if he rejects the setup but will suffer a loss of $200(.06 - .04) = \$4$ if he accepts.　　The probability that the rule (20,2) will lead to *acceptance* can be read as .66 from Figure

10.2 or evaluated as .6605 from Table I; the probability that it will lead to the *rejection* is correspondingly .3395.   The *conditional* expected terminal loss of the rule *given p* = .06 is then shown in Table 11.2 to be $2.64.

Table 11.2
Conditional Expected Terminal Loss of Rule (20,2) Given p = .06

Sample outcome	Resulting decision	Probability	Terminal loss	
			Conditional	Expected
$r < 2$	Accept	.6605	$4	$2.64
$r \geq 2$	Reject	.3395	0	0
		1.0000		$2.64

A complete description of *any* decision rule in terms of conditional expected terminal loss can be obtained by carrying out computations of this sort for a number of values of p and then plotting them and fairing in a curve.   Curves of this sort are shown in Figure 11.1 for the rules with $n = 20$ and values of c from 1 through 3 which were originally described in Figure 10.3.

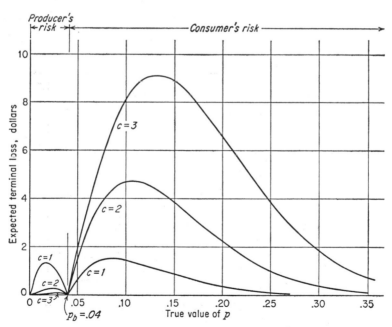

Figure 11.1. Terminal loss under the decision rules (20,1), (20,2), and (20,3).

Short-cut Computation. Tables 11.1 and 11.2 follow the general pattern for computation of an expected value which was set up at the beginning of this course:

1. List all possible events;
2. Assign a probability to each event;
3. Assign a conditional value (in this case, a loss) to each event;
4. Multiply each value by the corresponding probability and add the products.

This procedure can be cut short in problems like the ones we are now discussing where (1) a decision rule will lead to one or the other of *just two* possible acts and (2) we are working in terms of *opportunity loss* rather than profit or cost. Because at least one of the two possible acts must have zero loss by the definition of opportunity loss (cf. Section 4.2), the expected loss for any p will be simply the loss of the wrong act multiplied by the probability that the decision rule will lead to the wrong act.

This short-cut method of computation is illustrated graphically in Figure 11.2 for the rule (20,1). The two straight lines in this figure give the *loss* of the wrong act (reject if $p < .04$, accept if $p > .04$) as read from Figure 10.1, while the two curved lines give the *probability* of the wrong act under the rule (20,1) as read from Figure 10.3. The *product* of the heights of these two curves at any value of p gives the height of

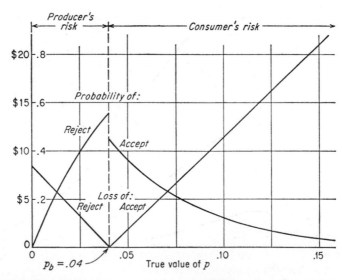

Figure 11.2. Conditional losses and probabilities of wrong decision under the rule (20,1).

the curve for $c = 1$ in Figure 11.1 at that value of p, as the student should verify for $p = .02$ and $.06$.

11.1.2 General Shape of Curves of Conditional Expected Terminal Loss

The method of computation illustrated by Figure 11.2 makes it clear that in any *two*-action problem the graph of conditional expected terminal *loss* under any sensible decision rule will have the general "butterfly" shape of the curves in Figure 11.1. At $p = 0$ there cannot be any defectives in the sample and *any* sensible decision rule will *certainly* lead to the right act, i.e., to acceptance, so that conditional expected terminal loss is zero. As p increases toward the break-even value p_b, the *probability* of getting c or more defectives and therefore of rejecting and incurring a loss *increases*, but at the same time the terminal *loss* which will be incurred by taking the wrong act *decreases*, becoming zero when $p = p_b$, with the result that the product of probability times loss at first increases from zero and then decreases to zero again as shown in the left-hand branches of the curves in Figure 11.1. The student can himself supply the corresponding arguments for the right-hand branches, i.e., for the part of each curve *above* p_b.

11.2 Unconditional Expected Terminal Loss; Optimal Decision Rules When Sample Size Is Predetermined

In order to simplify our discussion by proceding one step at a time, let us suppose for a moment that the manufacturer of our quality-control example is obliged for one reason or another to fix his sample size (the n of his decision rule) at 20, so that his only problem is to select the best rejection number c. Then examining Figure 11.1 we see that

By changing c with n held fixed the manufacturer can reduce his conditional expected terminal loss for $p < p_b$ at the cost of increasing his conditional expected terminal loss for $p > p_b$ or vice versa, but he cannot reduce his conditional expected terminal loss for all p simultaneously.

His problem is thus one of selecting the best balance between these two "kinds" of conditional expected terminal loss.

11.2.1 Minimax Decision Rules

Examining Figure 11.1 more carefully, the student will probably be struck by the fact that if the manufacturer chooses $c = 1$ his conditional expected terminal loss will scarcely exceed \$1.50 for *any* value of p, whereas with $c = 2$ the conditional expected terminal loss goes nearly to

$4.75 (at $p = .11$) and with $c = 3$ it goes above $9.00. This may suggest that the manufacturer should obviously set $c = 1$ if he is obliged to set $n = 20$, and this is in fact the solution called for by the *minimax-loss principle* which we have already encountered in Section 4.5: among all the decisions (in this case, values of c) which are under consideration, choose the one for which the greatest conditional loss is least. The principle applies just as well to conditional expected terminal losses under a decision rule as to conditional definite losses in an inventory problem of the kind we were studying in Chapter 4.

11.2.2 $\tilde{p}$ as a Basic Random Variable

The student will remember, however, that when we took a close look at the minimax-loss principle in connection with the simple inventory problems discussed in Chapter 4, we saw that it not only could, but in most cases would, lead to acts which any sensible businessman would reject at once because they forced him to violate sound business judgment. Specifically, the businessman might in some situations be willing to bet at very long odds that demand would exceed the minimax stock by a substantial amount, while in other situations he might be willing to bet at very long odds that demand would fall far short of the minimax stock; and in either case he would wish to base his stocking decision on what he knew or believed about demand rather than on an arbitrary "principle." We concluded that the stock level should be chosen, not by use of the minimax principle, but by (1) assigning a *probability* to every possible value of the *basic random variable* "demand," (2) using these probabilities to compute the *expected loss* of each possible stock level, and (3) selecting the stock level with the lowest expected loss.

The expected losses which have appeared up to now in our sampling problem cannot be used in this way because they are *conditional* expectations, depending on p; so that when we compare any two values of c we always find that while one is better for *some* values of p, the other is better for other values, and no clear choice is possible. If, however, we digress for a moment to ask how the manufacturer would have chosen between the acts "accept" and "reject" if the possibility of sampling had not entered the picture, we shall quickly find a way out of our difficulty.

Terminal Decision if No Sample Is Taken. If no sample is to be taken and the manufacturer must choose directly between the acts "accept" and "reject," we know from the original discussion of this problem in Section 10.1 that the costs of the two acts and therefore their opportunity losses depend on p; the losses were shown to be given by the formulas

$$\text{Loss of acceptance} = \begin{cases} \$0 & \text{if } p \leq .04, \\ \$200(p - .04) & \text{if } p > .04; \end{cases}$$

$$\text{Loss of rejection} = \begin{cases} \$200(.04 - p) & \text{if } p < .04, \\ \$0 & \text{if } p \geq .04. \end{cases}$$

The fraction defective is thus the *basic random variable* of this decision problem, just as "demand" was the basic random variable of the inventory problems in Chapter 4; and if we are to apply the methods of Chapter 4 to our present problem, a probability distribution must be assigned to the random variable $\tilde{p}$.

Suppose then that the machine operator of our present example has set up his machine a great many times in the past, that records have been kept of the fraction defective in those runs for which the setup was *not* readjusted by the expert mechanic, and that from these records the manufacturer computes the frequency distribution of fraction defective shown in Table 11.3.   Since the runs are fairly large (500 pieces), the fraction

Table 11.3
Historical Distribution of Fraction Defective

Fraction defective	Relative frequency
.01	.7
.05	.1
.15	.1
.25	.1
	1.0

defective in any run can be taken as roughly equal to the value of the process average p during that run; and if the manufacturer has no information other than this—no reason to think that the operator's skill has changed, etc.—he may reasonably take Table 11.3 as giving the *probability* distribution for the process average $\tilde{p}$ in any new run for which the setup is not checked.†

From the formulas for the conditional losses of the two acts given just above we can now compute the conditional losses shown in Table 11.4 for the four values of $\tilde{p}$ which Table 11.3 shows to be *possible*.   We again remind the student that, from the point of view we are now taking, each of the four p's in Table 11.3 or 11.4 is to be considered, not as a *prob-*

---

† In order to simplify the computations, we assume that the process average fraction defective always has one of just four possible values.   The only change which a more realistic distribution would make in the analysis would be an increase in the *amount* of arithmetic required to find the solution—there would be no change in the *nature* of the arithmetic.

Table 11.4
Loss Table

p	Act	
	Accept	Reject
.01	$ 0	$6
.05	2	0
.15	22	0
.25	42	0

ability, but as a *value* of a basic random variable: $\tilde{p}$ *plays exactly the same role in our present problem that the demand $\tilde{z}$ plays in a problem of inventory control.*

From the *conditional* losses shown for all possible p's in Table 11.4 and the probabilities assigned to all possible p's in Table 11.3, we can now compute the (unconditional) *expected* losses of the two terminal acts as shown in Table 11.5. Since the expected loss of rejection is less than the expected loss of acceptance, the manufacturer should choose rejection *if* a terminal act is to be chosen without sampling.

Table 11.5
Expected Losses of Immediate Terminal Decisions

p	$P(p)$	Loss of acceptance		Loss of rejection	
		Conditional	Expected	Conditional	Expected
.01	.7	$ 0	$0	$6	$4.20
.05	.1	2	.20	0	0
.15	.1	22	2.20	0	0
.25	.1	42	4.20	0	0
	1.0		$6.60		$4.20

11.2.3 Bayes Decision Rules

We are now ready to face our real problem, that of choosing the best value of c to use in conjunction with a sample of size $n = 20$. With a moment's thought we can see that

A decision to set $c = 1$ (or 2, or 3, or any other value) is an "act" in exactly the same sense that a decision to accept or reject is an "act"; and an act such as "set $c = 1$" has a conditional terminal loss depending on the unknown true p exactly as an act such as "accept" has a conditional terminal loss depending on p.

The conditional terminal losses of the acts "set $c = 1$," "set $c = 2$," and "set $c = 3$" are given for every possible p by the curves in Figure 11.1,† from which we can read the losses shown in Table 11.6 for the four particular values of p which may actually occur according to Table 11.3. *Table* 11.6 *is identical in principle to Table* 11.4, and it becomes obvious that

The acts "$c = 1$," "$c = 2$," and "$c = 3$" should be compared in exactly the same way that the acts "accept" and "reject" are compared: by computing the *unconditional* expected terminal loss of each act.

Table 11.6
Terminal-loss Table, $n = 20$

p	Act		
	$c = 1$	$c = 2$	$c = 3$
.01	$1.09	$ .10	$ .06
.05	.72	1.47	1.85
.15	.85	3.86	8.91
.25	.13	1.02	3.83

The *unconditional* expected terminal losses of the rejection numbers 1, 2, and 3 (or of the acts "set $c = 1$" and so forth) are computed according to this principle in Table 11.7, where the conditional losses are taken from Table 11.6 and the probabilities from Table 11.3. One very striking fact emerges immediately. The act $c = 1$, which looked so good in Figure 11.1, is in fact substantially less good than $c = 2$. The explanation, of course, lies in the probabilities $P(p)$ in the second column of Table 11.7. If we think of the unconditional expected terminal loss of each act in Table 11.7 as a *weighted average* of the conditional terminal losses of that act, these probabilities are the weights; and

Because so much weight is attached to the conditional loss of each act given $p = .01$, it pays to choose an act (value of c) with a very low loss at $p = .01$ even though this act has fairly high losses for values of p above .04.

† The fact that these are conditional *expected* losses rather than conditional "definite" losses, as in the inventory problems of Chapter 4, is irrelevant, since if the utility of money is linear (as we assume in all these problems) an expected loss of any given amount is exactly equivalent to a definite loss of that same amount. Actually, the conditional losses shown in Table 11.4 for the *terminal* acts "accept" and "reject" are also expectations rather than "definite" losses, since the formulas from which they are calculated were derived from the argument that the *expected* number of defectives in a run of 500 pieces is $500p$.

Table 11.7
Unconditional Expected Terminal Losses of Various Rejection
Numbers, $n = 20$

p	$P(p)$	Loss of $c = 1$		Loss of $c = 2$		Loss of $c = 3$	
		Conditional	Expected	Conditional	Expected	Conditional	Expected
.01	.7	$1.09	$.76	$ .10	$.07	$ .06	$.04
.05	.1	.72	.07	1.47	.15	1.85	.18
.15	.1	.85	.08	3.86	.39	8.91	.89
.25	.1	.13	.01	1.02	.10	3.83	.38
	1.0		$.92		$.71		$1.49

The name *Bayes decision rule* is given to any decision rule chosen by the method of Table 11.7, i.e., by (1) assigning probabilities to all possible values of the basic random variable $\tilde{p}$, (2) using these probabilities to compute the *unconditional* expected value (or "weighted average") of the conditional expected losses of each rule under consideration, and (3) selecting the rule with the lowest *unconditional* expected loss.

11.2.4   *Subjective Distributions of $\tilde{p}$*

The method which we have just described for choosing the best rejection number c is easy to apply and leads to definite, "objective" results when the probability distribution of the random variable $\tilde{p}$ rests on a solid base of historical relative frequencies, as we assumed in Sections 11.2.2 and 11.2.3; but what if the manufacturer had *not* had an objective base for his probability assignments? The answer to this question is the same as the answer to the question of how to determine an inventory level when there is no "objective" basis for assigning a probability distribution to the random variable "demand." In the inventory problem, the manufacturer *must* assign a distribution to "demand" by using his *best business judgment*, basing it on whatever evidence and reasoning he can; the upshot of the assignment will be that his stock will be low if in his best judgment demand will be small, his stock will be high if in his best judgment demand will be high. He may of course be wrong in his judgment—he may stock many and sell few—but no sensible businessman will entertain for a moment the notion that this implies that he should proceed in reverse, i.e., that he should stock a large quantity when in his best judgment demand will be small and vice versa.

Similarly in our quality-control example. The obligation to choose a rejection number c is exactly equivalent to an obligation to lay bets on the fraction defective p of the operator's setup; and *a manufacturer with common sense will want to decide for himself the odds at which he wishes to bet.* Observe, furthermore, that *it is only in very exceptional circumstances that a sensible man's judgment will lead him to choose the minimax c in a problem of the kind we are now discussing.* Reexamining Figure 11.1 we can see that the minimax solution $c = 1$ will have a weighted-*average* height or *un*conditional expected loss lower than that of $c = 2$ only if the weight or probability assigned to p's above the break-even value is at least nearly as great as the weight or probability assigned to p's below the break-even value. *If the manufacturer does feel that he would bet even money that his operator's setup will be bad, he should probably be looking for a new operator rather than wasting his time on the choice of a sampling plan to control his present operator.*

11.2.5   *The Book-club Example*

This same principle that the decision maker *must* lay bets and had better think seriously about the odds at which he wishes to bet applies in the marketing problem described in Section 10.5. It is true that the president of the book club does not know the "true" probability that any particular fraction p of his members will buy a copy of the book in question; and indeed it is not at all clear what is meant by the "true" probability of a unique event of this kind. The president did have a good deal of relevant evidence, however, even before the sample was taken: evidence in the form of sales records on more or less similar books; and *he would be acting irresponsibly if he acted in accordance with betting odds which did not take this evidence into account.* (Observe carefully, on the other hand, that he must *not* use the *sample* evidence in setting the betting odds which he will use to choose a rejection number c. This evidence will come in when the decision rule is *applied*, and it would therefore be double-counted if it were used in *choosing* the rule.)

Suppose, for example, that he has already reprinted 10 books on subjects of roughly the same level of difficulty and roughly the same level of general appeal as the one concerning which a decision must now be reached, and suppose that the frequency distribution of fraction ordering was as shown in Table 11.8. Suppose further that he knows that sales of the original edition of the book now in question were slightly lower than sales of the original editions of the ten books in the historical record. If then he had assigned a probability distribution to the $\tilde{p}$ of the current book before knowing the outcome of his sample mailing he would have wanted (1) to *smooth out* the distribution of Table 11.8 (cf. Chapter 7) and (2) to *adjust* the smoothed distribution a little toward the left—i.e., to put more weight on lower values of $\tilde{p}$. *Exactly* how this is done is for him to decide; we shall assume that he proceeds graphically by the two steps illustrated in Figure 11.3 and then reads off the probabilities shown

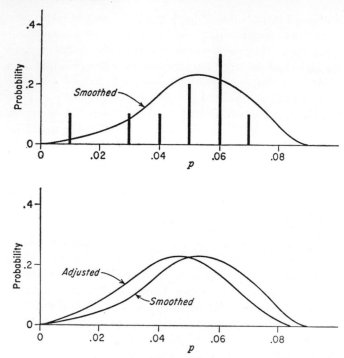

Figure 11.3. Frequency and probability distributions of $\tilde{p}$.

Table 11.8
Relative Frequencies

p	Relative frequency
.01	.1
.02	0
.03	.1
.04	.1
.05	.2
.06	.3
.07	.2
	1.0

in Table 11.9.†   It is left to the student as an exercise to show that,

† Merely in order to simplify the arithmetic we assume in Table 11.9 that $\tilde{p}$ must have 1 of just 8 possible values, just as we assumed in the quality-control example that $\tilde{p}$ must have 1 of just 4 possible values.   The *principles* of the analysis would be identical if we used the "adjusted" curve in Figure 11.3 to assign probabilities to a very large number of different values of $\tilde{p}$.

Table 11.9
Subjective Probabilities

p	Probability $P(p)$
.01	.04
.02	.08
.03	.15
.04	.22
.05	.23
.06	.17
.07	.09
.08	.02
	1.00

with a sample of size $n = 100$ and under the probability distribution of Table 11.9, the unconditional expected terminal losses of rejection numbers $c = 2$ through 5 are as shown in Table 11.10.

Actually, the best c could have been found with less calculations than those summarized in Table 11.10. It can be proved mathematically that in problems of this general type a graph of loss as a function of c can have at most *one* "dip"; and therefore the fact that loss is less for $c = 3$ than for $c = 2$ or 4 proves without further calculation that $c = 3$ has less loss than *any* other value of c.

Table 11.10
Unconditional Expected Terminal Losses, $n = 100$

c	Loss	c	Loss
2	$198	6	$299
3	152	7	399
4	156	8	491
5	211		

11.2.6　The Role of Utility

We saw in Section 10.7.2 that many statisticians believe or act as if they believe that it is in some sense more serious to disturb the *status quo* unnecessarily than to fail to disturb it when it ought to be disturbed; and we saw that as a result they often recommend procedures for choosing c (or equivalently, for selecting a test of significance) which might well have led the book-club president to choose $c = 7$ or even 8. Table 11.10 shows, however, that under the probability distribution of Table 11.9

these very "conservative" rejection numbers lead to expected losses which are more than three times those of $c = 3$.

Clearly, then, the president should *not* adopt a decision rule which gives him strong protection against an error of the first kind (an unprofitable decision to publish) at the cost of greatly increasing the risk of an error of the second kind (failure to publish when publication would be profitable) unless he has some better reason to do so than the mere fact that statisticians often advise people to do so.   We have seen in discussing the quality-control example that an extremely unbalanced distribution of $\tilde{p}$ can lead a man rationally to choose a decision rule which has much higher risks on one side of the break-even point than on the other; but the traditional reason for wanting unbalanced protection has nothing to do with subjective beliefs that $\tilde{p}$ is likely to be high or low.   It is purely and simply the feeling which we have already mentioned, that inaction is somehow safer than action, and *in some situations* this feeling may actually correspond to the businessman's reasoned preferences.

Thus, in the book-club example, publishing when $p = .02$ would lead to a $1500 *out-of-pocket* loss, whereas not publishing when $p = .06$ would lead only to *failure to realize* a possible $1500 profit; and as we saw in Chapter 2, a man would be in no sense *unreasonable* if he said that he would give up a better-than-even chance of winning $1500 in a gamble where losing involved actually paying $1500 out of pocket.   If the president of the book club *does* hold this attitude toward risk, then expected *monetary* value does not satisfy the test of Section 2.2.2 and we may *not* say that Table 11.10 shows that he should choose $c = 3$.   On the contrary, he will quite legitimately want to choose a c which gives him strong protection against out-of-pocket loss even though this does increase the risk of failing to realize a potential profit; and Figure 10.6 shows that this means that he should choose a c which is *higher* than 3.

This much is correct in the traditional approach when applied in situations where one of the two acts can produce out-of-pocket losses while the other cannot.   Even in these situations, however, the *right amount* of protection against out-of-pocket losses will not be obtained or even approached except by accident if the rejection number c (or equivalently the "test of significance") is chosen by the kind of procedure described in Section 10.7.2.   The *only* way of finding a rule which gives the *right* amount of protection is first to determine the president's utility for money in the way described in Section 2.3, then to compute the *expected utility* of each possible decision rule (each value of c if the sample size n is already fixed), and finally to choose the rule with the greatest expected utility.   Except that utility is substituted for monetary loss, the computations would be very similar to those we have already made; but the details are beyond the scope of this elementary course.

11.3   Expected Total Loss; Optimal Sample Size

Returning now to our assumption that *the decision maker's utility for money is linear* and that he therefore wishes to minimize expected monetary loss, we have seen that *if the sample size n is predetermined*, then the *best available* decision rule or (n,c) pair is the one whose c minimizes unconditional expected terminal loss when used in conjunction with the predetermined n. If, however, the decision maker is *free to choose the sample size n*, then the best decision rule can *not* be chosen by looking only at expected *terminal* loss, since this neglects the *cost of sampling*. By taking a large enough sample the businessman can reduce the conditional probabilities of wrong decision (cf. Figure 10.4) almost to nothing and thus reduce his unconditional expected terminal loss almost to nothing; but as the sample size increases, the cost of sampling increases.

11.3.1   Unconditional Expected Total Loss

What the businessman will want to minimize in such a situation is what we shall call his

> Unconditional expected *total* loss: the *sum* of (1) the cost of sampling, plus (2) the unconditional expected terminal loss due to the fact that a wrong terminal decision may be made after the sample has been taken.

When the cost of a sample of any given size n can be definitely calculated before the sample is taken, computation of the unconditional expected total loss of any given decision rule or (n,c) pair presents no new problems whatever.† Returning to our quality-control example, we saw in Table 11.7 that if the sample size is $n = 20$ the rejection number should be $c = 2$ and that the unconditional expected *terminal loss* of the rule (20,2) is \$.71. The *cost of sampling* in our example was shown in Section 10.1 to be given by the formula \$.25 + \$.02 n, so that for $n = 20$ we have \$.25 + \$.40 = \$.65. The unconditional expected *total loss* of the rule (20,2) is thus \$.71 + \$.65 = \$1.36.

11.3.2   Optimal Sample Size

As we have already said, the decision maker's objective is to find the (n,c) pair which has the lowest possible unconditional expected total loss. We already know how to find the best c for any *given* n; our last task is therefore to learn how to find the best n. We can simplify the discussion to follow by defining

---

† The more complicated case where the cost of sampling depends on the actual sample outcome will be discussed below in Section 11.3.3.

Loss of a given sample size n: the unconditional expected loss of the decision rule in which c has the *best* value for the given n.

Terminal loss, sampling cost, and total loss in our quality-control example are graphed in Figure 11.4 for $n = 1$ through 55, and the student should examine this graph before going on.

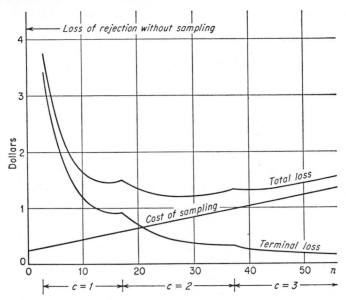

Figure 11.4. Terminal loss, cost of sampling, and total loss.

Behavior of Terminal Loss as n Increases.   It can be proved mathematically that *as n increases from 0 toward ∞,*

1. *Terminal* loss will first decrease and then increase if c is held fixed at any given value, but
2. If we start with $c = 1$ when $n = 1$ and increase c by one unit each time that *terminal* loss would otherwise start to increase, then c will have its optimal value for each n and *terminal* loss will decrease continuously, approaching zero.

The graph of *terminal* loss in Figure 11.4 was generated by this procedure, but we have not shown the portion for $n = 1$ and 2 because here the terminal loss with the lowest possible rejection number ($c = 1$) is greater than the loss of rejecting regardless of the sample outcome.

Determination of Optimal n.   Adding the cost of sampling to the terminal loss of n we obtain the *total* loss of n graphed in Figure 11.4, and we see that this total loss behaves in a somewhat peculiar way. It decreases as n increases from 3 to 15, then increases up to $n = 17$, decreases to $n = 27$, increases to $n = 37$, remains nearly flat to $n = 40$, then increases again. It *looks* as if $n = 27$ may have the least total cost of all possible n's, but it seems hard to be sure, and we wonder whether we ought to trace out the curve for much higher values of n. Actually, however, it is easy to prove that we need go no further—that we can say with certainty that $n = 27$ is the best of all possible n's. All that we have to do is observe that *total loss* at $n = 27$ is less than *sampling cost* at $n = 53$; then since no n can have a total loss which is less than the cost of sampling alone, we can be absolutely sure that the total loss of any n greater than 53 is greater than the total loss of $n = 27$.

11.3.3 *Unknown Sampling Cost*

In many situations the sampling cost which will *actually* be incurred by taking a sample of any given size n cannot be determined until the sample *outcome* is known, as when inspection sampling involves destruction of both the good and the defective pieces in the sample and the cost incurred by sampling therefore depends in part on the number of good pieces in the sample. In such situations we must define the expected total loss of a decision rule as the sum of the expected terminal loss and the *expected* cost of sampling.

To see how expected sampling cost can be easily evaluated before the sample is taken, let us return to our book-club example. In this situation the cost of sampling consisted of three parts, the first two of which could have been definitely known in advance but the third could not.

1. A fixed cost for designing the mailing and setting it up in print; assume that this amounted to $25.

2. A cost for actual printing and postage proportional to the number n of mailings sent out; assume that this amounted to $.10 per mailing.

3. A cost proportional to the number of orders received, each order costing the $7.50 difference between the $1.95 remitted with the order and the $9.45 which would have to be paid for a hard-cover copy with which to fill the order.

To find the expected value of the cost of filling the orders from a sample of size n *before* the sample was taken, we could have reasoned as follows: (1) *Given* that any particular fraction p of *all* members would order the book, the *conditional* expected number of orders received from a sample of size n is pn and the *conditional* expected cost is therefore $7.50 pn$. (2) Because this conditional cost is a linear function of the basic random variable $\tilde{p}$, we have by Section 6.3.1 that its *unconditional* expected value is $7.50 \ \mathrm{E}(\tilde{p}) \ n$, where $\mathrm{E}(\tilde{p})$ is the mean of the decision maker's probability distribution of $\tilde{p}$. We thus have for *total* expected sampling cost, including printing, mailing, *and* order filling,

Cost of sampling $= \$25 + \$.10\, n + \$7.50\, \mathrm{E}(\tilde{p})\, n.$

If the president assigns to $\tilde{p}$ the probability distribution shown in Table 11.9, then $\mathrm{E}(\tilde{p}) = .0449$, as the student should verify, and

Cost of sampling $= \$25 + \$.437\, n.$

PROBLEMS

1. Graph the conditional expected terminal loss of the decision rule ($n = 100$, $c = 6$) as applied in the book-club example described in Section 10.5.

2. Suppose that the manufacturer of the quality-control example has kept no records of the fraction defective produced in runs where the setup was not readjusted by the expert mechanic, but that there is one critical adjustment such that $\tilde{p}$ will have the value .02 if this adjustment is correct and the value .10 if it is incorrect.

   a. If the manufacturer is willing to bet at odds of 9 to 1 that the operator has made the adjustment correctly (i.e., if he assigns probability .9 to the event $\tilde{p} = .02$ and probability .1 to $\tilde{p} = .10$), what rejection number should he choose for use in conjunction with a sample of size $n = 20$?

   b. What is the *smallest* probability of $\tilde{p} = .10$ which will justify use of rejection number $c = 1$?

3. In the book-club example described in Section 10.5,

   a. Draw curves of conditional expected terminal loss for $c = 3$ and $c = 8$ and for p running from 0 to .10.

   b. Verify the unconditional expected losses for $c = 3$ and $c = 8$ as given in Table 11.10.

4. Suppose that the president thinks that, if he publishes the book, it will be either a definite "success," in the sense that $p = .06$ of the members will buy it, or else a definite "failure," in the sense that only $p = .02$ of the members will buy it. Assuming that his utility of money is linear and that he therefore wishes to minimize expected monetary loss,

   a. What c should he use if he thinks that "the chances are even" that the book will be a success?

   b. How large a probability must he assign to $\tilde{p} = .02$ to justify use of $c = 7$? $c = 8$?

5. What would be the optimal sample size in the quality-control example if the costs of acceptance and rejection were exactly as described in the text but sampling

   a. Cost $\$.02$ per unit as stated in the text but did *not* involve the $\$.25$ fixed cost?

   b. Cost $\$.20$ per unit with no fixed cost?

6. In the book-club example, suppose that, instead of sampling, the president had made an immediate choice between publishing and not publishing. If he would have assigned to $\tilde{p}$ the probability distribution of Table 11.9 and if he wants to minimize expected monetary loss, which act should he have chosen?

7. On the assumptions of Problem 6 and on the further assumption that sampling could be *expected* to cost $\$25 + \$.437\, n$, was the president's decision to sample $n = 100$ wiser (as evaluated *before* the sample *outcome* was known) than an immediate choice of a terminal act?

8. The Robinson Abrasives Company manufactured a wide variety of grinding wheels for industrial use. These wheels were subject to extreme stresses; and since breakage could result in severe damage to machinery and injury to machine operators, the company was anxious to maintain high-quality output and subjected the wheels to rigorous testing procedures.

The first step in the manufacture of a grinding wheel was to mix bonding material, abrasive, and water until a smooth uniform mixture was obtained and then pour the mixture into molds which were allowed to dry for a period of several days. The dried wheels were then placed on a shaving machine and turned to the desired dimension, bushings were inserted, and the finished product was tested for hardness, toughness, and strength. The strength test consisted in placing the wheel in a protective steel shell and rotating it at a speed 50 per cent greater than the maximum speed which would be used under ordinary operating conditions.

Failure of finished wheels in the strength test could be due to a variety of causes. If the wheels were improperly loaded in the kiln, warping or cracking or internal stresses could result; and on the average, about 5 per cent of all wheels failed on final test for reasons of this sort. The bonding material itself was of variable quality, and sometimes a substantial number of wheels in a single batch would fail because the cohesive strength of the material was inadequate. Although he could not be completely sure of the reason for some of the individual failures, the quality-control supervisor believed that about 70 per cent of all batches had no failures due to the raw material while 20 per cent of the batches had 5 per cent failures for this reason and 10 per cent of the batches had 20 per cent.

In September, 1955, the research department announced that it had developed and had available for immediate use in manufacturing a new bonding material which was much stronger than the old. Wheels made of this material were no better or worse than wheels made of the old material which succeeded in passing inspection, but the failures due to the raw material were completely eliminated and the company intended to purchase no more material of the old kind. At this time the company had on hand enough of the old bonding material to make 1000 grinding wheels 36 inches in diameter; and since there was no test which would give a reliable measurement of the strength of this material other than actually using it to produce finished wheels, the superintendent raised the question whether it ought to be scrapped in order to avoid the risk of wasting money in processing wheels which might fail on final test.

The cost of processing plus the cost of the materials other than the bonding material amounted to $15 per wheel, but enough new bonding material to produce one thousand 36-inch wheels would cost $1000 and the quality-control supervisor suggested that the batch of old material should be tested by actually using some of it in finished wheels before a decision was reached to accept or reject the remainder. He proposed that the test wheels be prepared and processed under carefully controlled conditions, so that the probability of failure due to improper loading would be negligible. They would be given the regular strength test, and a decision to accept or reject the batch would be based on the outcome of this test.

Trace expected total loss as a function of n for $n = 1$ through 10.

CHAPTER 12

Revision of Probabilities
in the Light of New Information

In Section 11.2.5 of the previous chapter we considered a situation in which the decision maker (the president in the book-club example) wished to choose the c of an (n,c) decision rule *after* he had already taken a sample of a particular size $n = 100$ and observed its actual outcome $r_o = 5$. We pointed out at that time that if the decision maker wanted to assign a probability distribution to the basic random variable $\tilde{p}$ so that he could then choose the c which would minimize his expected loss, he would have to be very careful to base the distribution on only that information which was available to him *before* the sample outcome $r_o = 5$ was known. Otherwise, this last information would in effect be counted twice: once in *choosing* the c of his decision rule and a second time in *applying* the decision rule by comparing the observed r_o with the chosen c. It may well have seemed to the student that this whole procedure was needlessly awkward and complex: that if the decision maker *did* incorporate the information contained in the known sample outcome into his distribution of $\tilde{p}$, then he could choose the better terminal act by simply computing the expected losses of the two *terminal acts* exactly as we did in Part One of the course and again in Table 11.5 of the last chapter; there would be no need to find a decision rule which would tell the decision maker what to do for all *conceivable* sample outcomes—those which did not occur as well as the single one which actually did.

This alternative and simpler method of choosing the optimal terminal act after the sample outcome is already known will be valid *provided* that the decision maker can assess a distribution of $\tilde{p}$ which takes *proper* account of *both* the information which was available before the sample was taken *and* the information obtained from the sample, and we shall now see how this can be done.

12.1 Bayes' Theorem

Before tackling any practical problems in which the decision maker must assign to $\tilde{p}$ a distribution which takes account of both sample and "other" information, let us consider an artificial example which will bring out the basic logic of the procedures we are about to use.   An urn contains 10 balls in the following mix:

1. ½ of all the balls are striped; of these striped balls, $\frac{2}{10}$ are red and $\frac{8}{10}$ are green.
2. ½ of all the balls are dotted; of these dotted balls, $\frac{6}{10}$ are red and $\frac{4}{10}$ are green.

This mix is shown graphically in Figure 12.1; notice that while the numbers *above* the bars give the *unconditional* relative frequencies of striped and dotted balls the numbers *within* the bars are the *conditional* relative frequencies of red and green *given* either striped or dotted.   One ball is now drawn from this urn in such a way that we are convinced that every ball had an equal chance of being drawn, and we wish to assess the probability that this ball is striped.

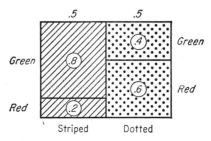

Figure 12.1. Original probabilities.

If the only information we have is that given above, then clearly we must assign probability .5 to the event "striped," since we have already assigned equal probability to every elementary event (each individual ball) and we know that half the elementary events are contained in the compound event "striped" (half of all the balls are striped).   Suppose, however, that before assessing the probability of "striped" we are given the *additional information* that the ball in question is *red*.   In this case our problem becomes one of assessing the probability that a *red* ball is striped, and we therefore reason as follows.

We originally assigned equal probability to every ball in the urn. The subsequent information that the ball drawn from the urn was red obviously leads us to change this assessment and assign 0 probability to all green balls and therefore to raise the total probability assigned to all red balls to 1, but it gives us no reason whatever to assign a higher probability to any one red ball than to any other and we therefore now assign equal probability to all red balls.   We can then argue that of all the balls in the urn, $.2 \times .5 = .1$ were red striped while $.6 \times .5 = .3$ were red

dotted, and therefore that the probability that this red ball is striped
is $.1/(.1 + .3) = .25$.

The reasoning can be expressed in terms of relative frequencies as
follows. Suppose that we draw one ball from the urn, record its description, replace the ball in the urn, stir the contents, and then repeat this
procedure a great number of times. Of *all* the balls drawn, about half
will be striped; but *if we look only at those occasions on which the ball is red*,
only a quarter of *these* balls will be striped.

The same reasoning is represented graphically in Figures 12.2 and
12.3. We start by reproducing in Figure 12.2 only that part of Figure
12.1 which corresponds to the event "red," since the information that the
ball is red means that the rest of Figure 12.1 is now totally irrelevant.

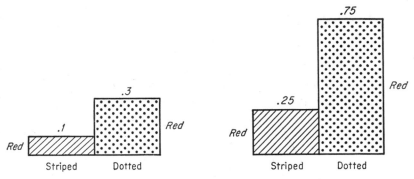

Figures 12.2 (*left*) and 12.3 (*right*). Revision of probabilities.

We then produce Figure 12.3 by enlarging Figure 12.2 in such a way that
its total area becomes 1; to do this we first calculate the *original* area of
each part of Figure 12.2 (the joint probabilities) from the data in Figure
12.1 and then divide the area of each part of Figure 12.2 by the total .4 of
these original areas in order to raise the revised area to 1.

The calculations can also be laid out in the form of a table like Table
12.1. The events in which we are really interested, striped and dotted,
are listed in the first column, and their original probabilities in the second.
Notice that these original probabilities are "basic"—they rest on our
judgment concerning the process by which the ball was drawn from the
urn and in no way depend on the theory of probability. The third
column shows the probability of "red" *given* the event "striped" and the
corresponding probability given the event "dotted"; again these are
"basic" probabilities which rest on judgment and not on the theory of
probability.

The theory of probability is then used to compute *revised* probabilities for the events "striped" and "dotted" from these two sets of basic

Table 12.1

Event of interest	Basic probabilities		Computed probabilities	
	Probability of event	Probability of red given the event	Joint probability of event and red	Probability of event given red
Striped	.5	.2	.1	.1/.4 = .25
Dotted	.5	.6	.3	.3/.4 = .75
	1.0		.4	1.00

probabilities; the work is shown in the last two columns of the table. We first use the multiplication rule (Section 8.4) to compute the *joint* probabilities of "red *and* striped" and "red *and* dotted" shown in the next to the last column as assessed before it was known that the ball was red. We then use the addition rule to compute the *marginal* probability (Section 8.6) of "red" as assessed before it was known that the ball was in fact red; this is the .4 total of the joint probabilities. Finally we apply the definition of conditional probability (Section 8.3) to compute the revised probabilities in the last column of the table.

The logic of this table can be expressed more compactly by the use of algebraic notation. Using S, D, and R to denote the events "striped," "dotted," and "red," we have by the multiplication rule (Section 8.4)

$$P(R,S) = P(S)\ P(R|S),$$
$$P(R,D) = P(D)\ P(R|D).$$

The addition rule gives us the marginal probability (Section 8.6)

$$P(R) = P(S)\ P(R|S) + P(D)\ P(R|D)$$

and the definition of conditional probability then gives (Section 8.3)

$$P(S|R) = \frac{P(S,R)}{P(R)} = \frac{P(S)\ P(R|S)}{P(S)\ P(R|S) + P(D)\ P(R|D)}.$$

This formula is known as *Bayes' theorem*, but it is important to realize that it is really nothing but the mathematical definition of conditional probability as given in Section 8.3 with $P(R)$ written out to show how it is actually calculated. Although the theory of probability can be used as an *aid* in assessing the distribution of a basic random variable, it cannot be too strongly emphasized that theory *by itself* can never determine the probability of any event. As we have emphasized from the outset (Section 1.6.1),

The theory of probability does not *replace* judgment and experience. Its utility lies rather in the fact that it allows us to *make more effective use* of our judgment and experience by assigning probabilities to those events on which our experience and judgment bear most directly rather than to events which will actually determine costs but with which we have had relatively little direct experience.

12.2 Bayes' Theorem Applied to Samples

Our first example of the use of Bayes' theorem to revise probabilities in the light of additional information was chosen to make the underlying logic as obvious as possible rather than to illustrate a common sort of practical use of the theorem.   In practical business applications of probability theory the additional information which we wish to consider usually comes from a sample, and we now proceed to examine three applications of Bayes' theorem in which the information is of this nature.

12.2.1   Samples of Size 1

Suppose that we are presented with an urn containing two kinds of deformed dice.   Half the dice are shaped in such a way that ace will turn up .2 of the time; half the dice are shaped so that ace will turn up .6 of the time.   Using p to denote the fraction of aces which a die would yield in the long run, we can say that $p = .2$ is the *process parameter* of the first kind of dice while $p = .6$ is the parameter of the second kind.

One die is drawn from the urn in such a way that we originally assess at .5 the probability that a die with $p = .2$ has been drawn.   A sample of the die's behavior is then taken by rolling it once; it comes up ace, and we now wish to revise the probability originally assigned to the proposition that the die is one with $p = .2$.

The analysis of the problem is carried out in Table 12.2, which is really identical to Table 12.1.   In terms of an infinite series of trials: if we repeated over and over the process of drawing a die and sampling its behavior by a single roll, we would roll an ace on .4 of all occasions; on

Table 12.2

Value of the basic random variable	Original probability	Conditional probability of sample	Joint probability	Revised probability
.2	.5	.2	.1	.25
.6	.5	.6	.3	.75
	1.0		.4	1.00

.1/.4 = .25 of *these* occasions it would turn out that we had drawn a die
with $p = .2$.

Application to a Production Process.   Suppose now that a manufacturer believes that when a certain machine is correctly set up it has a
process average fraction defective $p = .2$ but that when a poor job is
done the process average is $p = .6$; and suppose further that on the basis
of his records of *past* performance the manufacturer assigns probability .5
to the proposition that the setup which has just been made is "correct."
Before deciding whether or not to proceed with a production run, the
manufacturer obtains additional information on the quality of *this particular* setup by producing and inspecting a sample consisting of one
piece of product.   This piece proves defective.

The manufacturer should now assess at .25 the probability that this
particular setup is "correct."   The reasoning is identical to that used in
the two previous examples.   In terms of an infinite series of trials, the
setup is correct on .5 of *all* occasions, but it is correct on only .25 of *those
occasions on which the sample piece is defective.*

12.2.2   Samples of Size 2

Suppose next that the manufacturer produces a sample of *two* pieces
instead of just one (the die is rolled twice), and suppose that both the
sample pieces are defective (both rolls result in ace).   The revised probability which the manufacturer should assign to the event "correct setup"
($p = .2$) in the light of *this* evidence is computed in Table 12.3.

Table 12.3

Value of the basic random variable	Original probability	Conditional probability of the sample	Joint probability	Revised probability
.2	.5	.04	.02	.1
.6	.5	.36	.18	.9
	1.0		.20	1.0

The first two columns are identical to those of Table 12.2.   The third
column shows the conditional probability of getting two defectives (two
aces) in a row: if $p = .2$, this probability is $.2^2 = .04$; if $p = .6$, the probability is $.6^2 = .36$.   The fourth column gives the joint probability, as
evaluated *before* the sample is drawn, of *both* having a setup with the
specified value of p (drawing a die with the specified parameter) *and* then
producing two defectives (rolling two aces); the total of this column is
the marginal or unconditional probability of two defectives as assessed
before the sample was taken.   The last column is computed from the

fourth in the same way as before; the revised probability that the setup is correct $(p = .2)$ is .1.

If the entire process of setting up the machine and producing two pieces were repeated over and over, then (on the average) *both* pieces would be defective on 20 out of every 100 occasions. On only 1 of every 10 occasions *with two defectives in the sample* would the setup be of quality $p = .2$; on 9 it would be of quality $p = .6$.

12.2.3 Larger Samples

In the previous examples we have computed the conditional probability of the sample directly from first principles; let us now see how tables of a standard distribution can be used for this purpose. We assume as in Section 12.2.2 that the process average fraction defective p of a certain machine depends on the quality of the setup, but this time we come closer to realism by assuming that p can have any one of four different values instead of always having one or the other of just two values. The possible values of p are shown in the first column of Table 12.4; and to them we assign in column 2 the probabilities which the manufacturer of the quality-control example in Section 10.1 assigned on the basis of his previous experience with the regular operator's setups as recorded in Table 11.3.

Table 12.4

Value of the basic variable p	Original probability $P(p)$	Conditional probability $P_b(\tilde{r} = 1 \mid n = 20, p)$	Joint probability $P(\tilde{r} = 1, p)$	Revised probability $P(p \mid \tilde{r} = 1)$
.01	.7	.1652	.11564	.684
.05	.1	.3773	.03773	.223
.15	.1	.1368	.01368	.081
.25	.1	.0211	.00211	.012
	1.0		.16916	1.000

Suppose now that on one particular occasion the manufacturer runs off a sample of 20 pieces immediately after a setup is made and finds that there is one defective among them. The conditional probabilities of getting such a sample, given any specified value of p, can be found using the binomial table for $n = 20$; and it is these binomial probabilities $P_b(\tilde{r} = 1 \mid n = 20, p)$ which are shown in the third column of the table. The entry for $p = .05$, for example, is found by looking up

$$P_b(\tilde{r} \geq 1) - P_b(\tilde{r} \geq 2) = .6415 - .2642 = .3773.$$

The remainder of the calculation is carried out exactly as before: the first

joint probability is .7 $\times$ .1652 = .11564; the first revised probability is
.11564/.16916 = .684.

12.2.4 Column Totals

Notice carefully the following facts about the column totals in any
table like the four we have just studied.

1. The total of the *original* probabilities and the total of the *revised*
probabilities must always equal 1; they represent the total probability of
all possible values of the basic random variable and the variable is *sure* to
have *some* value.

2. The total of the *joint* probabilities will in general be *less than* 1.
This is the marginal probability of getting one particular sample "event"
(one defective, or a red ball), and this "event" was *not* sure to happen.

3. The total of the *conditional* probabilities is meaningless; it may be
either more than 1 or less than 1.

12.3 Definitions

12.3.1 Sample

We are now in a position to see exactly how information obtained
from a "sample" differs from the kind of evidence on which probability
distributions have been based up to now. In all the examples of this
chapter, *the conditional probability which we assigned to the observed sample
depended on the value of the basic random variable*—the probability that
there would be one defective among 20 pieces depended on the value of
the basic random variable $\bar{p}$, the process average fraction defective. *It
was because of this fact* that we could use the theory of probability to revise
the probability distribution of the basic random variable in the light of
the observed sample.

12.3.2 Prior and Posterior Probability

Henceforth we shall use the term *prior probabilities* for the probabilities assigned to the values of the basic random variable before some
particular sample is taken and the term *posterior probabilities* for the
probabilities as revised in the light of the additional information obtained
from that sample.

Notice (1) that this is the *only* distinction between prior and posterior
probabilities and (2) that the distinction is always *relative to some particular sample*. If the manufacturer of the quality-control example has
not taken and is not considering taking any sample, the .7 probability
assigned to $p = .01$ in column 2 of Table 12.4 is not a prior probability—
it is just a probability. If, on the other hand, two successive samples

are taken from the same process, the probabilities posterior to the first sample are the probabilities prior to the second sample. As regards a possible second sample, the value .684 in the last column of Table 12.4 is the *prior* probability that $p = .01$.

In problems where we deal with both a prior and a posterior distribution we shall sometimes use notation of the following sort to keep them distinct:

$P_0(p)$: the *prior* probability that $\tilde{p} = p$; the probability of p on 0 sample evidence.

$P_1(p)$: the *posterior* probability (after 1 sample has been taken) that $\tilde{p} = p$.

12.3.3   Likelihood

We shall use the term *likelihood* for the conditional probability of drawing the sample which was actually drawn, given some particular value of the basic random variable. By Table 12.4, the likelihood of one defective in a sample of 20 given $p = .01$ is .1652. Again we emphasize that the new term is introduced purely for convenience: *a likelihood is a probability in the same sense as any other probability.*

12.4   Terminal Decision after a Sample Has Been Taken

In Table 11.5 of the last chapter we computed the expected losses of acceptance and rejection under what we shall now call the manufacturer's *prior* distribution of $\tilde{p}$, found that they were respectively \$6.60 and \$4.20, and concluded that because the loss of rejection was the lesser of the two the manufacturer *should* reject *if* he were to make his choice without sampling. Now suppose that instead of making an immediate terminal decision he takes a sample of arbitrarily chosen size $n = 20$ and finds 1 defective in the sample. The revised or *posterior* distribution which the manufacturer should now assign to $\tilde{p}$ has been already computed in Table 12.4, and using this distribution we now compute in Table 12.5 the posterior expected losses of acceptance and rejection. Because the loss of acceptance is now less than the loss of rejection, the manufacturer should accept.

Observe that this result agrees with the conclusion reached in Section 11.2.3 concerning the best rejection number c to use in conjunction with a decision rule of the form

Sample $n = 20$ and reject if there are c or more defectives in the sample.

Table 12.5
Posterior Expected Losses of Terminal Decisions

p	$P_1(p)$	Loss of acceptance		Loss of rejection	
		Conditional	Expected	Conditional	Expected
.01	.684	$ 0	$0	$6	$4.10
.05	.223	2	.45	0	0
.15	.081	22	1.78	0	0
.25	.012	42	.50	0	0
	1.000		$2.73		$4.10

We saw there that c should be given the value 2 even though $c = 1$ had seemed very attractive when we looked at curves of *conditional* expected loss in Figure 11.1. Table 12.5 confirms that the manufacturer should *not* reject if $\tilde{r} = 1$; it is left to the student as an exercise to show by similar computations that he *should* reject if $\tilde{r} = 2$.

PROBLEMS

1. Peter is presented with two externally identical urns, one of which contains 10 white balls while the other contains 10 black balls, and he chooses one of the two urns by tossing a fair coin. He will be paid $1 if the chosen urn is the one containing all white balls. What is the expected value of this payment

  a. If Peter must set the price on the basis of only the information given above?

  b. If Peter has already drawn one ball from the chosen urn, seen that it is white, and replaced it in the urn before he sets the price?

2. Same as Problem 1 except that one urn contains eight white and two black balls, the other contains eight black and two white, and the payment will be made if the chosen urn is the one with eight white and two black.

3. In the quality-control problem of Section 10.1, assuming that the manufacturer adopts Table 11.3 as his prior distribution of $\tilde{p}$,

  a. Find the posterior distribution of $\tilde{p}$ after a sample of 10 has been taken and no defective found.

  b. Using the result of (*a*) as the prior distribution, find the distribution of $\tilde{p}$ after a second sample of 10 has been taken and 2 defectives have been found.

  c. Find the distribution of $\tilde{p}$ if a single sample of 20 is taken and 2 defectives are found.

  d. Compute the expected losses of acceptance and rejection in the situation of part *c*.

  4. In the book-club problem of Section 10.5, assuming that the president assigns to $\tilde{p}$ the prior distribution shown in Table 11.9, find the posterior distribution of $\tilde{p}$ and the posterior expected losses of publishing and not publishing.

CHAPTER 13

Suspension of Judgment and Summarization of Information

In the last three chapters we have been concerned with situations in which the decision maker could or would take *at most one* sample; *after* a sample had been taken the only problem remaining was to choose the better terminal act. Often, however, the decision maker is not compelled to make a terminal decision as soon as a single sample has been taken; he is free to postpone terminal action still further and wait for the information from *one more* sample, and this *may* be the better thing to do.

13.1 An Example from Marketing

In Section 10.5 we described the problem faced by the president of a book club who must choose between two terminal acts, "publish" and "do not publish," in a situation where the conditional terminal losses of the two acts depended on how large a fraction p of the club members would buy the book:

$$\text{Loss of publishing} = \begin{cases} \$75,000(.04 - p) & \text{if } p < .04, \\ \$0 & \text{if } p \geq .04; \end{cases}$$
$$\text{Loss of not publishing} = \begin{cases} \$0 & \text{if } p \leq .04, \\ \$75,000(p - .04) & \text{if } p > .04. \end{cases}$$

In order to obtain additional information on p, the president solicited orders from a sample consisting of 100 members and received orders from 5 of them.

In our earlier discussions of this problem we assumed that the president was obliged to reach a terminal decision immediately after receiving this sample information. We now assume instead that he is under no particular pressure to reach a terminal decision; he is free to take another sample of any size n he likes. The cost of the original sample was shown in Section 11.3.3 to be given by the formula $\$25 + \$.437\,n$, but the $25 represented the cost of designing the mailing piece and will not be incurred

198

if the same mailing is used again. We thus have for any *new* sample

Cost of sampling = \$.437 n.

13.2 Analysis by Test of Significance

In Section 10.7.3 we described how tests of significance are traditionally used as a method for choosing between two *terminal acts*, and this is their sole function according to the great majority of American books on statistical *theory*. In *actual practice*, however,

> Tests of significance are far more commonly used as a device for answering the quite different sort of question with which we are now concerned: *given* the outcome of a sample, should *any* final or terminal decision be reached or should judgment be suspended until more sample evidence is available?

This is also by far the most common kind of question to which statistical analysis is applied in research, as opposed to the making of actual business decisions. When a sociologist or a psychologist has collected data that tend to support a theory which he considered plausible even before the data were collected, he may ask whether the evidence in favor of his theory is or is not *conclusive;* but he is certainly *not* going to ask whether he should *reject* the theory when all the available evidence is in its favor. An enormous amount of confusion has arisen through failure to distinguish clearly between these *two totally different kinds of questions*.

Keeping this distinction in mind, let us now inquire whether the evidence supplied by the fact that five orders were received from a sample of 100 mailings is (1) sufficient to warrant a definite conclusion by the president of the book club or (2) so shaky that he should take another sample before deciding *either* that $p > .04$ and he should publish *or* that $p < .04$ and he should not publish.

The fact that $r_o = 5$ in a sample of $n = 100$ tends of course to support the view that the true p is *above* the break-even value $p_b = .04$, since if p were *equal* to p_b the expected number of orders would be $p_b n = 4$, and if p were *less* than p_b the expected number of orders would be still lower. On the other hand, 5 is not *very* far above 4, and this number of orders *could* have occurred by pure chance even though p was in fact equal to or even less than .04. This suggests that we might try to decide whether 5 is *far enough* above 4 to warrant a definite conclusion by computing the probability *given* $p = .04$ that pure chance could result in an r *at least this far* (i.e., 1 unit) above 4. For *if* this probability given $p = .04$ is very small we know that the probability of the same event given any p *below* .04 is still smaller; and it would then seem reasonably safe for the president to conclude that p is in fact *above* .04 and to go ahead and publish without spending money on more sample evidence.

Even though this reasoning seems appealing, we had better not accept it until we have seen how it would work if the sample had happened to give a different result—specifically, if r had come out equal to 3 (say) and thus *below* $p_b n = 4$. In this case the sample evidence would favor the view that the true p is below rather than above the break-even $p_b = .04$; the question would be whether it was *far enough* below 4 to warrant a *definite conclusion* that $p < .04$ and a definite decision *not* to publish. Our previous reasoning would then lead us to think that the question might be answered by computing the probability given $p = .04$ that pure chance would give an r at least 1 unit *below* 4.

Now one procedure which would work in either case would be simply to look at the actual outcome r_o and then (1) if $r_o > p_b n$, compute $P(\tilde{r} \geq r_o|n,p_b)$, or (2) if $r_o < p_b n$, compute $P(\tilde{r} \leq r_o|n,p_b)$. More commonly, however, statisticians have argued or implied that instead of thinking about how far r_o lies *above* $p_b n$ or how far it lies *below* $p_b n$, we should think about how far it lies *away from* $p_b n$ and measure the conclusiveness of the sample by computing the probability, given $p = p_b$, that pure chance could have yielded an r *at least this far from* $p_b n$ *in either direction*. Thus, in our example, where $r_o = 5$ is 1 unit away from $p_b n = .04$, we would compute

$$P_b(\tilde{r} \leq 3|100,.04) + P_b(\tilde{r} \geq 5|100,.04) = .4295 + .3711 = .8006,$$

from which we see that if in fact p *were* equal to p_b, pure chance could *easily* yield an r at least 1 unit greater or less than $p_b n$.

13.2.1   *Two-tail Tests of Significance*

Formally, the procedure used by most practicing statisticians for deciding whether a given sample warrants a final conclusion or whether judgment should be suspended until more evidence has been obtained can be put in the form of the following decision rule:

Defining $d_o = |r_o - p_b n|$, where n is the sample size, p_b is the break-even value, and r_o is the number of successes actually observed in the sample,† compute the *two-tail significance*

$$P_b(\tilde{r} \leq p_b n - d_o|n,p_b) + P_b(\tilde{r} \geq p_b n + d_o|n,p_b);$$

then reach a final conclusion or terminal decision if this quantity is no greater than some predetermined number α; otherwise, suspend judgment until more evidence has been obtained.

---

† The "absolute-value signs" around $|r_o - p_b n|$ indicate that the quantity between them is to be treated as positive whether or not it is so in fact. Thus $|3 - 7| = +4 = |7 - 3|$.

When the significance is numerically no greater than α, the sample evidence is said to be "significant at level α"; when it is greater than α, the sample evidence is said to be "not significant at level α."

Concerning the level α at which the test should be conducted, statisticians traditionally say that this is a matter of judgment which should depend on the circumstances of the case. In practice, however, α is virtually never made higher than .05; and it is absolutely certain that no statistician who uses procedures of this sort would ever dream of setting α as high as the .8006 which we computed to be the significance of the sample taken by the president of the book club. Using traditional procedures, the president should very definitely take another sample before reaching any final conclusion about p—i.e., before deciding whether or not to publish.

13.2.2   *The Null Hypothesis $p = p_b$*

The decision procedure which we have just described is often called a test of the "null hypothesis" that $p = p_b$ *exactly*. The *meaning* of the test, however, is obviously totally different from the meaning of the tests described in Section 10.7.3 for null hypotheses of the form $p \le p_b$. In that case we had a problem of terminal action; rejection of the null hypothesis implied acting as if $p > p_b$, and the alternative was to *accept* the null hypothesis and act as if $p \le p_b$. In the present case, on the contrary, rejection of the null hypothesis implies taking *whichever act looks better* on the available evidence; and the alternative is *not* to *accept* the hypothesis that $p = p_b$ but to *suspend judgment*.

Observe, however, that the difference between the two kinds of tests of significance does *not* arise because of the difference in *form* between null hypotheses of the type $p = p_b$ and those of the type $p \le p_b$ or $p \ge p_b$. In some situations we might in fact be quite ready to accept a null hypothesis which asserted that p was exactly equal to some specified value—e.g., the hypothesis that the long-run frequency p with which a person can guess whether a coin will fall heads or tails is exactly $\frac{1}{2}$. The difference between the two kinds of tests which we are now discussing is due to the *purpose* for which each kind of test is performed. In Section 10.7.3 we really wanted to know whether the hypothesis that $p \le p_b$ was true or false, whereas in the present chapter the null hypothesis that $p = p_b$ is *purely and simply a dummy*.

13.3   Analysis in Terms of Expected Loss

Although the test of significance described in the previous section seems to indicate overwhelmingly that the president of the book club ought to take another (and probably a larger) sample, we would still like to bring the losses of wrong decisions and the cost of any new sample into the analysis explicitly, especially since we have as yet no way of deciding *how large* the proposed new sample should be.   We learned in Chapter 11 how to make an economic analysis when the question was one of deciding, with no previous sample evidence to go on, whether a *single* sample should be taken and if so how large it should be; we now ask whether, even though one sample has already been taken, we can use this same kind of analysis to determine whether *one more* sample should be taken and if so how large it should be.

The answer is that we can. <u>Full account can be taken of the infor-</u><u>mation in the sample already at hand by using Bayes' theorem to make</u> <u>an appropriate revision of the decision maker's original distribution of</u> <u>the basic random variable $\bar{p}$, after which the expected total loss of any</u> <u>new</u> sample can be computed exactly as it was computed in Chapter 11. This conclusion is completely analogous to the one we reached in Chapter 12 concerning problems of terminal decision: if after a sample has been taken the decision maker's original distribution of $\bar{p}$ is revised appropriately by the use of Bayes' theorem, he can then compute the expected loss of any terminal act by exactly the same *method* that he would have used before the sample was taken.   More generally,

> Once the information in a sample has been incorporated via Bayes' theorem into the decision maker's distribution of *any* basic random variable, he can for *any* purpose whatsoever forget completely that a sample has been taken.

In our book-club example: if the president *originally* assigned to $\bar{p}$ the distribution shown in Table 11.9, then the student can verify that after observing 5 orders in a sample of 100 he should assign to $\bar{p}$ the

Table 13.1
Revised Distribution of $\bar{p}$

p	$P(p)$
.01	.001
.02	.021
.03	.112
.04	.258
.05	.305
.06	.205
.07	.085
.08	.013
	1.000

revised distribution shown in Table 13.1.   Given this revised distribution and a complete set of binomial tables, we can analyze our present
problem exactly as we analyzed the quality-control example in Chapter
11.   For any given sample size n, we find the best "rejection number" c
by computing (unconditional) expected terminal loss with various c's and
picking the lowest, just as we did in Section 11.2.5 except that we now
use the posterior rather than the prior distribution of $\tilde{p}$.   Repeating this
procedure for various n's, we can trace out the curve of expected terminal
loss shown in Figure 13.1; applying the formula given in Section 13.1 for
the cost of sampling, we can trace out the "curve" of sampling cost; and
adding terminal loss and sampling cost we obtain the curve of expected

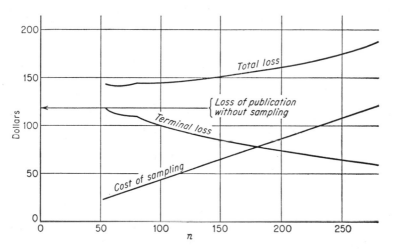

**Figure 13.1. Terminal loss, sampling cost, and total loss of a second
sample.**

total loss.   Finally, we compute the expected losses of the decisions
"publish" and "do not publish" *immediately* (i.e., *without* further sampling) and find that they are respectively \$118 and \$766.

Inspecting Figure 13.1 we see at once that *there is no sample size for
which expected total loss is as low as the loss of acceptance without further
sampling.*† The president should publish the book without spending any
more money on sampling, regardless of the fact that the sample already
taken is "significant" only at the .8006 level and not at the traditionally
required level .05.

† We do not need to compute expected total loss for sample sizes larger than about
270 because for such samples the cost of sampling alone is greater than the loss of
publication without sampling.

13.4 An Example from Marketing Research

A drug manufacturer who is thinking of developing and marketing a new cold remedy wishes to learn, among many other things, whether a person's choice of a remedy is more likely to be determined by a doctor or by a druggist. Accordingly he employs an agency specializing in telephone surveys to call telephone numbers chosen at random from telephone books all over the country and to ask each person who answers the telephone (1) whether when he last bought a cold remedy his choice of product was due to any individual's advice and (2) if so, whose advice; the calls are to be continued until 1000 answers have been obtained.†

The agency reports that of the 1000 persons answering the questions, 148 had not bought any cold remedy that they could remember, 221 had been buying the same product for so long that they had forgotten what led them to start, 476 had made their choice because of advertising in mass media, 56 because of advice from friends, 67 because of advice from doctors, and 32 because of advice from druggists. The manufacturer now wants to know whether the fact that 67 of the people in the *sample* were influenced by doctors against 32 influenced by druggists (1) really entitles him to conclude that more people in the *entire population* are influenced by doctors than by druggists, or (2) might be purely a result of chance. If the sample can *not* be considered reliable, he would consider purchasing additional interviews at a cost of $.50 each.

13.4.1 The Sampled Population

Let us observe immediately that the sampling method the agency has used cannot really give the manufacturer any information concerning the *whole* United States population, however large a sample is taken. Even if every telephone in the United States had been rung, the survey would have obtained answers only from that part of the population who (1) have telephones, (2) answered the telephone, and then (3) answered the interviewer's questions. We must therefore start by asking the manufacturer whether he is willing to rephrase his question as follows: "Among all people who would have responded to a 100% telephone survey, is the number whose choice of cold remedy was determined by a doctor greater or less than the number whose choice was determined by

† Actually, it would be prohibitively expensive to take a survey in the way we assume this one to have been taken. Instead, a certain number of cities would first be drawn, and a number of individuals would then be drawn within each city. The *technical analysis* of such a "clustered" sample would be much more complex than that of the "simple" sample we assume in the text, but the *general principles* would be identical and it is these general principles which we are trying to expound in this introductory course.

a druggist?" In the analysis which follows, we assume that the manufacturer's answer is yes—that since it would obviously be extremely expensive to try to get evidence bearing directly on his real question, he will make do with an answer to this substitute question.

13.4.2 Formalization of the Decision Problem

To formalize the manufacturer's decision problem, we now define *for the population consisting of all people who would have answered a* 100% *telephone survey*

N_{doc}: number of people whose choice was determined by a doctor;
N_{drug}: number of people whose choice was determined by a druggist;

$$ p = \frac{N_{doc}}{N_{doc} + N_{drug}}. $$

The manufacturer is interested only in the "subpopulation" of size $N_{doc} + N_{drug}$ within which the definition of p which we have just given classifies anyone who was influenced by a *doctor* as a "success"; and concerning this subpopulation he wishes *ultimately* to choose between two *hypotheses*: $p \leq \frac{1}{2}$ and $p > \frac{1}{2}$. By drawing 1000 people from the entire population, he has obtained a sample consisting of 67 successes and 32 failures or a total of $n = 99$ from the subpopulation in which he is interested. His problem is to decide whether (1) this sample evidence is sufficient to warrant an immediate choice between the two hypotheses—in which case he will obviously choose $p > \frac{1}{2}$—or (2) he should suspend judgment until more evidence has been collected.

13.5 Rectangular Prior Distributions

As we have seen in the book-club example, a complete analysis of any problem of this sort will depend upon the decision maker's *prior* distribution of $\tilde{p}$. If, however, we ask the drug manufacturer of our present example to assess this prior distribution, he is very likely to answer that we are wasting his time—that prior to learning the sample outcome he had only the vaguest notions about p and that his posterior probabilities or betting odds ought to depend wholly on the sample results.

13.5.1 Meaning of a Rectangular Prior Distribution

If the manufacturer does give this answer, our first task is to check whether he really means what he says; and we can do so by asking him a few questions of the following sort:

Suppose that, *before* you knew the sample outcome, someone who *knew* the true value of p had told you that it was either .13 or .28: would you then have been just as ready to take either side of an even-money bet on .13?   What if the two values had been .101 and .796, or .321 and .645?

If the president answers that he would indeed have had no preference in any bet of this sort, then he *has* in effect given us his prior distribution of $\tilde{p}$: it is the so-called *rectangular* distribution whose graph is shown in Figure 13.2 with the label "prior."   This distribution is *continuous* and therefore the vertical axis shows *probability per unit width* rather than probability (cf. what is said on histograms in Sections 3.3 and 3.5). The probability that $\tilde{p}$ lies, say, between .203 and .206 is the product of the

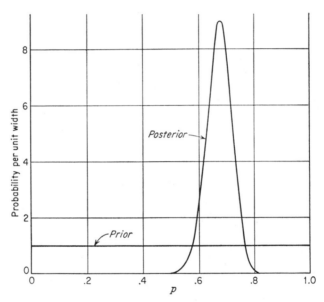

Figure 13.2. Prior and posterior distribution of $\tilde{p}$.

width of this interval times the height of the "curve," or .003 × 1 = .003; and similarly for any other interval.   Because the probability in an interval which has zero width is zero, the probability that $\tilde{p}$ has *precisely* any specified value p is zero, and therefore

$$P(\tilde{p} < p) = P(\tilde{p} \le p)$$

and similarly for the right tail.†

† The fact that the probability of any particular value p is zero does *not* mean that $\tilde{p}$ *cannot* have this value; it means only (very loosely speaking) that, because there are so many possible values for p, it would be unreasonable to put any money "on the nose" of any one value.   There *is* a finite probability that $\tilde{p}$ lies *within the interval* .5000000 to .5000001 or within any other nonzero *interval*, however narrow.

13.5.2   The Sampling Distribution

Although the subpopulation from which the manufacturer's sample was drawn is finite and therefore the distribution of the sample $\tilde{r}$ is not strictly binomial, the fact that the sample size $n = 99$ is extremely small relative to the subpopulation size $N_{doc} + N_{drug}$ means that the distribution of $\tilde{r}$ can be treated as binomial for all practical purposes *provided* that, when each successive member of the sample was drawn, every undrawn member of the subpopulation had an equal chance of being drawn.

13.5.3   Posterior Distributions When the Prior Distribution Is Rectangular and Sampling Is Binomial

We now give two extremely important mathematical facts without proof. When (1) the prior distribution of $\tilde{p}$ is *rectangular* and (2) the sampling distribution of $\tilde{r}$ is *binomial*, then after r_o successes have been observed in a sample of size n the posterior distribution of $\tilde{p}$ has *probability per unit width* given by the formula

$$\mathrm{P}'_1(p) = (n + 1)\mathrm{P}_b(r_o|n,p)$$

and has *cumulative probabilities* given by the formulas

$$\mathrm{P}_1(\tilde{p} \leq p) = \mathrm{P}_b(\tilde{r} \geq r_o + 1|n + 1, p),$$
$$\mathrm{P}_1(\tilde{p} \geq p) = \mathrm{P}_b(\tilde{r} \leq r_o|n + 1, p).$$

The binomial probabilities in terms of which these formulas are expressed are *not* true probabilities involving a real random variable $\tilde{r}$; the random variable in whose distribution we are interested is $\tilde{p}$, not $\tilde{r}$, and it simply happens that the *mathematical formulas* for the distribution of $\tilde{p}$ are the same as or similar to the *mathematical formulas* for certain binomial probabilities.   The reason for expressing the formulas in binomial equivalents is purely and simply that this makes it easy to evaluate the formulas numerically by use of binomial tables.

"Gentle" Prior Distributions.   If the drug manufacturer is actually shown the graph of a strictly rectangular prior distribution which is given in Figure 13.2 with the label "prior" and again in Figure 13.3 with the label (0,0), he is very likely to say that this was *not* what he really meant: he should have said that he was *nearly* as ready to bet on $\tilde{p} = .13$ as on $\tilde{p} = .28$, and so forth.   In particular, he may not like the implication that $\tilde{p}$ is just as likely to lie between 0 and .01 as it is to lie between a pair of less extreme values such as .30 and .31, say.   On further reflection he may decide that he would not even have been willing to bet exactly even money that $\tilde{p}$ was above or below ½—when he stops

to think about it, he recalls that he *did* have a *little* prior information which would have led him to favor one side or the other.

Supposing that the manufacturer does react in this way, we can ask him to draw a rough sketch of a curve which *does* properly represent his *prior* betting odds, and he might give us something which looks roughly like either the curve labeled (4,1) or the curve labeled (4,3) in Figure 13.3. We must then ask whether the *posterior* distribution graphed in Figure 13.2 has any validity whatever now that the prior distribution has been changed, and the answer is quite surprising: *the posterior distribution corresponding to either the* (4,1) *or the* (4,3) *prior is so nearly identical to the posterior corresponding to a rectangular or* (0,0) *prior that when all three are graphed to the scale of Figure* 13.2 *it is impossible to see any difference at all.*

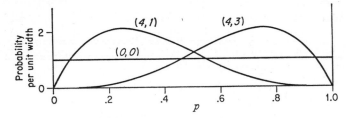

Figure 13.3. Prior distributions of $\tilde{p}$.

Although it would be beyond the scope of an elementary course to go into details of the theory of continuous prior and posterior distributions, we can suggest why it is that the three prior distributions of Figure 13.3 all yield nearly identical posteriors after a sample of 99 observations has been taken. The (4,1) prior can be interpreted as the posterior distribution which the manufacturer would have obtained if he had *originally* assigned a rectangular distribution to $\tilde{p}$ and then found 1 success in a sample of size 4; the (4,3) prior can be interpreted as the posterior given a rectangular prior and 3 successes in a sample of 4. The amount of information in a sample of size 4 is clearly very small relative to the amount in the manufacturer's *real* sample of size 99 and therefore has a negligible effect on the final distribution of $\tilde{p}$. More generally, *any* reasonably "gentle" prior distribution whose peak is not much higher than the peaks of the (4,1) and (4,3) distributions in Figure 13.3 will have a negligible effect on the posterior distribution after a sample of size 99 has been taken.

It would thus appear that in many situations where (1) a "large" sample has been taken, and (2) the decision maker's prior opinions are such that his prior distribution is not "very" sharply peaked, he can obtain good approximations to his exact posterior probabilities by simply using formulas which assume a rectangular prior, thus sparing himself the trouble of deciding what his *exact* prior betting odds would have been. Notice carefully, however, that *what constitutes a "large" sample or a "very" sharply peaked prior distribution is a relative matter.* The information contained in 4 fictitious observations would *not* have been negligible if the drug manufacturer's real sample had consisted of only 9 observations rather than 99; and on the other hand a prior distribution as peaked as the *posterior* distribution in Figure 13.2 and therefore equivalent to 99 fictitious observations would be roughly equivalent to a rectangular prior if the real sample consisted of 999 observations. *There is unfortunately no reliable substitute for a correct understanding and application of probability theory; a person in the drug manufacturer's position is always well advised to consult an expert rather than to try to use general-purpose formulas on his own.*

13.6 Suspension of Judgment When Terminal Losses Are Small and Ill-defined; The Common Sense of Statistical Significance

13.6.1 *Posterior Probability as a Rough-and-Ready Guide to Suspension of Judgment*

Now that we have the drug manufacturer's distribution of $\tilde{p}$ posterior to his sample of 99 observations, we are ready to attack his decision problem: should he make an immediate choice between the two hypotheses $p \leq \frac{1}{2}$ and $p > \frac{1}{2}$, or should he suspend judgment and collect more sample evidence?

If this problem is to be analyzed in the way the book-club example was analyzed in Section 13.2 above, our next step would be to determine (1) the *terminal-loss functions* which tell us, for every possible value of p, the loss which will result from a wrong choice of hypothesis, and (2) the *cost of sampling.* The latter is easy to estimate: since interviews cost 50 cents each, and since about one interview in ten is with a person influenced by either a doctor or a druggist, it will cost about \$5 on the average for each additional interview with a member of the subpopulation in which the manufacturer is interested.

The terminal losses, on the contrary, would be exceedingly difficult to estimate. The question about the relative influence of doctors and druggists is only one of many which bear on the manufacturer's decision whether or not to market the new product and, if he *is* to market it, how to promote it; so that it is clearly impossible to say *objectively* what the loss will really be in any particular case. If despite this it appeared that the loss due to a wrong choice could be really serious, we would ask the manufacturer to express his *best judgment* about the possible losses by *assigning* them definite subjective values (in money or utiles). This would obviously be a considerable bother to the manufacturer, however, and therefore we shall not ask him to assign these subjective values until we have got a *rough indication* of the "conclusiveness" of the existing evidence by simply computing the (posterior) *probability that the obvious choice is wrong*.

Since there were 67 successes in the sample of size 99, the hypothesis which should obviously be chosen if *any* choice is to be made is $p > \frac{1}{2}$. The probability that this obvious choice is *wrong* is the probability that $\tilde{p} \leq \frac{1}{2}$; and we therefore use the second formula in Section 13.5.3 to evaluate

$$P_1(\tilde{p} \leq \tfrac{1}{2}) = P_b(\tilde{r} \geq 68 | n = 100, p = \tfrac{1}{2}) = .0002.$$

It is immediately apparent that the manufacturer can without further ado take it as established that doctors are more influential than druggists in the choice of cold remedies—or far more accurately, that *this would be the indication of a 100% sample taken in the same way and by the same interviewers as the original sample*. It would be foolish to spend money on additional interviews when the chances are so poor that they would change the conclusion.

This conclusion depends only on the manufacturer's *posterior* distribution of $\tilde{p}$; the fact that the prior distribution was or was not rectangular is irrelevant once the posterior distribution has been found. We may therefore generalize this example to assert that

> In any decision problem in which the cost of further sampling is substantial and the loss of a wrong conclusion is not very serious, the fact that one of the two hypotheses has a *very* low posterior probability can reasonably be taken as a strong indication that the other, more probable hypothesis should be adopted without spending time or money on additional sampling.

Observe, however, that we may *not* assert the converse—it is *not* true that when neither hypothesis has a low posterior probability we *should* go on to collect more evidence before adopting either hypothesis or choosing either terminal act. In our book-club example, we have by Table 13.1 that the posterior probability that $\tilde{p} < .04$ and that publication will therefore result in a loss is .134, which is certainly not *very* low; and yet we saw in Section 13.3 above that the manufacturer should proceed forthwith to publish: collection of more information was *not* economically justified.

13.6.2   Statistical Significance and Posterior Probability

We are now ready to see how statistical significance can actually be of considerable practical use as a rough-and-ready guide to practical action, even though the two traditional uses which we described in Chapter 11 and the first part of this chapter are extremely misleading and dangerous.

Going back to Section 10.7.3, we remind the student that <u>if the decision maker is testing a null hypothesis of the form $p \leq p_b$ or $p \geq p_b$ and wishes to limit the conditional probability of *any* Type I error to some predetermined α, the (*one-tail*) statistical significance of r_o successes in a sample of size n is</u>

$P_b(\tilde{r} \geq r_o \| n, p_b)$	if the null hypothesis is $p \leq p_b$,
$P_b(\tilde{r} \leq r_o \| n, p_b)$	if the null hypothesis is $p \geq p_b$.

We have seen in Section 13.5.3, on the other hand, that *if* the decision maker treats $\tilde{p}$ as a random variable to which he assigns a *rectangular prior distribution*, then after observing r_o successes in a sample of size n the *posterior probabilities* that $\tilde{p}$ is to the left or right of p_b are respectively

$$P_1(\tilde{p} \leq p_b) = P_b(\tilde{r} \geq r_o + 1 | n + 1, p_b),$$
$$P_1(\tilde{p} \geq p_b) = P_b(\tilde{r} \leq r_o | n + 1, p_b);$$

and these formulas hold as approximations for any prior distribution which is not "very" peaked relative to a "large" sample size n. Comparing the two pairs of formulas we see that

> When the sample size is large and the prior distribution of $\tilde{p}$ can be treated as rectangular, the posterior probability that the null hypothesis is true is approximately equal to the *one-tail* statistical significance of the sample computed with reference to the *break-even value p_b*.

Thus, in our example, where there were 67 successes in a sample of 99, the *one-tail* significance of this result against the null hypothesis that $p \leq p_b$ is

$$P_b(\tilde{r} \geq 67 | n = 99, p = \tfrac{1}{2}) = .0003,$$

which is roughly equal to the .0002 posterior probability of $\tilde{p} < \tfrac{1}{2}$ on a rectangular prior.

Now the posterior probability that a hypothesis of the type $p \leq p_b$ is true is of no relevance whatever in the *terminal-action* problems to which one-tail tests are usually applied; but we have just seen in Section 13.6.1 that *under certain very special conditions* this posterior probability *is* use-

ful in problems of deciding whether or not to *suspend judgment*. We
conclude that

> When (1) the sample size is large, (2) the decision maker's prior
> distribution is "gentle" relative to the sample size, (3) the cost of
> sampling is substantial, and (4) the loss incurred by a wrong terminal
> act or conclusion would not be very serious, *then* a numerically
> *very* low one-tail significance *computed at the break-even point* can be
> taken as a strong indication that it is not worthwhile to collect more
> evidence.

The student should remember, however, that the *converse* of this conclusion is *not* necessarily true. As we pointed out in Section 13.6.1, a
posterior probability which is *not* very small does *not* necessarily indicate
that more sample evidence should be obtained before a terminal decision
is made; and the same statement necessarily applies to one-tail "statistical
significance" because the only bearing of this quantity on the question is
as a rough indication of posterior probability.

The only way in which sense can be made of the *two*-tail significance
which is usually computed in problems of this kind is to divide it by 2
and thus get the exact or approximate one-tail significance. If any problems exist in which two-tail significance is in itself an even roughly correct
indication of anything whatsoever, these problems are unknown to the
present author.†

13.7   Summarization of Information; Confidence Intervals

Although we succeeded in Section 13.6.1 in giving a clear-cut answer
to the question originally posed by the drug manufacturer of Section 13.4,
a little careful thought about this manufacturer's *real* problems may very
well lead us to doubt that he has posed the *right question*. If he has not
yet determined that he would like to take one particular terminal *act* if
$p \leq \frac{1}{2}$ and another particular terminal *act* if $p > \frac{1}{2}$, then why should
he be so interested in knowing whether p is above or below the particular
value $\frac{1}{2}$? Common sense would seem to say that while a certain amount
of background information about p may be useful at this stage in his
thinking, such information should not be focused down on the single
question whether or not p is greater than $\frac{1}{2}$. What he really needs is
some general-purpose description of the odds which it is reasonable to
assign to *any* set of values of $\tilde{p}$ in which he may be interested now or later.

† On the totally misleading nature of tests of significance in *terminal-action*
problems involving a *true* null hypothesis of the form $p = p_o$ (cf. Section 13.2.2), see
D. V. Lindley, A Statistical Paradox, *Biometrika*, vol. 44, pp. 187–192, 1957.

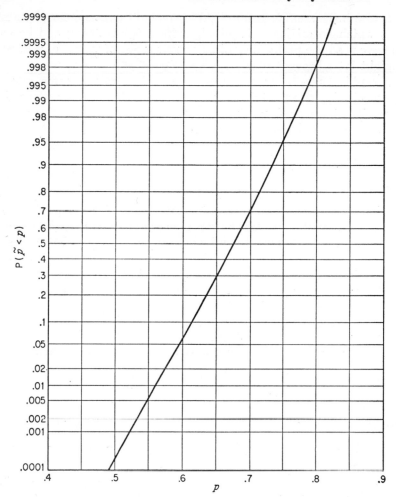

Figure 13.4. Drug manufacturer's posterior distribution.

13.7.1   *Graphs and Fractiles of Posterior Distributions*

Instead of obtaining from his statistician nothing but a computation of the posterior probability that $\tilde{p} < \frac{1}{2}$, the manufacturer might have done much better to ask for a graphical representation of the *complete posterior distribution of $\tilde{p}$*—either a graph of probability per unit width like the one labeled "posterior" in Figure 13.2, or a graph of the cumulative distribution like the one shown in Figure 13.4.†   From the cumu-

† This graph is drawn on "Normal-probability paper" (cf. Section 7.3.3) simply in order to make it possible to read the probabilities in the extreme tails of the distribution.

lative graph the manufacturer could have read the particular probability about which he originally inquired, $P_1(\tilde{p} < \frac{1}{2}) = .0002$; and he could also have read the probability of any other range of values of $\tilde{p}$ in which he might later become interested, e.g., $P(\tilde{p} < \frac{2}{3})$.

Graphical reports of posterior distributions may become unwieldy when a sample survey obtains answers to many different questions of the "yes-no" or "success-failure" type and thus produces posterior distributions of a large number of different $\tilde{p}$'s. Even in this case, however, a good deal of information about each distribution can be reported practically by stating a certain number of *fractiles* (cf. Section 6.1) of the posterior distribution. Thus in our drug example, the statistician could have reported that the three quartiles (that is, $F_{.25}$, $F_{.5}$, and $F_{.75}$) of the distribution were respectively $p = .643$, $p = .675$, and $p = .706$; or in very little more space he could have reported that the nine deciles (that is, $F_{.1}$, $F_{.2}$, . . . , $F_{.9}$) were respectively $p = .613$, .635, .650, .662, .675, .686, .699, .714, and .732. From this last report the manufacturer could have seen at once that because $p = \frac{1}{2}$ is below the first decile, $P(\tilde{p} < \frac{1}{2})$ is less than .1; he could also have seen that because $\frac{2}{3}$ is between the fourth and fifth deciles, $P(\tilde{p} < \frac{2}{3})$ is between .4 and .5; and so forth.

13.7.2 Confidence Intervals

If the manufacturer had not asked a specific question about a particular value of p such as $\frac{1}{2}$, statisticians would traditionally recommend that the person analyzing the data should proceed as follows. First, he should go to the manufacturer and tell him that he will express the results of his analysis by picking a smaller number p_1 and a larger number p_2 and then asserting that the true p is greater than p_1 but smaller than p_2. The numbers p_1 and p_2 will be selected by a procedure such that, if this *same procedure* were applied to a very large number of problems of this same general kind, the fraction of *false* statements would be *no greater* than γ (gamma), where γ can be any number between 0 and 1 that the manufacturer tells him to use. The writers who recommend this procedure assume that the manufacturer will answer that this kind of statement is just what he always wanted and will promptly specify the value γ that he wants the statistician to use; and by their examples they suggest, without saying definitely, that most manufacturers will set $\gamma = .05$, although a few may set $\gamma = .01$.

Construction of Confidence Intervals. If the manufacturer does say that a statement that $p_1 < p < p_2$ is the kind of report he wants and specifies a numerical value for the upper limit γ on the relative frequency with which any such report would be wrong, the statistician's remaining duties are relatively simple. Letting n denote the size of the sample which has been taken and r_o the number of successes actually observed, he has simply to go to the binomial tables and find the values p_1 and p_2 such that

$$P_b(\tilde{r} \geq r_o | n, p = p_1) = \tfrac{1}{2}\gamma,$$
$$P_b(\tilde{r} \leq r_o | n, p = p_2) = \tfrac{1}{2}\gamma.$$

It is proved in the appendix to this chapter that if the statistician applies this procedure to a very large number of *different samples,* from the same or from different populations, and on each occasion asserts that p lies between the p_1 and the p_2 *computed for that particular sample,* then the ratio of false statements to all statements would be *no greater* than γ, although it might be very much less than γ.

Looking at this last proposition the other way around, we can say that the fraction of all statements concocted in this way which would be *correct* would be *at least as great as* $1 - \gamma$; and therefore a statement of the form $p_1 < p < p_2$ concocted in this way is known as a $1 - \gamma$ *confidence interval.* If, for example, the relative frequency of incorrect statements is limited to $\gamma = .05$, then the statement $p_1 < p < p_2$ is called a .95 or 95% confidence interval, and it is sometimes said that we can be "at least 95% confident" that p is in fact between the stated limits p_1 and p_2.

In our example, suppose that the manufacturer does want a report of this kind and for one reason or another sets $\gamma = .05$—i.e., says that he wants a 95% confidence interval. There were $r_o = 67$ successes in a binomial sample of size $n = 99$, and it can easily be found from a complete set of binomial tables that

$$P_b(\tilde{r} \geq 67 | n = 99, p = .575) \doteq .025 = \tfrac{1}{2}\gamma,$$
$$P_b(\tilde{r} \leq 67 | n = 99, p = .768) \doteq .025 = \tfrac{1}{2}\gamma.$$

The statistician now asserts that the true p is between .575 and .768; and the manufacturer can feel assured that even if the statistician were to quit his job tomorrow and go to work constructing statements of this type about other problems for other employers, at least 95% of these statements would be correct.

13.7.3 *Confidence Intervals and Posterior Probability*

As to how this assurance should affect *this* manufacturer's conduct in any decision problem into which *this* sample enters as evidence, the statisticians who recommend reports in the form of confidence intervals have, somewhat surprisingly, nothing at all to say. The *implications* of the confidence interval are left entirely to the judgment of the manufacturer.

What nonstatisticians actually do when faced with a confidence interval has been well established by actual observation: they almost universally interpret the confidence interval statement *as if* it were a statement of posterior probability. They assume, in other words, that the report that p is between .575 and .768 "with confidence .95" implies that 95 to 5 is reasonable odds for a bet on the proposition that p is between .575 and .768. According to the advocates of confidence intervals, this interpretation is not so much wrong as meaningless, because the very concept of "reasonable odds" for a bet on p is meaningless in traditional statistics. To the businessman, however, the concept of reasonable odds for a bet of this sort is both familiar and meaningful; the question is simply whether the odds in question have been correctly calculated.

Now we have seen repeatedly that even after a sample has been taken, the "posterior" probabilities or betting odds which are reasonable in any particular decision maker's best judgment depend on his "prior" probabilities or betting odds; and therefore the fact that $p_1 < p < p_2$ is a .95 confidence interval calculated from the sample data alone cannot *by itself* possibly indicate that the businessman should bet 95 to 5 that $\tilde{p}$ lies between p_1 and p_2. There is actually *no* prior distribution for which the posterior probability that $\tilde{p}$ lies within any given confidence interval is *exactly* equal to the "confidence coefficient," but

> Provided that the sample size is large *and* the decision maker's prior distribution of $\tilde{p}$ is *rectangular* or at least "gentle" relative to the sample size, the posterior probability that $\tilde{p}$ lies within a $(1 - \gamma)$ confidence interval is *roughly* $1 - \gamma$.

To prove this assertion, we first observe that by the formulas in Section 13.5.3 the posterior probability on a rectangular prior that $\tilde{p}$ lies *outside* the interval from p_1 to p_2—i.e., the probability that it lies either below p_1 or above p_2—is

$$P_b(\tilde{r} \geq r_o + 1 | n + 1, p_1) + P_b(\tilde{r} \leq r_o | n + 1, p_2);$$

and this is *roughly* equal to the γ of the confidence interval because, by the rules in Section 13.7.2 for the construction of confidence intervals, p_1 and p_2 were chosen so as to make

$$P_b(\tilde{r} \geq r_o | n, p_1) + P_b(\tilde{r} \leq r_o | n, p_2) = \gamma.$$

Thus in our example, where by setting $\gamma = .05$ we obtained the confidence interval $.575 < p < .768$, we have for the posterior probability that $\tilde{p}$ lies outside this interval

$$P_b(\tilde{r} \geq 68 | 100, .575) + P_b(\tilde{r} \leq 67 | 100, .768) = .021 + .017 = .038.$$

In other words: *provided* again that the sample size is large and that the decision maker's prior distribution of $\tilde{p}$ is "gentle" relative to the sample size, the lower and upper limits of a $(1 - \gamma)$ confidence interval correspond roughly to the $\frac{1}{2}\gamma$ and $(1 - \frac{1}{2}\gamma)$ fractiles of the posterior distribution of $\tilde{p}$. Even when the proviso is duly met, it would still seem foolish to give *only* these rather extreme fractiles: for most purposes, the more detailed reports suggested in Section 13.7.1 above would be far more informative.

Contrast between "Confidence" and Posterior Probability. Simply to drive home the fact that the probability that $\tilde{p}$ lies within a $(1 - \gamma)$ confidence interval may be *totally* different from the "confidence coefficient" attached to the interval, let us observe that in extreme cases we may actually *know for certain* that p is outside a duly constructed confidence interval. Suppose, for example, that a sample of $n = 20$ pieces is drawn from a Bernoulli process which is *known* to have a long-run fraction defective $p = .1$. By pure chance we *may* get a sample containing 6 defectives; and if we do, the 95% confidence interval will have a *lower* limit $p_1 = .119$ because

$$P_b(\tilde{r} \geq 6 | n = 20, p = .119) \doteq .025 = \tfrac{1}{2}\gamma.$$

This will happen only rarely, of course, because the probability of getting 6 or more defectives from a process with $p = .1$ is only .0432, but this has no bearing on the essential *logic* of the point we wish the student to remember. *Confidence intervals are a good indication of sensible betting odds* only *if the decision maker's prior odds were at least roughly the same for all possible values of p.*

13.7.4 Appendix†

We shall now prove what we simply asserted in Section 13.7.2: that if a statistician were to compute $(1 - \gamma)$ confidence intervals by the procedure of Section 13.7.2, then in the long run the intervals which did *not* include the true p would amount to a fraction no greater than γ of the total. Observing that any *one* interval of the form $p_1 < p < p_2$ can be wrong *either* (1) because the computed p_1 is equal to or greater than the true p *or* (2) because the computed p_2 is equal to or less than the true p, we shall proceed by showing that the fraction of intervals in which either individual kind of error would occur does not exceed $\frac{1}{2}\gamma$. To make the discussion concrete, we assume that the statistician repeatedly draws samples of size $n = 20$ from the same Bernoulli process and that he sets $\gamma = .10$ so that $\frac{1}{2}\gamma = .05$.

Intervals Incorrect Because $p_1 \geq p$. Consider first the p_1's which

† The tortuous reasoning in this section is not required in any later part of the course.

the statistician will compute when his sample of size $n = 20$ contains 10, 11, or 12 successes. When he finds 10 successes, he will interpolate in the binomial tables to find that

$$P_b(\tilde{r} \geq 10|n = 20, p = .302) = .05$$

and he will state that p *is greater than* $p_1 = .302$. When he draws 11 successes, he will find that

$$P_b(\tilde{r} \geq 11|n = 20, p = .347) = .05$$

and he will state that p *is greater than* $p_1 = .347$. When he draws 12, he will find that

$$P_b(\tilde{r} \geq 12|n = 20, p = .393) = .05$$

and he will state that p *is greater than* $p_1 = .393$. Observe that p_1 increases as the number of successes in the sample increases.

Now suppose first that the true value of p in this population is in fact .393. Whenever the statistician draws 11 *or less* successes, he will state that p is greater than .347 or some *lower* number and all these statements will be *right*. Whenever he draws 12 *or more* successes, he will state that p is greater than .393 or some *higher* number and all these statements will be *wrong*. He will *actually draw* 12 or more successes in a fraction

$$P_b(\tilde{r} \geq 12|n = 20, p = .393) = .05$$

of all samples, and therefore exactly .05 of his statements will be wrong.

Suppose next that the true value of p is below .393 but not so low as .347. In this case the statistician will still make erroneous statements when and only when he draws 12 or more successes, but he will actually draw 12 or more successes somewhat *less* than .05 of the time. If, for example, the true value of p is .35, he will draw 12 or more successes and make an erroneous statement on only

$$P_b(\tilde{r} \geq 12|n = 20, p = .35) = .0196$$

of all occasions.

Finally, suppose that the true value of p is exactly .347. In this case the statistician will make an erroneous statement whenever he draws *eleven* or more successes and the fraction of wrong statements jumps back to .05 exactly.

The *general* way in which the procedure will work should now be clear. If p is below .347 but not so low as .302, errors will occur whenever 11 or more successes are drawn and this will happen on *less* than .05 of all draws. If $p = .302$ exactly, errors will occur whenever *ten* or more successes are drawn and this will happen on *exactly* .05 of all draws; and so forth.   We conclude that the method we have described does make it possible for the statistician to make statements in such a way that in the long run *not more than* $\frac{1}{2}\gamma$ of all statements would be wrong because $p_1 \geq p$, although it does *not* assure him that *exactly* this fraction of the statements would be wrong in the long run.

Intervals Incorrect Because $p_2 \leq p$.   Next consider the intervals which will be incorrect because the *upper* end p_2 of the interval is too *low*. If the statistician observes 11 successes in a sample of 20, he will find that

$$P_b(\tilde{r} \leq 11 | n = 20, p = .741) = .05$$

and assert that p is *less than* $p_2 = .741$.   Similarly he will compute $p_2 = .774$ if he observes 12 successes or $p_2 = .813$ if he observes 13 successes, as the student should verify.   Then by exactly the same kind of reasoning used in calculating the fraction of all p_1's which would be too *high*, we can show that the fraction of all p_2's which will be too *low* will be *exactly* .05 if the true p is .741, .774, or .813, etc., and will be *less than* .05 if the true p has any other value.

PROBLEMS

1. If the sample of size 100 taken by the president of the book club (Section 13.1) had resulted in 7 orders rather than 5, what would have been its two-tail significance against the null hypothesis $p = p_b$?

2. If the sample taken by the drug manufacturer of Section 13.4 had contained 100 rather than 99 persons who were influenced *either* by doctors or by druggists, and if 63 of the 100 had been influenced by doctors, what would have been the two-tail significance of this sample against the null hypothesis $p = \frac{1}{2}$?

3. Verify that if the president of the book club takes a *new* sample of size $n = 100$, the best rejection number is $c = 2$ and the expected terminal loss is $101, as shown in Figure 13.1.

4. Verify the height at $p = .6$ of the curve of the *posterior* distribution in Figure 13.2.

5. Graph the posterior distribution of $\tilde{p}$ which would result from a rectangular prior followed by
   a. 2 successes in a sample of 4.
   b. 33 successes in a sample of 49.

6. Graph the posterior distribution of $\tilde{p}$ which would result from the (4,1) prior of Figure 13.3 followed by 2 successes in a sample of 4.   (HINT: Read the next-to-the-last paragraph of Section 13.5.3 carefully and then compare Problem 3 in Chapter 12.)

7. If the drug manufacturer's prior distribution of $\tilde{p}$ was rectangular, what probability should he have assigned to the hypothesis $p < \frac{1}{2}$ after observing
   a. 33 successes in a sample of 49?
   b. 3 successes in a sample of 5?
   c. 5 successes in a sample of 5?

8. What is the one-tail significance of the three samples in Problem 7 against the less likely of the two hypotheses $p \leq \frac{1}{2}$ and $p \geq \frac{1}{2}$?

PART THREE

Introduction to the Normal Distribution

CHAPTER 14

Measures of Variability:
Variance and Standard Deviation

14.1 Introduction to Part Three

In Part Two of this course we were very considerably hampered in practical problem solving by the fact that our binomial tables covered only a few values of the sample size n. Examples in the text which required values of n not included in Table I at the end of this book were solved by the use of more complete tables, but if the student actually looks up these more complete tables he will find that they too are limited in their coverage. It is fortunate, therefore, that there are methods for accurately approximating binomial probabilities when tables of exact values are unavailable, and we now begin our study of the most frequently useful of these methods: the so-called *Normal approximation*.

What we shall learn in these two chapters will, moreover, be of use for other purposes which are really far more important than convenient approximation of binomial probabilities. The sampling problems considered in Part Two all involved either populations of individuals or processes generating individuals each of which could be *classified* as either a defective or a good piece, a buyer or a nonbuyer, or in general as a "success" or a "failure." Ultimately we shall want to consider problems where the individuals must be *measured* and described by a number. Thus instead of asking whether a part produced by a machine is defective because it is too long or not defective because it is not too long, the decision maker may want to know exactly *how* long it is. Or instead of asking whether a person will or will not buy a book, the decision maker may want to know *how many* books the person will buy. When we take up the study of such problems in Part Four of the course, we shall find ourselves continually obliged to make use of the same Normal approximation which we use in Part Three merely to approximate binomial probabilities.

In order to be able to use the Normal approximation, we must first learn a little more about how to describe a probability distribution by use of "summary measures." We saw in Chapter 6 that for some purposes any probability distribution can be adequately described by an appropriate *measure of location* such as the mean or a suitably chosen fractile; if we knew the value of this measure, we knew everything we needed to know about the distribution to solve the particular decision problem at hand.   In the problems we are about to encounter we shall make continual use of the mean as a measure of the location of a distribution, but we shall find that we also need a summary measure of another aspect of the distribution, viz., its "spread," "scatter," "dispersion," or *variability*.

Just as there are many possible measures of the location of a distribution, there are many possible measures of its variability; and in both cases we must choose *the particular measure which is appropriate to the purpose at hand*.   For a reason which will be explained in Section 14.4 below, the only measures of variability which are suitable for the *sampling* problems with which we shall be dealing are the "variance" and its square root, the "standard deviation"; and these are therefore the only measures of variability which we shall study in this course.   The subject of the present chapter is the study of these two measures as such; in Chapter 15 we shall then go on to *use* these measures in studying the Normal approximation.

14.2   Definition of the Variance and Standard Deviation

It naturally occurs to us that the variability of a set of values might logically be measured by

1. Selecting some *central value* such as the mean,
2. Computing the *absolute magnitude of the difference* between this central value and each individual value in the set,
3. *Averaging* these "absolute deviations."

Actually, however, it turns out that the measure of variability defined by these operations is *not* practical for use in sampling problems.

14.2.1   The Variance

A much more useful measure is obtained if instead of averaging the deviations themselves we average the *squares of the deviations*, and accordingly we define the

Variance of a set of values: the arithmetic average of the *squares* of the differences between the individual values and the mean value.

As an example, let us use the data of Table 6.1.   The mean of the values in this table is 2.7, and therefore the variance is $\frac{1}{10}[(2 - 2.7)^2 + (4 - 2.7)^2 + (0 - 2.7)^2 + (2 - 2.7)^2 + (4 - 2.7)^2 + (3 - 2.7)^2 +$

$(3 - 2.7)^2 + (1 - 2.7)^2 + (3 - 2.7)^2 + (5 - 2.7)^2] = \frac{1}{10}(.49 + 1.69 + 7.29 + .49 + 1.69 + .09 + .09 + 2.89 + .09 + 5.29) = 20.10/10 = 2.01$.

14.2.2 The Standard Deviation

The variance measures the dispersion of a set of values in rather peculiar units. The variance of the set of values of number defective computed just above comes out as 2.01 defectives-squared; the variance of a set of heights of men would come out in inches-squared or something of the sort. It is often more convenient to have a measure of dispersion which is in the same units as the variable itself—in number of defectives or in inches or feet. Therefore we very commonly use as our measure of dispersion the

Standard deviation: the square root of the variance.

The standard deviation of the values of number defective in our example is $\sqrt{2.01} = 1.42$.

14.3 Computation of the Variance from Relative Frequencies or Probabilities

The variance of a set of values can be computed by using their *relative frequencies* as *weights* in exactly the same way that the mean is computed by the use of relative frequencies as weights. The student should review the procedure for computation of the mean as described in Section 6.2.2 before proceeding further in the present chapter.

Let us reexamine the computation of the variance of the values in Table 6.1 as we carried it out above. If we rearrange the data in order of increasing value of the variable we have Table 14.1. The variance is the *average* square, or $20.10/10 = 2.01$.

Instead of writing down two identical rows for the value 2, three rows for 3, and two rows for 4, we can get the same result by writing the square of each value of the deviation once and weighting it by the number of times that the value occurs. This is done in Table 14.2, and again we get the variance by dividing the *sum of squares* by the *sum of the weights*, i.e. by the total number of occurrences. Furthermore we will still get exactly the same result if, instead of dividing the total of the last column by 10, we divide each of the individual products by 10; and instead of doing that, we can divide each of the numbers of occurrences by 10 before computing the products. The last three columns of Table 14.2 would then be as shown in Table 14.3; and since the sum of the weights is now 1, the variance is simply the total in the last column.

Table 14.1

Value of the random variable	Deviation	Deviation squared
0	−2.7	7.29
1	−1.7	2.89
2	− .7	.49
2	− .7	.49
3	+ .3	.09
3	+ .3	.09
3	+ .3	.09
4	+1.3	1.69
4	+1.3	1.69
5	+2.3	5.29
		20.10

Table 14.2

Value of the random variable	Deviation	Deviation squared	Number of occurrences	Product
0	−2.7	7.29	1	7.29
1	−1.7	2.89	1	2.89
2	− .7	.49	2	.98
3	+ .3	.09	3	.27
4	+1.3	1.69	2	3.38
5	+2.3	5.29	1	5.29
			10	20.10

Table 14.3

Deviation squared	Number of occurrences divided by 10	Product
7.29	.1	.729
2.89	.1	.289
.49	.2	.098
.09	.3	.027
1.69	.2	.338
5.29	.1	.529
	1.0	2.010

We now observe that the entries in the second column of Table 14.3 are simply the relative frequencies of the corresponding values of the random variable, and generalizing we conclude that

The variance is computed from a frequency distribution by computing the squared deviations from the mean of the distribution, weighting them by their relative frequencies, and adding these products. Since relative frequencies always add to 1, the sum of the weights is 1 and there is no need to divide by it to get the weighted average.

No new problems arise when we wish to compute the variance of a probability distribution:

The variance of a probability distribution is computed by using the probabilities in exactly the same way that relative frequencies are used in computing the variance of a frequency distribution.

Notation. It is standard practice to use the symbol σ (sigma) to denote the standard deviation of a random variable; when necessary, we shall add the name of the variable in parentheses. Thus:

$\sigma(\tilde{z})$ = standard deviation of the random variable $\tilde{z}$,
$\sigma^2(\tilde{z})$ = variance of the random variable $\tilde{z}$.

14.4   Mean and Variance of a Sum of Random Variables

In the great majority of the problems which we shall encounter in the remainder of this course we shall need to know the expectation and variance of a random variable which is the *sum* of a number of other random variables—e.g., the mean and variance of the sum of the values of the n items in a sample when the value of each individual item is itself a random variable. There is never any difficulty in finding the *expectation* of such a sum when the expectations of the individual variables included in the sum are known, since it can easily be proved that

The expectation of a sum of random variables is the sum of their individual expectations.

In symbols:

$$E(\tilde{x} + \tilde{y} + \tilde{z} + \cdots) = E(\tilde{x}) + E(\tilde{y}) + E(\tilde{z}) + \cdots$$
Any random variables

This proposition applies to *all random variables without restriction*, and it appeals immediately to our intuition. The expected total length of three pieces produced by a machine is simply the sum of the expected lengths of the three individual pieces.

We shall now state a somewhat similar proposition about the *variance* of a sum of random variables, but before even stating it we call attention to the fact that *this* proposition does *not* apply to *all* sums of random variables. It does apply, however, when the random variables in the sum are *independent* (cf. Section 8.5),† and we shall have very frequent occasion to make use of it in this connection. The proposition is the following:

   The variance of a sum of independent random variables is the sum of their individual variances.

In symbols:

$$\sigma^2(\tilde{x} + \tilde{y} + \tilde{z} + \cdots) = \sigma^2(\tilde{x}) + \sigma^2(\tilde{y}) + \sigma^2(\tilde{z}) + \cdots$$

Independent random variables

This is the reason for the great importance of the variance as a measure of variability: no other measure of variability has this "additive" property.

In particular, the *standard deviation* is *not* additive:

   The standard deviation of a sum of random variables is obtained by taking the square root of the variance of the sum.

14.5   Mean and Variance of the Binomial Distribution

In Chapters 9 to 13 we have studied the binomial distribution of $\tilde{r}$ given n and p, and (as we said at the beginning of this chapter) we shall need to know the variance of this distribution in order to compute the Normal approximation to binomial probabilities.

Let us first consider the binomial distribution of the number of successes on *one* trial. If we arbitrarily assign the *value* 1 to a success and the *value* 0 to a failure, we can say that the event of a single trial determines the value of a *random variable* $\tilde{x}$. The *expectation* of this random variable is computed in Table 14.4 in the same way in which we compute the expectation of any random variable, and we find that $E(\tilde{x}) = p$.

   The method of Table 14.3 above can now be used to compute the variance of this random variable $\tilde{x}$. The work is shown in Table 14.5, where the variance is the total of the last column. Since $p + q = 1$, this total reduces to pq.

---

† The proposition actually applies even when the random variables in the sum are *not* independent provided only that they are *uncorrelated,* but the subject of correlation is beyond the scope of this course.

Table 14.4

Value of the random variable x	Probability $P(x)$	Expectation $x \, P(x)$
0	q	0
1	p	p
	1	p

Table 14.5

Value x of the random variable	Deviation $x - E(x)$	Deviation squared	Probability $P(x)$	Product
0	$0 - p = -p$	p^2	q	$p^2q = p(pq)$
1	$1 - p = q$	q^2	p	$q^2p = q(pq)$
			1	$(p + q)pq$

The reason for assigning "values" to successes and failures is simply that it permits us to regard the number of successes $\tilde{r}$ in any number n of Bernoulli trials as *the sum of the values of n random variables $\tilde{x}_1$, $\tilde{x}_2$, ..., $\tilde{x}_n$ describing the individual trials*—if there are three successes in 10 trials, 3 trials have value 1, 7 trials have value 0, and the sum of these 10 values is 3. Consequently the addition theorem for expectations tells us that

$$E(\tilde{r}) = E(\tilde{x}_1) + E(\tilde{x}_2) + \cdots + E(\tilde{x}_n).$$

We have seen that $E(\tilde{x}) = p$, and therefore we have now proved the result which was simply asserted in Section 9.2.2: if n Bernoulli trials all have the same probability p of success, then

$$E(\tilde{r}) = np \qquad \textit{Binomial distribution}$$

Since Bernoulli trials are *independent* by definition, we can also apply the addition theorem for variances to get the variance of the binomial distribution for the number of successes $\tilde{r}$ in any number of trials n with constant probability p. Since the random variable $\tilde{x}$ describing any one trial has variance pq, we have immediately

$$\sigma^2(\tilde{r}) = npq \qquad \textit{Binomial distribution}$$

14.6   Mean and Variance of Continuous Distributions

We have already in Section 13.5 encountered and used the concept of a *continuous* probability distribution under which the random variable is not restricted to a certain set of spaced-out possible values such as 0, 1, 2, 3, . . . or .00, .01, .02, .03, . . . , but can take on *any value whatever* within a certain range.   In the example of Section 13.5 the permissible range was 0 to 1 because the random variable represented a fraction defective; in other cases the permissible range can be 0 to ∞ or even − ∞ to ∞.

The mean and variance of a continuous distribution can be approximated by converting the continuous distribution into a "discrete" or noncontinuous distribution.   To accomplish this conversion we simply (1) cut the horizontal axis into a number of intervals or "brackets" of equal width, (2) approximate the probability within any interval by multiplying the width of the interval by the height of the curve at the

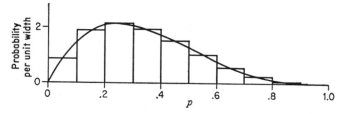

Figure 14.1. Approximation of a continuous by a discrete distribution.

mid-point of the interval, and (3) treat all this probability as belonging to the value at the mid-point of the interval.

Figure 14.1 and Table 14.6 show how this can be done for the (4,1) distribution of Figure 13.3.   Arbitrarily choosing to take brackets of width .1, we draw vertical lines at the edges of the brackets and then draw horizontal lines which cut the curve at the mid-point of each bracket. The area of each bar of the histogram thus formed is computed by multiplying width times height; thus for the first bar we have .1 × .85 = .085. This area or probability is then entirely assigned to the p at the mid-point of the bracket—to $p = .05$ in our example; all other p's in the bracket are treated *as if* they were impossible.   The area of any bar of such a histogram is of course only approximately equal to the area under the corresponding portion of the curve; it is for this reason that the total area of the histogram is 1.007 instead of 1.

Having approximated the continuous distribution by a discrete one, we can compute the mean and variance of this substitute discrete distribution in the way described in Section 14.3 above, and we can treat

Table 14.6

Bracket	Value at mid-point p	Height at mid-point $P'(p)$	Probability = width × height $P(p)$
0– .1	.05	.85	.085
.1– .2	.15	1.84	.184
.2– .3	.25	2.11	.211
.3– .4	.35	1.92	.192
.4– .5	.45	1.50	.150
.5– .6	.55	1.00	.100
.6– .7	.65	.56	.056
.7– .8	.75	.23	.023
.8– .9	.85	.06	.006
.9–1.0	.95	0	1.007

these computed values as approximations to the mean and standard deviation of the true continuous distribution. Clearly the approximation will be better the narrower the brackets that are used; the "exact" mean and variance of a continuous distribution are in fact *defined* to be the limit approached by the approximate method as the widths of the brackets approach 0. We shall see moreover that in certain cases—in *all* cases that will be of importance in this course—there are formulas for the mean and variance (obtained by use of the calculus) which spare us the need actually to carry out this process of approximation. The student must, however, remember the underlying logic.

14.7 Summary

14.7.1 Definitions

The *variance* is the mean of the *squares* of the deviations of a set of values from their mean value.

The *standard deviation* is the square root of the variance.

14.7.2 Additivity

The *expected value* of the sum of any random variables whatever is the sum of the individual expected values.

The *variance* of a sum of *independent*† random variables is the sum of the individual variances.

No other measure of variability is additive; the standard deviation of a

† See the footnote in Section 14.4 above.

sum of random variables is obtained by taking the square root of the variance of the sum.

14.7.3   Binomial Distribution

The mean of the binomial distribution of $\bar{r}$ given n and p is np.

The variance of the binomial distribution of $\bar{r}$ given n and p is npq.

PROBLEMS

1. Show that the mean, variance, and standard deviation of the frequency distribution of $\bar{p}$ in Table 11.3 (Section 11.2.2) are respectively .052, .006116, and .0782.

2. Compute the mean, variance, and standard deviation of the probability distribution of $\bar{p}$ given in

    a. Table 11.9 (Section 11.2.5).

    b. Table 13.1 (Section 13.3).

3. Compute the mean, variance, and standard deviation of the binomial distribution of $\bar{r}$ given

    a. $n = 50$, $p = .1$.

    b. $n = 50$, $p = .5$.

    c. $n = 99$, $p = .5$.

CHAPTER 15

The Normal Distribution and the Normal Approximation to the Binomial Distribution

We are now ready first simply to *describe* the so-called Normal probability distribution and then to see how it can be used to approximate binomial probabilities.

15.1 The Normal Distribution

15.1.1 *Normal Distributions in General*

Considered purely as a mathematical entity, without any regard to its meaning in the real world, the Normal distribution is a *continuous* distribution with *probability per unit width* given by the formula

$$P'_N(z|M,S) = \frac{1}{S\sqrt{2\pi}} e^{-\frac{1}{2}\left(\frac{z-M}{S}\right)^2},$$

where e is simply a mathematical constant approximately equal to 2.718. In this formula z represents *any* random variable which happens to have a Normal distribution. The quantities M and S are the *parameters* of the distribution, just as n and p were the parameters of the binomial distribution (cf. Section 9.2.1); the formula actually defines a whole family of different distributions, one for each possible combination of numerical values for M and S.

15.1.2 *Graphic Representation of a Normal Distribution*

To give a graphical idea of the meaning of the formula for the Normal distribution and of the way in which the numerical values of the parameters affect the distribution, we show three different Normal distributions in Figures 15.1 and 15.2. In Figure 15.1 the two distributions have the same standard deviation S but different means M; in Figure 15.2 the two distributions have the same mean M but different standard deviations S; the distribution with $M = 1$, $S = 2$ is common to both figures.

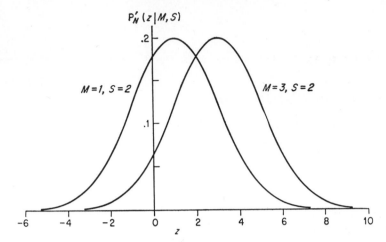

Figure 15.1. Normal distributions with the same standard deviation but different means.

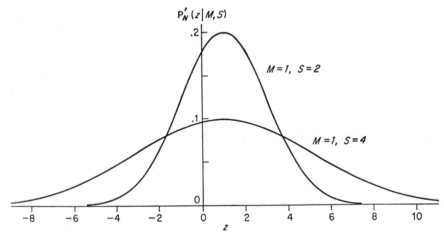

Figure 15.2. Normal distributions with the same mean but different standard deviations.

In all cases—i.e., for all values of the parameters M and S—the Normal distribution extends in principle from $z = -\infty$ to $z = +\infty$, although the height of the curve becomes too low to graph as soon as z is at a distance greater than about $3S$ away from the point where $z = M$. The distribution, as we have already said, is *continuous*, and as we saw in Section 13.5.1 in dealing with another type of continuous distribution this means that:

1. The probability that $\tilde{z}$ lies *between* any two values z_1 and z_2 is equal to the area under the curve between those two points on the horizontal axis;
2. The probability that $\tilde{z}$ has *precisely* any specified value is treated as 0 even though it is not *impossible* that $\tilde{z}$ has this value.

Accordingly

$$P_N(\tilde{z} < z|M,S) = P_N(\tilde{z} \le z|M,S),$$
$$P_N(\tilde{z} < z|M,S) + P_N(\tilde{z} > z|M,S) = 1.$$

15.1.3   *Mean and Variance of a Normal Distribution*

It can be shown by calculus that if any random variable $\tilde{z}$ has a Normal distribution with parameters M and S, then the *mean* or *expectation* of $\tilde{z}$ is equal to the value of the parameter M while the *standard deviation* of $\tilde{z}$ is equal to the value of the parameter S; the *variance* of $\tilde{z}$ is accordingly equal to S^2.

15.1.4   *The Unit or Standardized Normal Distribution*

The particular Normal distribution in which the parameter M has the value 0 and the parameter S has the value 1 is known as the *unit* or *standardized* Normal distribution; the name "unit" comes from the fact that the variance and standard deviation of this distribution have the value 1. A random variable which has a unit Normal distribution is usually called $\tilde{u}$ rather than some other name; and by substituting $M = 0$ and $S = 1$ in the formula for the general Normal distribution we can see that $\tilde{u}$ has probability per unit width

$$P'_{N*}(u) = \frac{1}{\sqrt{2\pi}} e^{-\frac{1}{2}u^2}.$$

The star on the subscript N represents the fact that the parameters have the "standard" values $M = 0$, $S = 1$, and eliminates the need of writing them out in the form $P'_N(u|M = 0, S = 1)$. This distribution is graphed in Figure 15.3; observe that it is *perfectly symmetric about the point $u = 0$*.

15.1.5   *Standard Measure*

If in order to use the Normal distribution we had to have a separate table for every possible combination of the parameters M and S—the way we have to have a separate binomial table for every combination of n and p—the task of tabulation would obviously be hopeless. Fortunately, however, all that we need is a *single* table of probabilities per unit width and a *single* table of cumulative probabilities or tail areas. The reason is as follows.

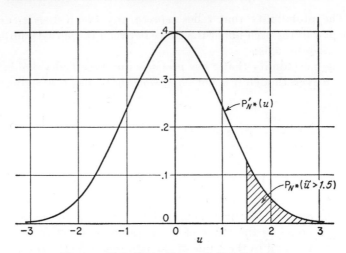

Figure 15.3. Unit Normal distribution.

Let $\tilde{z}$ be any random variable which has a Normal distribution with parameters M and S, where M and S may have any values whatever; and let z be any particular value of $\tilde{z}$ for which we want to compute either the probability per unit width $P'_N(z|M,S)$ or a cumulative probability such as $P_N(\tilde{z} < z|M,S)$ or $P_N(\tilde{z} > z|M,S)$. If now we *express the value z in standard measure* by computing

$$u \equiv \frac{z - M}{S} \qquad \text{\textit{Definition of standard measure}}$$

then it is obvious from the formulas in Sections 15.1.1 and 15.1.4 that

$$P'_N(z|M,S) = \frac{1}{S} P'_{N*}(u)$$

and it can be proved by calculus that

$$P_N(\tilde{z} > z|M,S) = P_{N*}(\tilde{u} > u)$$

and similarly for the left tail.

Observe that *the value of z in standard measure is the distance from the mean of $\tilde{z}$ to the particular value z expressed as a multiple of the standard* *deviation of ẑ.* If, for example, ẑ has mean 4 and standard deviation 3, then the particular value $z = 10$ is 2 standard deviations *above* the mean; in standard measure this particular value is

$$u = \frac{10 - 4}{3} = 2.$$

The particular value $z = 1$ is 1 standard deviation *below* the mean; in standard measure this particular value is

$$u = \frac{1 - 4}{3} = -1.$$

In expressing values in standard measure the student must be very careful not to neglect algebraic signs or to get z and M reversed in the formula for u.

15.1.6   *Tables of the Normal Distribution*

1. *Probability per Unit Width.* Table II at the end of this book is a table of $P'_{N\cdot}(u)$—i.e., of the height of the *unit* Normal curve shown in Figure 15.3 or of probability per unit width under the unit Normal distribution. The table has entries only for *positive* values of $\tilde{u}$, but it is obvious from Figure 15.3 that the height at any negative value of $\tilde{u}$ (-2, say) is equal to the height at the corresponding positive value ($+2$, say). The student should learn how to read the table by using it to verify that

$$P'_{N\cdot}(2) = P'_{N\cdot}(-2) = .05399;$$
$$P'_{N\cdot}(3) = P'_{N\cdot}(-3) = .004432;$$
$$P'_{N\cdot}(3.06) = P'_{N\cdot}(-3.06) = .003695.$$

If ẑ has a *non*standardized Normal distribution with mean $M = 7$ and standard deviation $S = 4$, then to find the probability per unit width at the particular value $z = 6$ we compute the standardized value

$$u = \frac{6 - 7}{4} = -.25$$

and use Table II to evaluate

$$P'_N(6 | M = 7, S = 4) = \frac{1}{S} P'_{N\cdot}(-.25) = \frac{1}{4} P'_{N\cdot}(+.25) = \frac{1}{4} \times .3867$$
$$= .0967.$$

2. *Cumulative Probabilities.* Table III at the end of this book is a table of $P_{N\cdot}(\tilde{u} > u)$—i.e., of *right*-tail areas like the one shaded in Figure 15.3. This table also has entries only for positive values of $\tilde{u}$, but again the symmetry of Figure 15.3 makes it obvious that for a negative u the *left* tail is equal to the *right* tail for the corresponding positive u; for

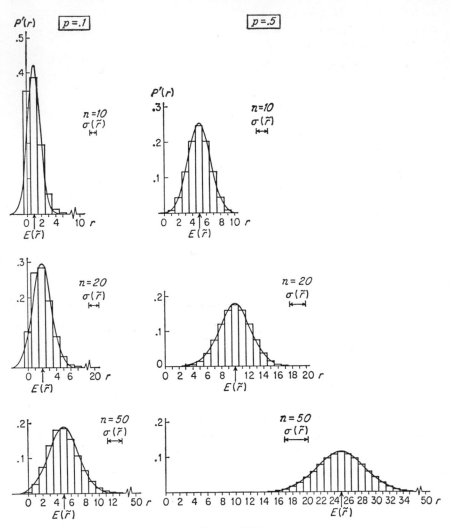

Figure 15.4

example,

$$P_{N\bullet}(\tilde{u} < -2) = P_{N\bullet}(\tilde{u} > +2) = .02275.$$

To get left tails for positive u or right tails for negative u we simply use the table to find the tail we do *not* want and then subtract from the total area under the curve, i.e., from 1.

If $\tilde{z}$ has a *non*standardized Normal distribution with mean $M = 7$ and standard deviation $S = 4$, then to find the probability that $\tilde{z}$ lies *above* the particular value $z = 6$, we compute the standardized value

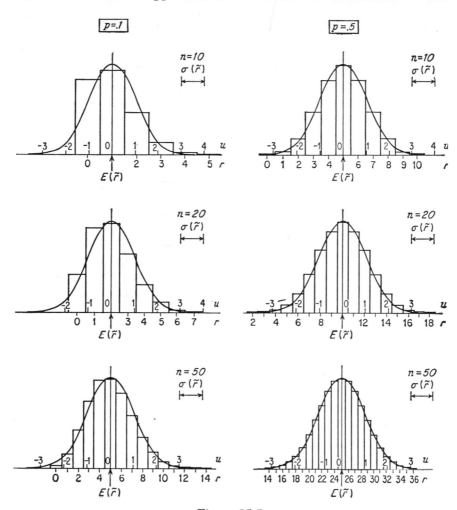

Figure 15.5

$u = -.25$ as before and then use Table III to evaluate

$$P_N(\tilde{z} > 6 | M = 7, S = 4) = P_{N*}(\tilde{u} > -.25)$$
$$= 1 - P_{N*}(\tilde{u} < -.25)$$
$$= 1 - P_{N*}(\tilde{u} > +.25)$$
$$= 1 - .4013 = .5987.$$

Remember what was pointed out in Section 15.1.2: because the Normal distribution is continuous, the probability that $\tilde{z}$ is *equal to or greater than* any value z is the same thing as the probability that $\tilde{z}$ is simply *greater than z*.

15.2   Behavior of the Binomial Distribution as n Increases

Figure 15.4 shows histograms of the binomial distributions of $\tilde{r}$ given $p = .1$ and $.5$ and $n = 10$, 20, and 50. The means and standard deviations of these distributions are computed in Table 15.1; and superimposed upon each histogram in the figure is a Normal distribution having the *same mean and standard deviation* as the histogram.

Figure 15.5 represents exactly the same binomial histograms and Normal distributions as before but with their means lined up above each

Table 15.1

	$p = .1$			$p = .5$	
n	$E(\tilde{r}) = pn$	$\sigma(\tilde{r}) = \sqrt{npq}$	n	$E(\tilde{r}) = pn$	$\sigma(\tilde{r}) = \sqrt{npq}$
10	1	.95	10	5	1.58
20	2	1.34	20	10	2.24
50	5	2.12	50	25	3.54

other and with the scales chosen in such a way that the standard deviations of all the distributions are represented by the *same* width on the paper.

From the two figures we would guess that *as n increases, the binomial histogram for any p approaches a Normal distribution with the same mean and standard deviation*, and it can be proved that this guess is correct. Formally: *Given any p and any standardized value*

$$u = \frac{r - E(\tilde{r})}{\sigma(\tilde{r})},$$

1. There is some n above which the *ratio* of the height of the histogram to the height of the Normal curve becomes and remains as close to 1 as we like;

2. There is some n above which the *difference* between the area in either tail of the histogram and the area in the corresponding tail of the Normal curve becomes and remains as close to 0 as we like.

15.3   Normal Approximations to Binomial Probabilities

The theorems which we have just stated make it clear that, if n is "large enough,"

1. The area of any bar in the binomial histogram can be approximated by multiplying its width by the height of the corresponding Normal curve at its mid-point.

2. The area of all the bars in a tail of the binomial histogram can be approximated by finding the area under the corresponding Normal curve beyond the inner edge of the first bar included in the tail in question.

How large an n is "large enough" depends *both* on the degree of accuracy we require for the decision problem at hand *and* on the particular p and standardized value u that are involved in the problem. To aid the student in deciding whether the Normal approximation can be used in any given situation, we show in Figures 15.6 to 15.9 both probabilities per unit width and left-tail cumulative probabilities for selected binomial distributions (curves labeled B) and their Normal approximations (curves labeled N).

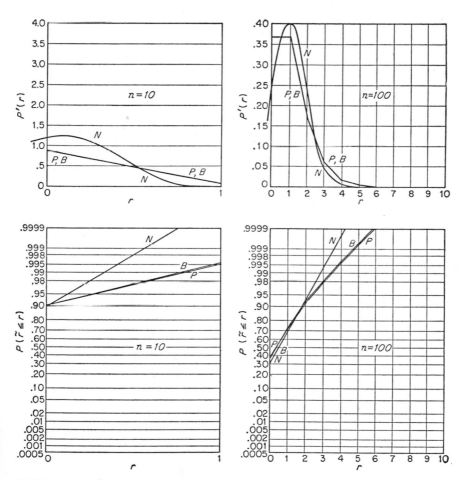

Figure 15.6. Binomial distributions with Normal and Poisson approximations. $p = .01$.

To warn the student that a little knowledge can be a dangerous thing, we also show in each case *another* approximation to the binomial, the so-called Poisson approximation. From these figures it is apparent that:

1. Both the Normal and the Poisson approximations improve as n increases;
2. The Normal approximation is better when p is neither too small nor too large.

If p is close to 0 or 1, then unless n is *very* large anyone who has a binomial probability to compute should get advice from a statistician rather than blithely go ahead to use the Normal approximation.

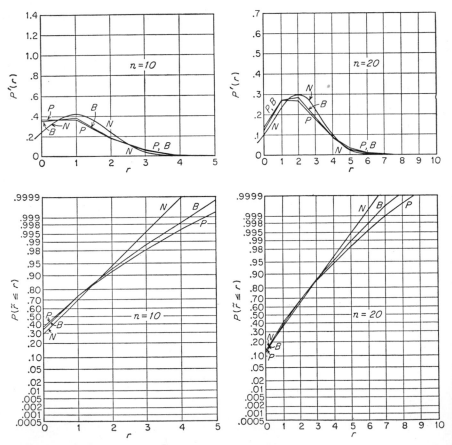

Figure 15.7. Binomial distributions with Normal and Poisson approximations. $p = .1$.

With this warning in mind, we give a few examples of the actual computation of Normal approximations to binomial probabilities.

15.3.1   *Approximation of Tail Areas*

Example 1.   To approximate the binomial probability

$$P_b(\tilde{r} \geq 8|n = 50, p = .1)$$

we first compute (using for the last step the square roots in Table VI at the back of this book)

$$E(\tilde{r}) = np = 50 \times .1 = 5,$$
$$\sigma^2(\tilde{r}) = npq = 50 \times .1 \times .9 = 4.5,$$
$$\sigma(\tilde{r}) = \sqrt{4.5} = 2.121.$$

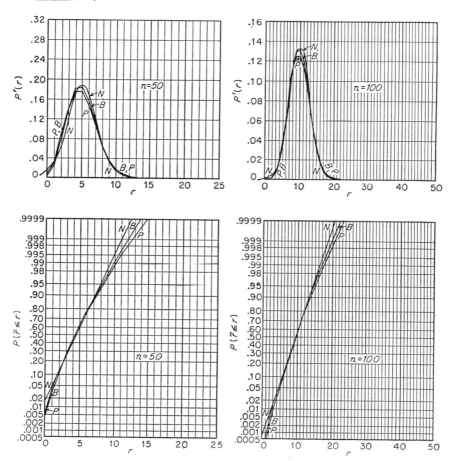

Figure 15.8. Binomial distributions with Normal and Poisson approximations. $p = .1$.

We then refer to the histogram in Figure 15.4 for $n = 50$, $p = .1$, and see that what we want is the area to the *right* of the *left edge* of the bar for $r = 8$.   This left edge lies at $r = 7\frac{1}{2}$, and therefore we compute

$$u = \frac{r - E(\tilde{r})}{\sigma(\tilde{r})} = \frac{7\frac{1}{2} - 5}{2.121} = 1.18.$$

We then look in Table III of the *cumulative* unit Normal distribution and find

$$P_{N \cdot}(\tilde{u} > 1.18) = .1190.$$

This is our approximation; the *exact* answer given by the binomial

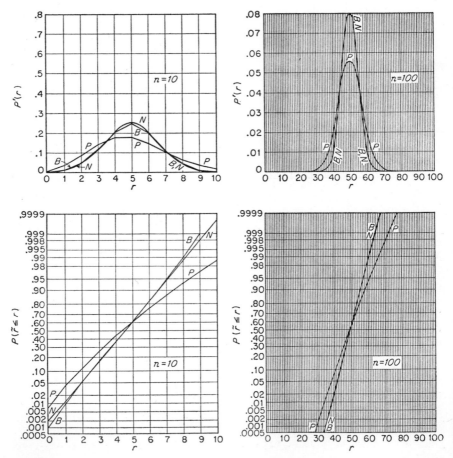

Figure 15.9. Binomial distributions with Normal and Poisson approximations. $p = .5$.

Table I is

$$P_b(\tilde{r} \geq 8 | n = 50, p = .1) = .1221.$$

Example 2. To approximate $P_b(\tilde{r} \leq 7 | n = 50, p = .1)$, our previous example shows that we should compute $P_{N*}(\tilde{u} < 1.18)$. Since Table III is a right-tail table, we do this by computing

$$P_{N*}(\tilde{u} < 1.18) = 1 - P_{N*}(\tilde{u} > 1.18) = 1 - .1190 = .8810.$$

Example 3. To approximate $P_b(\tilde{r} > 22 | n = 50, p = .5)$, we first compute

$$E(\tilde{r}) = 50 \times .5 = 25,$$
$$\sigma^2(\tilde{r}) = 50 \times .5 \times .5 = 12.5,$$
$$\sigma(\tilde{r}) = \sqrt{12.5} = 3.53.$$

In contrast to Example 1, it is the area to the right of the *right* edge of the bar for $r = 22$ which we want this time, and we therefore compute

$$u = \frac{22\tfrac{1}{2} - 25}{3.53} = -.708.$$

For most purposes we would round this result to $-.71$ and compute

$$P_{N*}(\tilde{u} > -.71) = P_{N*}(\tilde{u} < +.71) = 1 - P_{N*}(\tilde{u} > +.71)$$
$$= 1 - .2389 = .7611.$$

Unless instructed otherwise, the student may round in this way in all assigned exercises. If, however, we want a more accurate approximation, we will interpolate in Table III to find

$$P_{N*}(\tilde{u} > +.708) = .2395,$$

and thus $P_{N*}(\tilde{u} > -.708) = .7605$. The exact answer from Table I is

$$P_b(\tilde{r} > 22 | n = 50, p = .5) = .7601.$$

15.3.2 *Approximation of Individual Probabilities*†

Example. To approximate $P_b(\tilde{r} = 22 | n = 50, p = .5)$, we first compute

$$E(\tilde{r}) = 25, \qquad \sigma(\tilde{r}) = 3.53,$$

as shown in Example 3 of the previous section. We then refer to the histogram in Figure 15.4 for $n = 50$, $p = .5$, and remembering that we want the area of the *individual bar* for $r = 22$, we see that we can approximate its height by the height of the Normal curve at its *mid-point*. We therefore compute

† The contents of this section will not be required in any subsequent chapter.

$$u = \frac{22 - 25}{3.53} = -.85$$

and then use the formula for P'_N in Section 15.1.5 and Table II of $P'_{N^\bullet}$ at the end of the book to compute

$$P'_N(r|M = 25, S = 3.53) = \frac{1}{S} P'_{N^\bullet}(u) = \frac{1}{3.53} P'_{N^\bullet}(-.85)$$

$$= \frac{.2780}{3.53} = .0788.$$

This is the approximate *height* of the bar for $r = 22$; and since the *width* of the bar is 1, it is also its approximate *area* and therefore the approximate probability that $\tilde{r} = 22$. The *exact* probability from the binomial tables is

$$P_b(\tilde{r} = 22|n = 50, p = .5) = .0788.$$

The probability of an individual value of $\tilde{r}$—the area of an individual bar in the binomial histogram—is a little simpler to approximate than a tail area because we do not have to watch out for the $\pm\frac{1}{2}$ which takes us from the center to the edge of the bar. On the other hand we do have to remember that the answer cannot simply be read from the table of heights of the *unit* Normal curve; the reading of Table II must be multiplied by the factor $1/S$, where $S = \sigma(\tilde{r})$.

PROBLEMS

1. Find the following ordinates and areas of the unit Normal distribution. In some cases it will be necessary to use the symmetry of the distribution: sketch the distribution, locate the ordinate or area you seek, and then locate an equal ordinate or area which can be found in the tables.

a. $P'(0)$.   b. $P(\tilde{u} > 0)$.   c. $P'(+2)$.
d. $P'(-3)$.   e. $P'(-3.26)$.   f. $P(\tilde{u} > +1)$.
g. $P(\tilde{u} > +1.87)$.   h. $P(\tilde{u} < -2)$.   i. $P(\tilde{u} > -2)$.
j. $P(\tilde{u} < +2)$.   k. $P(\tilde{u} < -3)$.   l. $P(\tilde{u} < +3)$.

2. Use the Normal approximation to evaluate the following binomial probabilities for $n = 2500$, $p = .2$.

a. $P(\tilde{r} = 530)$.   b. $P(\tilde{r} \geq 530)$.
c. $P(\tilde{r} > 530)$.   d. $P(\tilde{r} < 530)$.

3. A sample of size $n = 200$ is taken and $r_o = 130$ successes are found.

a. What is the significance of the sample against the null hypothesis $p \leq \frac{1}{2}$?

b. If the decision maker's prior distribution was rectangular, what is the posterior probability that $\tilde{p} \leq \frac{1}{2}$?

c. Graph the decision maker's posterior distribution in ordinary and cumulative form.

4. In the problem discussed in Sections 13.1 and 13.3, verify that if the president of the book club takes a *new* sample of size $n = 260$, the best rejection number is $c = 8$ and the expected terminal loss is $64, as shown in Figure 13.1.

PART FOUR

Sampling of Measured Values

The Central Limit Theorem and Large-sample Theory

We now turn our attention away from problems in which samples are taken in order to learn something about the *fraction p of successes* contained in a population or generated by a random process to problems in which samples are taken in order to learn something about the *mean size or value* of the individuals contained in a population or generated by a random process. A decision problem may turn, for example, on the *mean number of units* which each potential customer will buy rather than on the fraction p who will buy one unit each, or on the *mean yield* per batch of raw material put through some chemical process rather than on the fraction p of batches which are in some sense defective. In dealing with this new class of problems we shall use the notation

x: the value attached to some individual member of a population or some individual item generated by a random process.

μ: the mean of all the x's contained in the population or which could potentially be generated by the process.

The student will find that it helps a great deal to realize that this new class of problems is not really so different from the old as may appear at first glance. As we saw in Section 14.5, we can regard a success generated by a Bernoulli process as an individual with "value" $x = 1$ and a failure as an individual with "value" $x = 0$; and if we do, then p is the *mean "value"* of all the x's which the process could potentially produce and r is the *total "value"* of all the x's in a sample. The only *real* difference between the old and the new class of problems lies in the *sampling distribution* of

$\tilde{l}$: the *total value* of the $\tilde{x}$'s in a sample where each $\tilde{x}$ can have any of a wide variety of possible *measured* values.

Clearly the total $\tilde{l}$ of a sample of $\tilde{x}$'s which may have any measured value in a wide range will not have the same distribution as the total $\tilde{r}$ of a sample of $\tilde{x}$'s each of which has either value 0 or value 1. What is more, the problem of finding the distribution of $\tilde{l}$ is not only different from, but much more complicated than, the problem of finding the distribution of $\bar{r}$.   We saw in Chapter 9 that the conditional distribution of $\bar{r}$ for given p was *wholly determined* by the given p, but it is easy to see that the distribution of $\bar{l}$ for a given μ *cannot* in general be wholly determined by the given μ.   Consider Figure 16.1, where we show the *frequency distributions of all the individual x's which are contained in four different populations or could potentially be generated by four different random processes all of which have exactly the same mean μ and standard deviation σ.   It is obvious as soon as we think about it that if we take samples of the same size n from each of these four populations, the sam-*

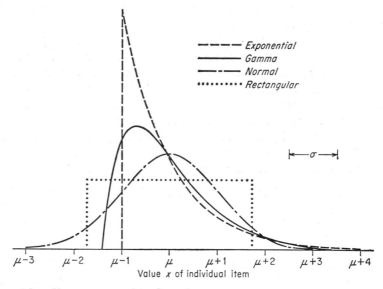

Figure 16.1. Various possible distributions of the individual values in a population.

pling distribution of $\bar{l}$ will be different in all four cases even though the four means and standard deviations are exactly the same.

16.1   Exact Sampling Distributions

If we *knew* the shape of the process or population from which we were about to sample, the fact which we have just brought out would give rise to purely technical problems.   A statistician could derive the conditional distribution, given μ, of a sample from any one of the four processes or populations in Figure 16.1; and in fact the distribution *has* been derived for all these cases and many others as well.   A much more serious difficulty arises from the fact that in most (not all) practical applications we do *not* know the "shape" of the process or population.

As for the applications to be discussed in this course, we sample because we do not know the *mean* of the process or population; and it is only under very exceptional circumstances that we know as much about the *shape* of a process or population as we know about its mean.†

We shall see in this chapter, however, that the distribution of the sample total $\tilde{t}$ fortunately depends *less and less* on the shape of the process or population as the sample size n increases.   If n is "large enough"—and we shall discuss exactly what this means—we can find an approximation to the distribution of $\tilde{t}$ which does *not* depend on the shape of the process or population and yet is accurate enough for all practical purposes.

16.2   Independent vs. Dependent Drawings

If we look at the conditional probability distribution, given μ, of a *single* value $\tilde{x}$ drawn from one of the processes or populations graphed in Figure 16.1 (or any other process or population, for that matter), we see that this *probability* distribution is identical to the *frequency* distribution of all the values which are contained in the population or which could potentially be generated by the process.   If $\frac{1}{4}$ of all these values are larger than 7, say, there is a probability $\frac{1}{4}$ that a member drawn at random will be larger than 7.

The problem becomes more complicated, however, when *more than one* sample value $\tilde{x}$ is drawn from the population or process.   In Section 9.4 we saw that there was a difference between the distributions of the number $\tilde{r}$ of successes in samples taken (1) from a Bernoulli *process* with parameter p and (2) *without replacement* from a *finite population* in which the proportion of successes is p.   The difference arose essentially from the fact that in the former case the probability of a success remained *constant* from one draw to the next, whereas in the latter case each successive draw *changed the proportion* of successes remaining in the population and thereby changed the probability of a success on the next draw.

There will obviously be a difference of this same kind between the distributions of the sample total $\tilde{t}$ (1) in samples drawn from a process generating measured values $\tilde{x}$ in such a way that *the value of any $\tilde{x}$ drawn into the sample has no effect on the value of any subsequent $\tilde{x}$* and (2) in samples drawn without replacement from a finite population, in which case each successive draw *changes the proportions* among the values of the individuals remaining in the population.   In the former case any one of the graphs in Figure 16.1 describes the probability distribution of the next $\tilde{x}$ to be drawn regardless of the values of the $\tilde{x}$'s already drawn; in the

† The principal exceptions are cases where theoretical knowledge of the nature of the underlying mechanism of a random process tells us that its output must be approximately describable by some particular mathematical curve.

latter case this conditional probability distribution changes in both shape and mean after each draw is made: the distribution of any $\tilde{x}$ after the first depends on the values of the previous $\tilde{x}$'s.

We shall proceed in this chapter exactly as we proceeded in Chapter 9. We first study the distribution of $\tilde{t}$ in samples drawn from a random process such that *the probability distribution of each successive $\tilde{x}$ is independent of the values of all previous $\tilde{x}$'s*. After this problem has been solved, we shall go on to see how the results must be modified to obtain the distribution of $\tilde{t}$ in samples drawn *without replacement from a finite population*.

16.3   The Central Limit Theorem Concerning Sums of Independent Random Variables

In addition to the four processes whose output is graphed in Figure 16.1, let us look for a moment at the two additional processes whose out-

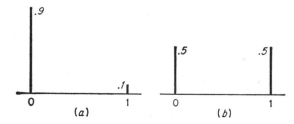

Figure 16.2. Two-valued processes.

put is graphed in Figure 16.2.   In this latter figure every $\tilde{x}$ generated by the process must have either the value 0 or the value 1; the only difference between the two processes is in the relative frequencies of the two values 0 and 1.   The outputs of these two processes are obviously *extremely* different in shape from the output of the Normal process graphed in Figure 16.1; and as we have already emphasized, the *probability* distribution of the value $\tilde{x}$ of any individual drawn from any process is identical to the frequency distribution of the whole potential output of the process.

The two processes graphed in Figure 16.2 are, however, the Bernoulli processes with parameters $p = .1$ and $.5$ which we studied in Section 15.2; and we saw in that section that even though the distribution of an individual value $\tilde{x}$ generated by either process is violently non-Normal, *the distribution of the total value $\tilde{r}$ of all the $\tilde{x}$'s in a sample becomes closer and closer to a Normal distribution as the number n of $\tilde{x}$'s in the sample increases*. More specifically, we saw that

If $\tilde{r}$ is the sum of n independent two-valued random variables all having the same probability distribution, then as n increases the distribution of $\tilde{r}$ is more and more closely approximated by a Normal distribution with mean $E(\tilde{r})$ equal to the expected value of the sum and with variance $\sigma^2(\tilde{r})$ equal to the variance of the sum.

16.3.1 The Central Limit Theorem

We are now ready to state a new, very remarkable, and extremely important fact: the above statement can be generalized to apply to almost *any* sum of independent random variables all having the same probability distribution, *regardless of the nature of this common distribution.*   It is true in general that

If $\tilde{t}$ is the sum of n independent random variables all having the same probability distribution, then as n increases the distribution of $\tilde{t}$ is more and more closely approximated by a Normal distribution with mean equal to the expected value of $\tilde{t}$ and variance equal to the variance of $\tilde{t}$; and this is true regardless of the nature of the distribution of the individual variables.†

From this it follows at once that if we wish to compute probabilities such as $P(\tilde{t} > t)$, then *provided that the number of independent $\tilde{x}$'s included in the sum $\tilde{t}$ is large enough,* probabilities can be approximated by using the procedure of Section 15.1.5: we first substitute the "standardized" value

$$u = \frac{t - E(\tilde{t})}{\sigma(\tilde{t})}$$

for the natural value t and then use Table III of the unit Normal distribution to evaluate

$$P(\tilde{t} > t) \doteq P_{N\ast}(\tilde{u} > u).$$

16.3.2 "Rapidity of Convergence" to Normality

From what we have just said it follows that, before we can make any practical use of the central limit theorem, we must know how large a sample size n is "large enough" to make the approximation "accurate enough" for the purpose at hand; in other words, we must know something about the *rapidity* with which the distribution of $\tilde{t}$ "converges" to Normality as n increases.

Now we saw in Figures 15.6 through 15.9 that in the case of two-

† The only independent random variables with identical distributions to which this statement does not apply are those which have infinite means or standard deviations, and such variables almost never occur in practical business problems.   On the other hand, the statement does apply under certain conditions even to sums of independent variables which do not have identical individual distributions.

valued or Bernoulli processes the rapidity of convergence depends on the value of the process parameter p—i.e. on the "shape" of the probability distribution of any individual $\tilde{x}$. For the very symmetric distribution of $\tilde{x}$ with $p = .5$ (Figure 16.2b), the distribution of $\tilde{r}$ is very close to Normal for n as small as 10 (Figure 15.9), whereas for the extremely asymmetric distribution of $\tilde{x}$ for $p = .01$, the distribution of $\tilde{r}$ is far from Normal even when $n = 100$ (Figure 15.6).

In exactly the same way the Normality of the distribution of the total $\tilde{l}$ of n measured $\tilde{x}$'s depends on the shape of the distribution of an individual $\tilde{x}$ as well as on the number n. If the $\tilde{x}$'s are drawn from a *Normal* process—i.e., if each individual $\tilde{x}$ in the sample is itself Normal— then $\tilde{l}$ is *exactly* Normal for any n. As for other processes, we can start by examining Figure 16.3, where we show the *exact* distribution of $\tilde{l}$ in samples of size $n = 10$ from the three non-Normal processes graphed in Figure 16.1, together with the Normal approximation to all three distributions.

From Figure 16.3 it is apparent that *for n as small as* 10, (1) the distribution of $\tilde{l}$ in samples from a *rectangular* process is very close to Normal, but (2) the distribution of $\tilde{l}$ drawn from "gamma" processes of the type graphed in Figure 16.1 is not yet close to Normal, and (3) the distribution of $\tilde{l}$ drawn from an "exponential" process is still farther from Normal. We must therefore investigate the two latter types of process for larger values of n, and this is done in Figure 16.4. This figure shows the exact distribution of $\tilde{l}$ in samples of size $n = 10$, 20, and 50 from an *exponential* process, and the same curves give the exact distribution of $\tilde{l}$ in samples of size $n = 5$, 10, and 25 respectively from a *gamma* process of the type graphed in Figure 16.1. We conclude that for the extremely J-shaped exponential process the Normal approximation will be extremely poor unless n is at least 50—better 100 or more—and that even for the less asymmetric gamma process the approximation is no good unless n is at least 25, or better 50.

Usually, of course, we will *not know* the exact shape of the process from which a sample is drawn; it is ordinarily *because* we lack this knowledge that we want to use the Normal approximation instead of the exact distribution of $\tilde{l}$. In most circumstances, however, we *will* be able to learn enough about the shape of the process to say whether it is (1) *roughly* Normal, (2) fairly symmetric but flatter than Normal and thus *roughly* rectangular, (3) skewed, with a relatively small fraction of very high values bringing up the average or mean well above the great majority of the individual values, in which case it is very *roughly* of the gamma shape shown in Figure 16.1, or finally (4) actually J-shaped and thus *roughly* like the exponential process. For most practical purposes such rough knowledge of the shape of the process will be adequate to decide

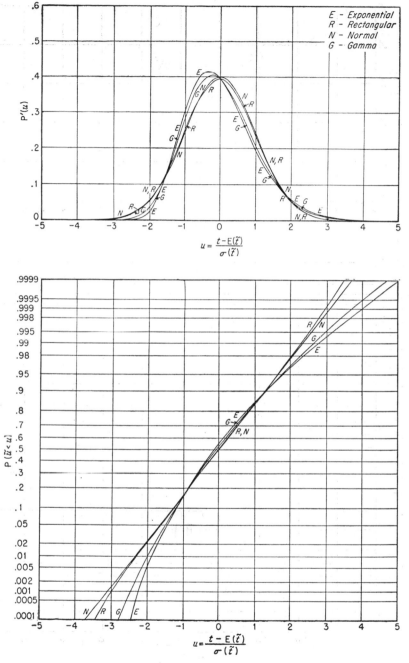

Figure 16.3. Distributions of sample totals with Normal approximations, $n = 10$.

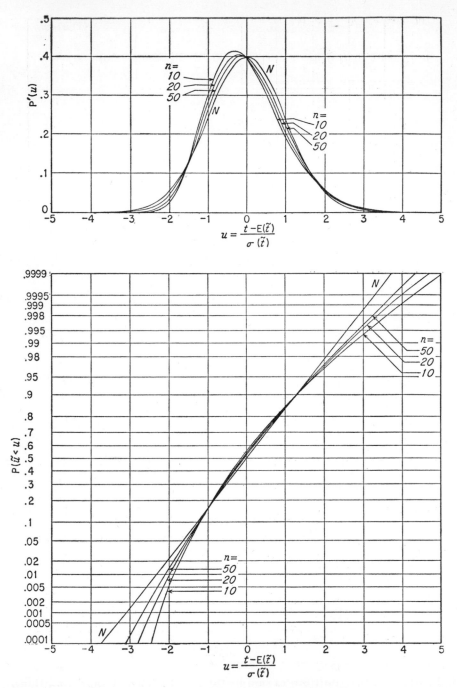

Figure 16.4. Distributions of sample totals with Normal approximation.

whether or not it is legitimate to use the Normal approximation to the distribution of the sample total $\tilde{t}$.

16.4   Mean and Variance of $\tilde{t}$

16.4.1   *Process Variance Known*

Even though we know the circumstances under which the exact distribution of $\tilde{t}$ can be legitimately approximated by a Normal distribution with the same mean and variance, this will be of little use to us unless we know how to compute the mean and variance of the exact distribution of $\tilde{t}$.   These quantities will of course depend on the characteristics of the process generating the $\tilde{x}$'s of which the sum $\tilde{t}$ is composed, but fortunately they do *not* depend on a *complete description* of the process.   Redefining

> μ: the *mean* of all the x's which could be generated by the process,
> σ: the *standard deviation* of all the x's which could be generated by the process,

and remembering that the *probability* distribution of any individual $\tilde{x}$ drawn from the process is identical to the *frequency* distribution describing the whole output of the process, we have at once for the mean and variance of any *one* of the $\tilde{x}$'s in the sum $\tilde{t}$:

$$E(\tilde{x}) = \mu,$$
$$\sigma^2(\tilde{x}) = \sigma^2.$$

Then since the additivity theorems in Section 14.4 tell us that the mean and variance of any sum of independent random variables are equal respectively to the sums of the individual means and variances, we have at once for the sum $\tilde{t}$ of n independent $\tilde{x}$'s

$$E(\tilde{t}) = n\mu,$$
$$\sigma^2(\tilde{t}) = n\sigma^2.$$

Thus provided that we *know* the *process* variance σ^2, that is, the variance of the *individual* $\tilde{x}$'s, we can compute conditional probabilities such as $P(\tilde{t} > t|\mu)$ for any *given* μ by computing

$$u = \frac{t - E(\tilde{t})}{\sigma(\tilde{t})} = \frac{t - n\mu}{\sigma \sqrt{n}}$$

and then using Table III to look up the right-hand member of

$$P(\tilde{t} > t|\mu) \doteq P_{N*}(\tilde{u} > u).$$

16.4.2   *Process Variance Unknown*

From what we have just said it would seem that if we do *not* know the process variance σ^2, then even though n is large enough to warrant our saying that l is approximately Normal, we cannot actually use the Normal approximation because we cannot compute $\sigma(l)$. Since the sample is taken only because we do *not* know the mean μ of the process, the student may well ask how we can possibly know its variance σ^2. The answer is that while we almost never *literally know* the process variance, we very frequently have enough data to make an *estimate* of this variance which is reliable enough to be treated *as if* it were the true value of the variance. How the estimate is made and how we decide whether it is "reliable enough" to be treated as if it were the true value of σ^2 will be explained at the end of this chapter.

16.5   Samples from Finite Populations

We now turn from the problem of the distribution of the total l of the values in a sample from a random process generating *independent* $\tilde{x}$'s to the distribution of l in a sample drawn *without replacement* from a *finite population*.

16.5.1   *General Effect of the Finiteness of the Population*

When we examined the problem of sampling from a *two-valued* finite population in Section 9.4.2, we saw that the distribution of the sample total $\tilde{r}$ would be nearly identical to the distribution of $\tilde{r}$ in samples from a Bernoulli process unless the sample took in a *substantial* fraction of the entire population; and the same argument that we used to establish this fact for a two-valued population establishes it for a population of measured values. If the sample is small relative to the population, then even after all but one of the sample members have been drawn, the proportions among the values of the undrawn members must be *nearly* the same as the proportions in the original population. Consequently,

Provided that the sample size is small relative to the size of the population, the probability distribution of each successive $\tilde{x}$ drawn into the sample will be *virtually* independent of the previous x's and therefore the distribution of the sample total l will be *virtually* the same as if the $\tilde{x}$'s were actually independent.

From this it follows at once that

If a sample drawn without replacement from a finite population is (1) large enough in *absolute* size for the Normal approximation to be justified if the $\tilde{x}$'s were strictly independent, and at the same time (2) small enough *relative* to the total size of the population to make the $\tilde{x}$'s virtually independent, then the distribution of the sample total l can be legitimately approximated by a Normal distribution.

16.5.2   The "Finite-population Correction"

How small is small enough to make the $\bar{x}$'s "virtually" independent can be investigated more systematically by looking at the effect of the finiteness of the population on the standard deviation of the sample total t.   It can be proved that if the size of the population is N and the size of the sample is n, then *regardless of the shape* of the population the standard deviation of t is *exactly*

$$\sigma(t) = (\sigma \sqrt{n}) \sqrt{\frac{N - n}{N - 1}}.$$

The factor in parentheses on the right is the value given in Section 16.4.1 for the standard deviation of t in a sample from a process generating *independent* $\bar{x}$'s; the effect of the finiteness of the population is simply to reduce this standard deviation by the factor $\sqrt{(N - n)/(N - 1)}$, which is sometimes called the "finite-population correction."

Unless the *population* size N is *extremely* small, the value of the finite-population correction for any *sample* size n will be negligibly changed by dropping the 1 in the denominator and writing the correction in the form

$$\sqrt{\frac{N - n}{N}} = \sqrt{1 - \frac{n}{N}}.$$

It thus appears that, except for extremely small populations, the factor depends only on the *sampling ratio* n/N, which expresses the sample size as a fraction of the total size of the population.

In Table 16.1 we show the numerical value of the approximate finite-population correction for various values of the sampling ratio, and we

Table 16.1
Approximate Finite-population Correction

n/N	$\sqrt{1 - n/N}$
0	1.000
.01	.995
.05	.975
.10	.949
.20	.894
.50	.707

see at once that if the sampling ratio is below .05, the standard deviation of t will differ by less than $(1 - .975) = 2\frac{1}{2}\%$ from the value it would have if the sample were drawn from a process generating completely independent $\bar{x}$'s.   We can conclude immediately that *if the sample takes in less than 5 per cent of the whole population,*

1. The finiteness of the population will have no material effect on the *Normality* of the distribution of $\bar{t}$, so that the Normal approximation will be valid if the absolute sample size n is large enough to make it so for samples drawn from a process rather than a finite population.

2. The finite-population correction can itself be disregarded in computing the standard deviation of the Normal approximation, since an error of less than $2\frac{1}{2}$ per cent in the standard deviation is completely negligible in view of the fact that, in any case, we have only an *approximation* to the true distribution of $\bar{t}$.

If on the contrary the sample takes in a substantial part of the entire population, the finiteness of the population may affect the Normality of $\bar{t}$ as well as its standard deviation.   The problem of deciding how to approximate the distribution of $\bar{t}$ in such cases may be delicate; and therefore in this elementary course *we shall deal only with samples taking in so small a part of the total population that the finiteness of the population can be completely disregarded.*   We lose very little, moreover, by restricting ourselves in this way, since the vast majority of samples actually taken in real problems comprise not just less than 5 per cent of the population but far less.

16.6   Use of the Sample Mean

16.6.1   *Equivalence of Sample Total and Sample Mean*

Although problems involving the mean μ of a process generating or a population containing measured values can be analyzed by using the sample total t in exactly the same way that the sample total r was used in Part Two of this course, the standard practice is to use the *mean* of the x's in the sample rather than their total.   This sample mean is usually denoted by the symbol $\bar{x}$ (read x bar); it is related to the sample total t by the obvious formula

$$\bar{x} = \frac{t}{n} \quad \text{or} \quad \frac{r}{n}$$

where n is the number of x's in the sample.

The sample mean $\bar{x}$ obviously conveys exactly the same information about a sample that is conveyed by the sample total t or r.   In Part Two we used the sample total r because the fact that binomial tables always show r rather than $\bar{x} = r/n$ made the use of r much more *convenient*. This advantage disappears, however, when we use the Normal approximation; and the only reason for using t rather than $\bar{x} = t/n$ in the previous sections of this chapter was to bring out the essential similarity between problems involving two-valued random variables and problems involving measured random variables.   In the remainder of this course we shall shift over to use of $\bar{x}$ rather than t simply because almost every statistical analysis which the student will encounter will make use of $\bar{x}$ rather than t.

16.6.2   *Distribution of the Sample Mean*

If we are to use the sample mean $\bar{x}$ rather than the sample total t in analyzing problems of decision under uncertainty, we shall have to compute probabilities of the form $P(\tilde{x} > \bar{x}|\mu)$ where we would otherwise have computed probabilities of the form $P(\tilde{t} > t|\mu)$. We must, in other words, determine the *conditional distribution of $\tilde{x}$ given μ*. This problem is trivial, however, if we already know the distribution of the sample total $\tilde{t}$.

Shape of the Distribution of $\tilde{x}$. Suppose that we have a graph of some particular distribution of $\tilde{t}$, exact or approximate; an arbitrarily chosen example is shown as Figure 16.5. Since every value t on the horizontal axis corresponds to an $\bar{x} = t/n$ exactly $1/n$ times as large,

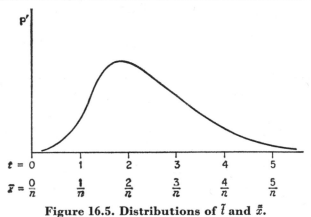

Figure 16.5. Distributions of $\tilde{t}$ and $\bar{\tilde{x}}$.

we can convert this graph of the distribution of $\tilde{t}$ into a graph of the distribution of $\tilde{x}$ by simply *changing the scale* on the horizontal axis by the factor $1/n$.† In other words,

The shape of the distribution of $\tilde{\tilde{x}}$ is identical to the shape of the distribution of $\tilde{t}$, and therefore we may use the Normal approximation to the exact distribution of $\tilde{\tilde{x}}$ whenever we may use the Normal approximation to the distribution of $\tilde{t}$.

Expected Value of $\tilde{x}$. Considering all the possible values $\bar{x}$ which the sample mean $\tilde{x}$ might have, and remembering that every one of them is simply $1/n$ times the corresponding sample total t, we see at once that the average or *expected* value of $\tilde{x}$ must be simply $1/n$ times the expected

† We must also multiply the scale on the vertical axis by the factor n in order to keep the area under the curve unchanged, but this need not concern us in computing *cumulative* probabilities, and cumulative probabilities are the only probabilities **we** shall use in the remainder of this course.

value of l.   We have already seen that the expected value of l is n times the population or process mean μ, and therefore

$$E(\bar{x}) = \mu \qquad \textit{Expected value of sample mean}$$

Variance of $\bar{x}$.   To compute the variance of any random variable we take a weighted average of the *squares* of the *differences* between *each possible* value of the variable and its *expected* value.   Since (1) each *possible* value of $\bar{x}$ is $1/n$ times the corresponding value of l and since (2) the *expected* value of $\bar{x}$ is $1/n$ times the expected value of l, every *difference* between a particular $\bar{x}$ and $E(\bar{x})$ will be $1/n$ times the corresponding difference between t and $E(l)$.   Therefore each *squared* difference $[\bar{x} - E(\bar{x})]^2$ will be $1/n^2$ times the corresponding $[t - E(l)]^2$; and if this is true for *every possible* squared difference, it is true for the *weighted-average* squared difference or *variance*.   We have seen that (neglecting the finite-population correction, if any) the variance of l is $n\sigma^2$; and multiplying this by $1/n^2$ we obtain

$$\sigma^2(\bar{x}) = \frac{\sigma^2}{n} \qquad \textit{Variance of sample mean}$$

Conclusion.   Whenever the use of the Normal approximation is warranted, conditional probabilities may be computed from the formula

$$P(\bar{x} > \bar{x}|\mu) \doteq P_{N^*}(\bar{u} > u)$$

where $\qquad u = \dfrac{\bar{x} - \mu}{\sigma/\sqrt{n}} \qquad$ *Normal approximation for* $\bar{x}$

16.7   Estimation of the Process or Population Variance

We now take up the last of the many problems which must be solved before we can deal with any practical decision problem involving the mean μ of all the values that are contained in a population or could potentially be generated by a random process.   We cannot use the Normal approximation to the distribution of $\bar{x}$ unless we can calculate $\sigma(\bar{x})$; we cannot calculate $\sigma(\bar{x}) = \sigma/\sqrt{n}$ unless we know the variance σ^2 of all the individual x's generated by the process or contained in the population; and usually we do not know σ^2.   We have already remarked, however, that we often *are* able to make an *estimate* of σ^2 which is reliable enough to be treated for practical purposes *as if* it were the *true value* of σ^2, and in this section we shall learn first how to estimate σ^2 and then how to decide whether this estimate is in fact reliable enough to be treated as if it were the true value of σ^2.

16.7.1 The Estimate s

If we wished to compute the variance of a finite population and if we knew the value x of *every one* of the N members of the population, we would first simply apply the *definition* of a mean in Section 6.2 to compute the population mean μ and then apply the *definition* of variance in Section 14.1 to compute the population variance σ^2. These two definitions can be written more briefly in the form

$$\mu = \frac{1}{N} \Sigma x$$

$$\sigma^2 = \frac{1}{N} \Sigma (x - \mu)^2$$

Definitions of mean and variance

The symbol Σ (capital sigma) is to be taken as an *instruction* to compute the value of the quantity which follows it for *every* value x and then *add* the results. Thus if we have a population consisting of just $N = 3$ members whose values x are respectively 5, 6, and 10, the formulas or definitions tell us to compute

$$\mu = \tfrac{1}{3}(5 + 6 + 10) = \tfrac{1}{3}(21) = 7,$$
$$\sigma^2 = \tfrac{1}{3}[(5 - 7)^2 + (6 - 7)^2 + (10 - 7)^2] = \tfrac{1}{3}(4 + 1 + 9) = 14\tfrac{2}{3}.$$

Now in actual applications we never know the value x of *all* the individuals that are contained in a population or could potentially be generated by a process; but we often have a *sample* of these values, and we naturally think of these sample values as being more or less "representative" of all the values. It is tempting, therefore, to try to *estimate* the variance of *all* the values by simply applying the definitions of mean and variance to the n values in the sample. Remembering to distinguish in our notation between the mean μ of the entire process or population and the mean $\bar{x}$ of the sample, we would start by computing

$$\bar{x} = \frac{1}{n} \Sigma x \qquad \text{*Definition of sample mean*}$$

where the sum includes all the values in the *sample*. The variance of the values in the *sample* is then (again by definition)

$$\frac{1}{n} \Sigma (x - \bar{x})^2 \qquad \text{*Definition of sample variance*}$$

and it is this quantity which we are tempted to take as an *estimate* of the variance of all the values which are contained in the *population* or could be generated by the *process*.

For extremely small samples, however, this estimate behaves in a very peculiar way, as we can best see by looking at samples of size $n = 1$. In this case the sample "mean" $\bar{x}$ is exactly equal to the single value x which constitutes the sample, so that *regardless* of the population or process variance the *sample* variance will necessarily be

$$\frac{1}{n} \Sigma(x - \bar{x})^2 = \frac{1}{1} (x - x)^2 = 0.$$

To take this result as an estimate of the *population* or *process* variance is clearly nonsensical.

A difficulty of the same general sort will be present in any very small sample even though it contains more than a single x, since the *cause* of the difficulty lies essentially in the fact that the definition of the *population* or *process* variance involves terms of the form $(x - \mu)^2$ whereas the *sample* variance involves terms of the form $(x - \bar{x})^2$. The sample x's will naturally tend to be "closer" to their *own* mean $\bar{x}$ than to the mean μ of all the x's in the population or process, and therefore *the sample variance will have a systematic tendency to be lower than the population variance*.

The standard remedy for this difficulty is to make the *estimate* of the *population or process variance* somewhat larger than the sample variance by using a divisor $n - 1$ instead of n: the usual estimate is

$$s^2 = \frac{1}{n - 1} \Sigma(x - \bar{x})^2 \qquad \text{*Usual estimate of population or process variance*}$$

The quantity $n - 1$ is called the "number of degrees of freedom" in the estimate s^2, one degree of freedom having been "lost" or "used up" because the sample mean $\bar{x}$ tends to be closer than μ to the sample x's. In the extreme case $n = 1$, there are *no* degrees of freedom: the formula for s^2 takes on the meaningless form

$$\frac{1}{1 - 1} (x - x)^2 = \frac{0}{0},$$

and this agrees perfectly with the fact that a sample of size 1 contains absolutely *no information* about the *variability* of the population or process.

It is true, of course, that this line of argument does not by any means prove that s^2 is the *best possible* estimate of σ^2. Determining what *is* the best estimate is in any given situation usually an extremely difficult problem—so difficult, in fact, that in the vast majority of applied problems a statistician will conclude that finding the best estimate is not worth the trouble and will use the "standard" estimate s^2 without further ado.

16.7.2 Use of s as if It Were the True σ

Suppose then that in some problem we do treat σ as if it were known to have the value s even though the true value is actually unknown. When we standardize $\bar{x}$ in the usual manner we will *not* get the *true* value of

$$u = \frac{\bar{x} - \mu}{\sigma(\bar{x})} = \frac{\bar{x} - \mu}{\sigma/\sqrt{n}};$$

what we will get is an "estimate" of u which we shall call "u hat":

$$\hat{u} = \frac{\bar{x} - \mu}{s/\sqrt{n}}.$$

Before the sample is taken, *both* $\tilde{x}$ and $\tilde{s}$ are random variables, and therefore the distribution of the random variable

$$\tilde{\hat{x}} = \frac{\tilde{x} - \mu}{\tilde{s}/\sqrt{n}}$$

is different from the distribution of

$$\tilde{u} = \frac{\tilde{x} - \mu}{\sigma/\sqrt{n}}.$$

Assuming that the sample size is large enough to make $\tilde{x}$ approximately Normal, we know that it would be legitimate to treat $\tilde{u}$ as unit-Normal and to use Table III to evaluate

$$P(\tilde{x} > \bar{x}|\mu) \doteq P_{N*}(\tilde{u} > u).$$

Treating s as if it were σ and using Table III to evaluate

$$P(\tilde{x} > \bar{x}|\mu) \doteq P_{N*}(\tilde{\hat{u}} > \hat{u})$$

amounts to treating the estimate $\tilde{\hat{u}}$ as if it had the *same unit-Normal distribution* as the true value $\tilde{u}$. What we want to know is whether this is likely to result in a serious error; and the only way of getting a definite answer to this question is to examine the *exact* distribution of the estimate $\tilde{\hat{u}}$.

The Student Distribution. The exact distribution of $\tilde{\hat{u}}$ depends of course on the exact distributions of $\tilde{x}$ and $\tilde{s}$, and these in turn depend on the exact shape of the process or population from which the sample is drawn. We shall try to give the student an idea of the *order of magnitude*

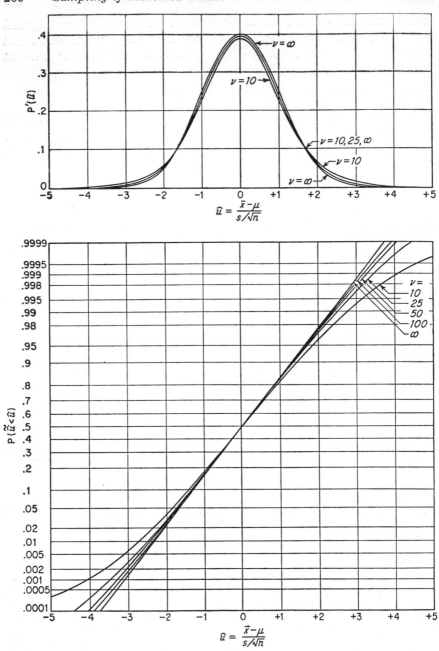

Figure 16.6. Student distributions with Normal limit.

of the difference between the unit-Normal distribution and the exact distribution of $\tilde{u}$ by examining just one case, viz., the case where the frequency distribution of the process or population is itself *Normal*. In this case the estimate $\tilde{u}$ has what is known as a *Student* distribution with one parameter which we shall call ν (nu); the numerical value of the parameter is equal to the *number of degrees of freedom in the estimate s*.

Figure 16.6 shows *Student* distributions with parameters $\nu = 10, 25, 50,$ and 100; the curves labeled ∞ represent the *unit-Normal* distribution. We observe immediately that as the number ν of degrees of freedom in the estimate s increases, the Student distribution of $\tilde{u}$ approaches a unit-Normal distribution; and we also observe that the approach is already very close for 25 degrees of freedom. We conclude that

> In the majority of practical problems it will be legitimate to treat $\tilde{u}$ *as if* it were unit-Normal—i.e., to treat σ *as if* it were known to have the value of its estimate s—provided that the estimate s is obtained from a sample with at least 25 degrees of freedom.

Analysis of a decision problem becomes *very* complex when we can *not* treat σ as if it were known to have the value s; in this elementary course we shall consider only problems where it can.

PROBLEMS

1. Compute the expectation and variance of the *total* value of $n = 10$ observations drawn from a process generating independent $\tilde{x}$'s with mean 90 and standard deviation 20.

2. Compute the expectation and *exact* variance of the *mean* of $n = 10$ items drawn without replacement from a finite population of size $N = 1000$ whose mean is 90 and whose variance is 400.

3. What error would be made in Problem 2 if the finiteness of the population were disregarded?

4. A population of size $N = 1000$ has unknown mean μ and known standard deviation $\sigma = 20$. A sample of size 10 is drawn from this population. We wish to evaluate the conditional probability, given $\mu = 90$, that the sample total $\tilde{t}$ will be greater than 1100. Read from Figure 16.3 both the true probability and the Normal approximation to the true value assuming that the *shape* of the population is

   a. Rectangular.

   b. Exponential.

   c. Gamma of the type graphed in Figure 16.1.

5. Same as Problem 1, except that we require the probability that the sample mean $\tilde{x}$ will be less than 75.

6. The values of the 5 items in a sample are 10, 8, 7, 10, and 5.

   a. Compute the variance of these values.

   b. Estimate the variance of the population from which the sample was drawn.

   c. If you wished to compute the probability, given $\mu = 10$, that the mean of *another* sample of size 5 from this same population would exceed 12, could you use the Normal approximation? Why?

CHAPTER 17

Statistical Decision Rules with Normal Sampling

We are now ready to begin the actual analysis of decision problems in which (1) the profits, costs, or losses of the various possible acts depend on the unknown mean μ of some process or population, (2) the sampling distribution of the sample mean $\bar{x}$ can be treated as Normal, and (3) the variance σ^2 of the population or process can be treated as known. We shall restrict ourselves to the simplest possible problems, viz., those in which there are *only two possible terminal acts*, just as we did when we were studying binomial sampling in Part Two of the course. Apart from the substitution of μ for p and of a Normal $\bar{x}$ for a binomial $\tilde{r}$, the present chapter very closely resembles Chapter 10, and the student may do well to review the main ideas of that chapter before studying the present one.

17.1 An Example from Chemical Processing

A certain chemical is produced from a liquid raw material. The final product must contain at least 3 pounds of constituent X per gallon. With *regular processing*, the amount of constituent X in the final product is 50 per cent of the amount of X in 1 gallon of the raw material. By *special processing* at an extra cost of $400, the yield can be raised to 75 per cent. The X content of the final product is always very precisely measured, and when it is below 3 pounds per gallon the deficit is made up with pure X, which costs $10 per pound. A batch of raw material sufficient to produce 100 gallons of final product is about to be processed, and the manufacturer wishes to decide whether to use regular or special processing. In what follows we shall refer to use of *regular* processing as *acceptance of the batch* of raw material and to use of *special* processing as *rejection* of the batch.

To simplify the discussion, we shall measure the X content of a given lot of raw material in terms of its yield under regular processing, which we shall call the *normal yield* of the material and which we shall denote by the symbol mu:

μ: yield of the raw material under regular processing.

Thus if there is 5.0 pounds of X in a gallon of raw material, we shall say that its normal yield is $\mu = 2.5$ pounds per gallon.

17.1.1   Conditional Costs and Losses

Special processing at a cost of \$400 will produce the required 3 pounds per gallon of X in the final product from raw material having any normal yield at least as great as $\mu = 2$; and we shall assume that on the basis of past experience the manufacturer feels absolutely sure that μ will not be less than 2. Since no pure X will have to be added, the total cost of *rejection* will be simply this \$400.

If the normal yield is 2.0 pounds per gallon but the batch is accepted and regular processing is used, $3.0 - 2.0 = 1.0$ pound of pure X will have

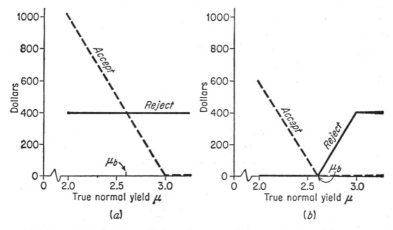

Figure 17.1. (*a*) **Conditional costs;** (*b*) **conditional losses.**

to be added per gallon, or 100 pounds for the entire batch. At \$10 per pound, this gives a conditional cost of acceptance amounting to \$1000. More generally: for any μ less than 3, the amount of pure X which will have to be added is $100(3 - \mu)$ gallons and therefore

$$\text{Cost of acceptance} = \$10 \times 100(3 - \mu) = \$3000 - \$1000\,\mu.$$

For $\mu > 3$ the conditional cost of acceptance is 0.

These costs are graphed in Figure 17.1, and it is easy to calculate that the *break-even value* at which it makes no difference whether the manufacturer accepts or rejects the batch is

$$\mu_b = \frac{\$3000 - \$400}{\$1000} = 2.6.$$

It is equally easy to see that the opportunity losses are given by

●━●

$$\text{Loss of acceptance} = \begin{cases} \$1000(2.6 - \mu) & \text{if } \mu < 2.6 \\ 0 & \text{if } \mu \geq 2.6 \end{cases}$$

$$\text{Loss of rejection} = \begin{cases} \$0 & \text{if } \mu \leq 2.6 \\ \$1000(\mu - 2.6) & \text{if } 2.6 < \mu < 3.0 \\ \$400 & \text{if } \mu \geq 3.0 \end{cases}$$

●━●

17.1.2   *Availability of Additional Information*

If he likes, the manufacturer can obtain additional information about the true normal yield μ of the batch about to be processed by taking one or more test-tubes-full of material from the batch and assaying each one with a measuring process which has been calibrated to read directly in normal yield. Each such measurement involves operator's time worth about $2.

17.1.3   *Characteristics of the Measuring Process*

Although any one batch of the liquid raw material is completely homogeneous, so that the *true* normal yields of the material in any number of test-tubes-full drawn from the same batch will be absolutely identical, measurement of the normal yield of each test-tube-full is difficult and inaccurate, and therefore a set of *measurements* on any single batch will *not* be all the same. On the last previous batch, for example, nine successive measurements *indicated* normal yields of 1.84, 1.75, 1.39, 1.65, 3.53, 1.03, 2.73, 2.86, and 1.96. The fact that a measuring instrument can be *read* to two decimal places does not mean that it is *accurate* to two decimal places. Notice that here as in many practical problems _the variability is in the measuring process itself and not in the object of measurement;_ the measurements actually made on the present batch constitute a sample from a *random process* which *could* have generated an *infinite number of measurements of a single fixed quantity.*

In order to determine the characteristics of his measuring process, the manufacturer had previously conducted an extensive investigation. During this investigation numerous measurements were made on each of a large number of batches of raw material and each of these measurements was later compared with a precise determination of the actual yield under regular processing of the batch on which the measurement had been made. Examination of the *errors of measurement* had brought out four important facts:

1. The mean of all the errors was virtually 0.
2. The standard deviation of all the errors was .9.

3. The shape of the distribution of the errors was Normal for all practical purposes.

4a. There was no observable tendency for a high error to be followed by a high error, etc.: the errors of measurement were *independent of each other*.

4b. There was no observable relation between the magnitude or sign of the errors made on any one batch and the true yield of that batch; the errors of measurement were *independent of* μ.

In discussing the Bernoulli process in Chapter 9, we emphasized that we could not treat a process as a Bernoulli process *merely* because it generated successes and failures; we had to be sure that the successive trials were *independent* and that the probability of a success was the *same* on each trial. When we are dealing with a random process which generates measured values rather than successes and failures, we must similarly make very sure that we know the characteristics of the process before we start computing any probabilities. In the present situation we know these characteristics because the manufacturer's very careful investigation shows that, as applied to *any one* batch of raw material, the measuring process:

1. Is of known type, generating *independent, Normally distributed* values $\tilde{x}$;
2. Has mean μ *equal to the true normal yield* of the batch being measured;
3. Has standard deviation $\sigma = .9$.

All our subsequent conclusions will depend for their validity on the truth of these three assertions; we have adopted a certain *model* of the real measuring process and *our conclusions depend on the validity of the model*.

17.2   The Decision Rule and Its Error Characteristic

17.2.1   *The Form of the Appropriate Decision Rule*

The great variability of the individual measurements generated by the measuring process when applied to any one batch suggests that if the manufacturer is to obtain information about the present batch which is reliable enough to be worth the trouble, he should take a fair number of measurements and then *average* them. His final decision will, in other words, be based on the mean $\bar{x}$ of the x's in a sample of some size n; and given this fact it is obvious and can be proved that the manufacturer should adopt a decision rule of the general form:

Take a sample of size n and compute the mean $\bar{x}$ of the individual measurements x in the sample. Then if $\bar{x}$ is *less than or equal to* some predetermined critical value *c*, *reject* the batch (give it special processing); if $\bar{x}$ is greater than *c*, *accept* the batch (give it regular processing).

Notice that because of the economics of the problem the manufacturer will reject for *low* values of $\bar{x}$; contrast the problem of Section 10.2 where the manufacturer would reject for *high* values of *r*.

Exactly as in the problem of Section 10.2, however, the manufacturer's problem is to determine the best values for *n* and *c*; and again here as there the first step of the analysis must be to learn how to describe any given decision rule or (*n,c*) pair by an *error characteristic* showing for *every possible* true value of μ the *conditional* probability, *given* that particular value of μ, that the decision rule will lead to a wrong decision. We arbitrarily take as an example the rule *n* = 9, *c* = 2.5, or more briefly (9,2.5)—i.e., the rule "make nine measurements and then accept the batch if their average $\bar{x}$ is greater than 2.5; otherwise reject."

17.2.2   Distribution of $\bar{\bar{x}}$

The manufacturer's investigation of the measuring process has shown that the individual measurements $\bar{x}$ are themselves virtually Normal, so that the mean $\bar{\bar{x}}$ of *n* = 9 measurements can certainly be treated as Normal (cf. Section 16.3.2).   The manufacturer's investigation has also shown that (1) the mean of the measuring process is equal to the true normal yield μ and (2) the standard deviation of the process is σ = .9. Applying the formulas in Section 16.6.2 we have for the distribution of the sample mean $\bar{\bar{x}}$

$$E(\bar{\bar{x}}) = \mu,$$

$$\sigma(\bar{\bar{x}}) = \frac{\sigma}{\sqrt{n}} = \frac{.9}{\sqrt{9}} = .3.$$

To compute the *conditional* probability, *given* any possible μ, that $\bar{\bar{x}}$ will be greater than 2.5 and that the batch will therefore be *accepted* under the rule (9,2.5), we now have only to put the critical value *c* in standard measure,

$$u_c = \frac{c - \mu}{\sigma(\bar{\bar{x}})} = \frac{2.5 - \mu}{.3},$$

and then use Table III to evaluate

$$P(\bar{\bar{x}} > 2.5|\mu) = P_{N^*}(\bar{u} > u_c).$$

Thus taking μ = 2.1 as a first example, we have

$$u_c = \frac{2.5 - 2.1}{.3} = 1.33,$$

$$P(\bar{\bar{x}} > 2.5|\mu = 2.1) = P_{N^*}(\bar{u} > 1.33) = .09176.$$

Taking $\mu = 2.9$ as a second example, we have

$$u_c = \frac{2.5 - 2.9}{.3} = -1.33,$$

$$
\begin{aligned}
P(\bar{x} > 2.5 | \mu = 2.9) &= P_{N^*}(\tilde{u} > -1.33) \\
&= 1 - P_{N^*}(\tilde{u} < -1.33) \\
&= 1 - P_{N^*}(\tilde{u} > +1.33) = 1 - .09176 = .90824.
\end{aligned}
$$

17.2.3   The Error Characteristic of the Rule

We can now obtain the conditional probability, given any particular μ, that the decision rule will lead to a *wrong* decision, by merely observing that acceptance is wrong if μ is in fact less than 2.6, while rejection is wrong if μ is greater than 2.6. (Be very careful not to confuse the *break-even* value $\mu_b = 2.6$ of the basic unknown μ with the *critical* value $c = 2.5$ of the sample mean $\bar{x}$.) Using our previous formula for the probability of acceptance we have

$$
P(\text{wrong decision} | \mu) =
\begin{cases}
P_{N^*}(\tilde{u} > u_c) & \text{if } \mu < 2.6 \\
P_{N^*}(\tilde{u} < u_c) & \text{if } \mu > 2.6
\end{cases}
$$

where

$$u_c = \frac{c - \mu}{\sigma(\bar{x})} = \frac{2.5 - \mu}{.3}$$

In Table 17.1 we show the computation of the conditional probability of a wrong decision given each of several different possible μ's, and in Figure 17.2 we graph these probabilities to depict the *error* characteristic of the rule (9,2.5).

Table 17.1
Conditional Probabilities of Wrong Decision under the Rule (9,2.5)

μ	$u_c = \dfrac{2.5 - \mu}{.3}$	$P(\text{accept} \| \mu) = P_{N^*}(\tilde{u} > u_c)$	$P(\text{wrong decision} \| \mu)$
2.0	-1.67	.953	.047
2.2	-1.00	.841	.159
2.4	$-.33$	.629	.371
2.5999	$+.33$	.371	.629
2.6001	$+.33$	.371	.371
2.8	$+1.00$	.159	.159
3.0	$+1.67$	.047	.047
3.2	$+2.33$	.010	.010

17.2.4   Effect of Changes in n and c

In Figure 17.3 we show the error characteristics of a number of decision rules all of which have the same sample size $n = 9$ but various

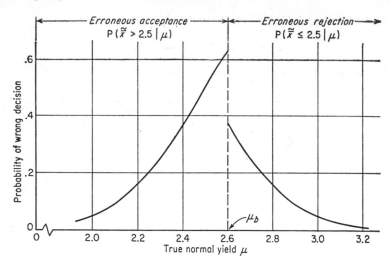

Figure 17.2. Error characteristic of the decision rule (9,2.5).

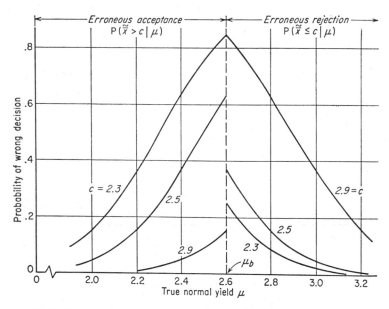

Figure 17.3. Error characteristics of the decision rules (9,2.3), (9,2.5), (9,2.9).

critical values c, and we observe exactly what we observed in Section 10.3.1:

> By changing c with n fixed, the manufacturer can reduce the chances of accepting a poor batch at the cost of increasing the chances of rejecting a good batch or vice versa, but he cannot reduce the chances of both kinds of wrong decision together.

In Figure 17.4 we show the error characteristics of a number of decision rules with various sample sizes n, the critical value c being chosen for each n in such a way as to give the *same* probability of accept-

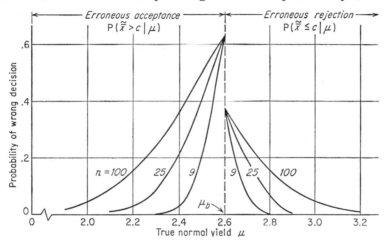

Figure 17.4. Error characteristics of the decision rules (9,2.5), (25,2.54), (100,2.57).

ing a batch of *break-even* quality, and we observe exactly what we observed in Section 10.3.2:

> By increasing n and changing c appropriately, the manufacturer can reduce *both* the chances of accepting a poor batch *and* the chances of rejecting a good batch; but by so doing he increases the cost of sampling.

17.3 Choice of a Decision Rule by Specification of Two Conditional Probabilities

In principle, the manufacturer should choose a particular decision rule or (n,c) pair by comparing the conditional probabilities of wrong decision for *all* values of μ under all possible (n,c) combinations; but as we saw in Section 10.4, this is so hard to do that statisticians traditionally recommend the following simplified procedure.

1a. Remembering that a loss will be incurred if a batch with $\mu < \mu_b$ is accepted (given regular processing), and remembering that this loss is the larger the farther μ is below μ_b, decide what value μ_1 of μ is just far enough below μ_b to make the loss of acceptance "serious."

1b. Decide just how large a conditional probability of acceptance you are willing to tolerate *if* $\mu = \mu_1$. We shall call this specified value α.

2a. Remembering that a loss will be incurred if a batch with $\mu > \mu_b$ is rejected (is given special processing), and remembering that this loss is more serious the farther μ is above μ_b, decide what value μ_2 of μ is just far enough above μ_b to make the loss of rejection "serious."

2b. Decide just how large a conditional probability of rejection you are willing to tolerate *if* $\mu = \mu_2$. We shall call this specified value β.

3. Use the (n,c) pair which comes as close as possible to satisfying these two requirements.

If our manufacturer is willing to play this game he may say, for example, (1) that losses of $99.99 or less are not serious but that losses of $100.00 or more are, and (2) that he is willing to tolerate a conditional probability $\alpha = \beta = .05$ of making the wrong decision if μ has such a value that the wrong decision would entail a $100 loss. From the formulas for the losses in Section 17.1.1 it is easy to calculate that $\mu_1 = 2.5$ and $\mu_2 = 2.7$, since

$$\$1000(2.6 - 2.5) = \$1000(2.7 - 2.6) = \$100.$$

We now have to find the (n,c) pair such that

$$P(\text{acceptance}|\mu = 2.5) = P(\bar{x} > c|\mu = 2.5) = \alpha = .05,$$
$$P(\text{rejection}|\mu = 2.7) = P(\bar{x} \leq c|\mu = 2.7) = \beta = .05,$$

Defining

$$u_1 = \frac{c - \mu_1}{\sigma/\sqrt{n}} = \frac{c - 2.5}{.9/\sqrt{n}}, \qquad u_2 = \frac{c - \mu_2}{\sigma/\sqrt{n}} = \frac{c - 2.7}{.9/\sqrt{n}},$$

our two requirements can be written

$$P_{N*}(\bar{u} > u_1) = \alpha = .05, \qquad P_{N*}(\bar{u} < u_2) = \beta = .05.$$

Looking in Table III we find that we must set $u_1 = 1.645$ if we wish the first of these two probabilities to equal .05, and by symmetry we see that we must set $u_2 = -1.645$ if we wish the second probability to equal .05. Referring back to the definitions of u_1 and u_2 we see that we must therefore choose n and c such that

$$\frac{c - 2.5}{.9/\sqrt{n}} = 1.645 \qquad \text{and} \qquad \frac{c - 2.7}{.9/\sqrt{n}} = -1.645.$$

These two "simultaneous equations" in n and c can now be solved by elementary algebra to obtain

$$n = 14.8^2 = 219, \qquad c = 2.60.$$

The manufacturer should have 219 measurements made if he wishes to reduce the conditional probabilities of a $100 loss due to either kind of wrong decision to $\alpha = \beta = .05$. The critical value c is equal to the break-even value μ_b because (1) α and β are given the same values at the same distances from μ_b and (2) the Normal distribution is symmetric.

It may seem that the sampling cost of $528 which will be incurred by making 219 measurements at $2 each is somewhat high in view of the fact that if the batch is simply rejected without sampling the resulting loss cannot exceed $400. If it does, the manufacturer would traditionally be advised to try higher values for α and β until he finds a pair which give whatever he thinks is the best balance of sampling cost and chance of loss due to a wrong decision. We leave to the student the investigation of the way in which sampling cost varies with α and β, merely pointing out that the reasoning which led to the particular values $n = 219$ and $c = 2.60$ can be generalized to give

$$n = \left(\frac{u_\alpha - u_\beta}{\mu_2 - \mu_1} \sigma \right)^2, \qquad c = \frac{\mu_2 u_\alpha - \mu_1 u_\beta}{u_\alpha - u_\beta},$$

where u_α and u_β are numbers chosen so that

$$P_{N^*}(\tilde{u} > u_\alpha) = \alpha, \qquad P_{N^*}(\tilde{u} < u_\beta) = \beta.$$

In applying the formulas, be sure to observe the algebraic signs of u_α and u_β; thus in the example we have already worked out,

$$u_\alpha = 1.645, \qquad u_\beta = -1.645,$$

$$n = \left[\frac{1.645 - (-1.645)}{2.7 - 2.5} (.9) \right]^2 = 14.8^2 = 219,$$

$$c = \frac{2.7(1.645) - 2.5(-1.645)}{1.645 - (-1.645)} = \frac{8.554}{3.29} = 2.60.$$

17.4 An Example from Store Testing

A manufacturer of instant coffee is considering a more modern-looking design for the jar and label with which he packages his product. The proposed new jars and labels can be bought for the same price as the old and the only extra cost involved in the change would be about $20,000 for minor modifications in the jar-filling machines. The manufacturer believes that if the new package proves successful it will be successfully imitated by the rest of the industry after about 2 years; and since his margin net of freight averages $.11 per ounce, this means that the new package must increase his sales by $20,000/$.11 = 182,000 ounces within the 2-year period in order to break even.   His sales have been running about 70 million ounces per year, so that an increase of this magnitude is readily conceivable; his real worry is whether a change to the new design might actually reduce his sales.

17.4.1   The Experiment

In order to obtain more information about the true effect on sales of the proposed package change, the manufacturer has had a store test conducted.   From a list containing the names and addresses of 400,000 grocery outlets—virtually every outlet in the United States—100 stores were drawn at random and divided at random into two groups of 50 each. In group A, sales of the product in the old package were first audited for 1 month by recording opening inventory, purchases, and closing inventory.   At the end of the month those stores which carried the manufacturer's product were supplied with the product in the new package, any leftover stock of the old being removed, and sales were again audited for 1 month.   In group B the procedure was the same except that the order in which the packages were used was reversed, the new package being used in the first month, the old one in the second.   The agency which actually carried out the test charged a fixed fee of $1000 for setup plus $75 for each store in the sample, or $8500 in all.

After all the data were in, they were used to compute *for each one of the* 100 *stores separately*

> *x*: ounces sold in the month in which the *new* package was stocked
> *minus* ounces sold in the month in which the *old* package was stocked.

The 100 individual *x*'s were then used to compute

$$\bar{x}_o = \tfrac{1}{100} \Sigma x = .157,$$
$$s = \sqrt{\tfrac{1}{99} \Sigma (\bar{x} - x)^2} = 1.25.$$

The manufacturer now wishes to decide whether he should definitely adopt the new package for his entire production during the next two years or should give up the idea and stick to the old package during this period of time.

17.5   Decision Rules and Risks of Error

In Section 10.7 we dealt with a situation which was exactly like the present one in the sense that the decision maker had *already taken* a sample and wished merely to use its known outcome as the basis for a choice of terminal act, but we saw that statisticians nevertheless traditionally recommend that the problem be analyzed *as if* the sample had not yet been taken. The decision maker there and here should first choose an (n,c) decision rule and *then* make his choice of terminal act by comparing the observed $\bar{x}_o = .157$ with the chosen c. The only effect of the fact that the sample has actually already been taken is to restrict the decision maker to rules with n equal to the size of the sample actually taken, i.e., to rules with $n = 100$.

17.5.1 The Form of the Decision Rule

Since a high sample $\bar{x}$ tends to indicate that the new package is better than the old while a low (possibly negative) $\bar{x}$ would tend to indicate that the new package is worse than the old, the decision rule should obviously be of the form

Take a sample of $n = 100$ observations x and compute their mean $\bar{x}$; then if $\bar{x}$ is greater than some predetermined critical value c, *accept the new* package; otherwise reject.

The only problem is to choose the critical value c, and this is to be done as usual by comparing the error characteristics of all possible c's.

17.5.2 The True Effect μ

To construct an error characteristic we must be able to compute the conditional probability of a wrong decision given any possible value of the quantity of interest to the decision maker. The quantity of interest in our present problem is the effect which the new package would have on the manufacturer's total sales over a 2-year period, since as we have already seen the new package will be profitable if and only if it increases these total sales by more than 182,000 ounces. Analysis of the problem will be easier, however, if we work in terms of average effect per store per month over the 2-year period rather than in terms of total effect. We shall therefore think of the package change as a *process* which would produce a *change x in each individual month's sales in each individual store in the United States*, and we shall define

μ: the mean of all the *changes* in individual store-month sales which the package change would produce.

Since there are 400,000 stores in the United States and since the manufacturer believes that the package change will affect sales over a period of 2 years or 24 months, there are $24 \times 400,000 = 9,600,000$ store-months on which the process will have an effect if the new package is adopted. We saw in Section 17.4 that the *break-even value* for total sales is 182,000 ounces, from which it follows that

$$\mu_b = \frac{182,000}{9,600,000} = .019.$$

The package change will be profitable if and only if it increases average sales per store per month by .019 ounce.

To express the opportunity losses in terms of μ, we observe that if μ is actually below μ_b but the new package is accepted, *total* sales will be $9,600,000(\mu_b - \mu)$ ounces below the quantity required to break even. Since the manufacturer's margin is $.11 per ounce, the reduction in profit will be

$$\$.11 \times 9,600,000(\mu_b - \mu) = \$1,056,000(\mu_b - \mu).$$

This result, plus similar reasoning about the potential increase in profit which the manufacturer will fail to realize if he rejects the new package when in fact $\mu > \mu_b$, gives us the formulas

$$\text{Loss of acceptance} = \begin{cases} \$1,056,000(\mu_b - \mu) & \text{if } \mu < \mu_b \\ \$0 & \text{if } \mu \geq \mu_b \end{cases}$$

$$\text{Loss of rejection} = \begin{cases} \$0 & \text{if } \mu \leq \mu_b \\ \$1,056,000(\mu - \mu_b) & \text{if } \mu > \mu_b \end{cases}$$

17.5.3   *Distribution of $\tilde{x}$*

The reason for introducing the average effect μ is that it simplifies the problem of finding the sampling distribution of the $\tilde{x}$ of the store test.

Expectation of $\tilde{x}$.   The 100 $\tilde{x}$'s actually measured in the store test were generated by the same package-change process that will generate 9,600,000 new $\tilde{x}$'s if the new package is adopted; and since the mean of this process is μ we have by the formula in Section 16.6.2

$$E(\tilde{x}) = \mu.$$

Standard Deviation of $\tilde{x}$.   The standard deviation σ of the $\tilde{x}$-generating process can be estimated from the data in the sample in the way described in Section 16.7.1. The estimate, already given in Section 17.4.1, is

$$s = 1.25.$$

Since this estimate rests on 99 degrees of freedom, we may treat it as a sure thing and proceed to use the formula in Section 16.6.2 to compute

$$\sigma(\tilde{x}) = \frac{\sigma}{\sqrt{n}} \doteq \frac{s}{n} = \frac{1.25}{\sqrt{100}} = .125.$$

Normality of $\bar{x}$. The individual $\bar{x}$'s generated by the process will have a more or less J-shaped distribution because the total volumes of business done by individual grocery stores have a more or less J-shaped distribution: a great many stores do a very small business each while relatively few stores do a relatively large business each. Even so, the sample is so large ($n = 100$) that we can treat the mean $\bar{x}$ as *Normally distributed* (cf. Section 16.3.2).

Conclusion. As evaluated before the store test was actually conducted, the *conditional* probability, *given* any particular true effect μ,

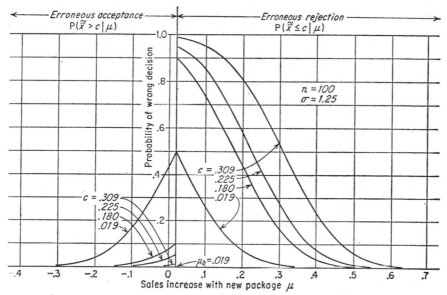

Figure 17.5. Error characteristics of the decision rules (100,.019), (100,.180), (100,.225), (100,.309).

that the sample mean $\bar{x}$ would be greater than any specified critical value c, can be found by computing

$$u_c = \frac{c - \mu}{\sigma(\bar{x})} = \frac{c - \mu}{.125}$$

and using Table III to evaluate

$$P(\bar{x} > c|\mu) = P_{N^*}(\tilde{u} > u_c).$$

17.5.4 Error Characteristics

Remembering that the decision rule calls for acceptance of the new package if $\bar{x} > c$ and that acceptance is a wrong decision if $\mu < \mu_b$, and vice versa for rejection, we have

$$P(\text{wrong decision}|\mu) = \begin{cases} P_{N \cdot}(\bar{a} > u_c) & \text{if } \mu < \mu_b, \\ P_{N \cdot}(\bar{a} < u_c) & \text{if } \mu > \mu_b. \end{cases}$$

In Figure 17.5 we depict error characteristics for selected critical values c.

17.6   Decision by Test of Significance

17.6.1   *Choice of c by Limitation of the Conditional Probabilities of One Kind of Error*

Although classical theory now calls for the manufacturer to choose the c of his decision rule by comparing curves like those in Figure 17.5 for every possible c and by looking at the risks which each c implies for every possible μ, we saw in discussing the book-club example in Section 10.7.2 that statisticians usually admit that this is very hard to do and approve a simplified procedure under which all that the manufacturer has to do is specify the conditional probability of wrong decision that he is willing to tolerate for one particular μ.   Such a procedure implies of course that the manufacturer must look at his problem asymmetrically: he can limit *either* the risk of accepting the new package when it is actually unprofitable *or* the risk of rejecting it when it would actually be profitable, but he cannot limit both kinds of risks simultaneously.   Again as we said in Section 10.7.2, most examples of the use of a procedure of this sort imply that changing the *status quo* for the worse is regarded as a more serious error than failing to change it for the better; and we shall illustrate the procedure for this case leaving it to the student to illustrate it for the other.

If the manufacturer is to choose his c by specifying the conditional probability of unprofitable acceptance given one particular μ, he must first pick the μ; and, once more as we saw in Section 10.7.2, two possibilities are commonly suggested.

1. The manufacturer may specify an upper limit α to the conditional probability of acceptance given any μ which makes acceptance unprofitable.   Since as shown by the curves in Figure 17.5 this probability increases with μ for any given c, all the conditional probabilities of erroneous acceptance can be kept down to α or less by choosing a c which makes the conditional probability exactly equal to α when μ has the break-even value .019.   If the manufacturer does specify the traditional limit $\alpha = .05$ on $P(\text{acceptance}|\mu) = P(\bar{x} > c|\mu)$ for all μ's which make acceptance unprofitable, he can find his c by first using Table III to find the value of

$$u_c = \frac{c - \mu_b}{\sigma(\bar{x})} = \frac{c - .019}{.125}$$

which will make

$$P(\bar{x} > c|\mu = .019) \doteq P_{N\bullet}(\bar{u} > u_c) = \alpha = .05.$$

Table III shows that for this to be true u_c must have the value 1.645, and we can then calculate

$$1.645 = \frac{c - .019}{.125},$$

$$c = .019 + .125 \times 1.645 = .225.$$

The error characteristic of the rule (100,.225) is one of those graphed in Figure 17.5.

Having thus chosen the decision rule (100,.225)—sample $n = 100$ and then accept the new package if $\bar{x} > .225$; otherwise reject— the manufacturer can decide what to do on the basis of the $\bar{x}_o = .156$ that he has already observed in the sample of size $n = 100$ which has already been taken. Although the sample seems to indicate that the new package would increase total sales over a 2-year period by

$$.156 \times 9,600,000 \doteq 1,500,000 \text{ ounces}$$

and thereby increase his profits by $\$.11 \times 1,500,000 = \$165,000$, the evidence is not decisive enough under the chosen rule: $x_o = .156$ is *below* $c = .225$ and the manufacturer should *reject* the new package.

2. Instead of limiting the conditional probability of acceptance given any μ which makes acceptance unprofitable by the slightest amount, the manufacturer may wish to specify an upper limit α on the conditional probability of acceptance given only those μ's which would make acceptance "*seriously*" unprofitable. Since it is hard to imagine that the manufacturer would regard a loss of as much as $\$100,000$ as "not serious," we shall suppose by way of example that he says that losses of $\$99,999.99$ or less are not serious but that losses of $\$100,000.00$ or more are; and since $\$100,000$ is a substantial amount of money, we shall suppose that he places a limit $\alpha = .01$ on the conditional probability of acceptance given any μ such that acceptance would result in a loss of $\$100,000$ or more. Then since (1) the loss of erroneous acceptance becomes less as μ increases, while (2) the conditional probability of acceptance becomes less as μ decreases, we see that he can accomplish his objective by (1) finding the value μ_o of μ for which the loss of erroneous acceptance is exactly $\$100,000$ and (2) choosing his c such that the conditional probability of acceptance given $\mu = \mu_o$ is exactly $\alpha = .01$.

From the formula for the loss of acceptance in Section 17.5.2 we easily calculate that $\mu_o = -.076$ because this makes the loss of acceptance equal to

$$\$1,056,000(\mu_b - \mu_o) = \$1,056,000[.019 - (-.076)] \doteq \$100,000.$$

He can then find his c by using Table III to find the value of

$$u_c = \frac{c - \mu_o}{\sigma(\bar{x})} = \frac{c - (-.076)}{.125}$$

which will make

$$P(\bar{x} > c | \mu = -.076) = P_{N^*}(\tilde{u} > u_c) = \alpha = .01.$$

Table III shows that for this to be true u_c must have the value 2.326, and we can then calculate

$$2.326 = \frac{c - (-.076)}{.125},$$
$$c = -.076 + .125 \times 2.326 = .215.$$

The rule is not greatly different from the one with $c = .225$ which is graphed in Figure 17.5; and again the manufacturer should *reject* the new package because the observed $x_o = .156$ is below the chosen c.

17.6.2   *Null Hypotheses and Tests of Significance*

We have already seen in Section 10.7.3 that *if* the manufacturer wishes *to behave in accordance with* a rule which would limit certain conditional probabilities of one kind of wrong decision to a predetermined α, he does not actually need to find the decision rule (i.e., the c) which will accomplish this.   Letting $\bar{x}_o$ denote the actually observed sample mean and μ_o the value of μ below which no conditional probability of acceptance is to exceed α, all that he has to do is to use the following *equivalent* decision rule:

Compute $P(\bar{x} > \bar{x}_o | \mu = \mu_o)$ and then *accept* the new package if this probability is *less than or equal to* α; otherwise reject.

Thus if the manufacturer wished to limit the conditional probability of acceptance to $\alpha = .05$ given any μ below the break-even point .019, he could make the right decision in the light of his observed $\bar{x}_o = .156$ by computing

$$u_o = \frac{\bar{x}_o - \mu_o}{\sigma(\bar{x})} = \frac{.156 - .019}{.125} = 1.10,$$
$$P(\bar{x} > .156 | \mu = .019) \doteq P_{N^*}(\tilde{u} > 1.10) \doteq .14,$$

and then rejecting because $.14 > .01$.

The proof that the "equivalent" decision rule will actually lead to the same decision that would be reached by actually choosing c in the way described in Section 17.6.1 is exactly like the corresponding proof in Section 10.7.3 and is left to the student as an exercise.   We also leave it to the student to show that if the manufacturer wants to place a limit α

on the conditional probabilities of erroneous *rejection* for all μ's *above* some value μ_o, he can do so by computing $P(\tilde{x} < \tilde{x}_o | \mu_o)$ and then rejecting only if this probability is equal to or less than the specified α.

If the manufacturer places a limit α on the conditional probabilities of erroneously accepting the new package, he is said to be testing the null hypothesis that $\mu < .019$ and that the new package should therefore be rejected. Observe that in this case rejection of the null hypothesis implies acceptance of the new package. If the manufacturer places a limit α on the conditional probabilities of erroneously rejecting the new package, he is said to be testing the null hypothesis that $\mu > .019$ and that the new package should therefore be accepted. In this case rejection of the null hypothesis implies rejection of the new package.

PROBLEMS

1. Mar-Pruf Finishes, Inc., was a relatively small firm operating in a segment of the industrial-finishes market which was dominated by the American Paint and Lacquer Company. Mar-Pruf's research chemists had recently developed a product to compete with American's type A-1 lacquer and the company was trying to decide whether or not to put this product on the market. Some preliminary market research had shown that while some firms considered the new Mar-Pruf product to be superior to American's A-1, the difference was not great enough to permit Mar-Pruf to charge a price appreciably higher than American's price of $8.75 per gallon. On the other hand, any attempt to seize American's market by charging a lower price was almost certain to produce a price war which American was sure to win because of its superior financial resources. It was clear that if the product was to be marketed at all it would have to be marketed at a price of $8.75 per gallon.

Mar-Pruf figured that if it installed the necessary equipment for economical manufacture of the new product it could realize a net contribution (selling price less variable cost of production, selling, and delivery) amounting to about $.40 per gallon; and after considering the amount of time during which a customer could be expected to continue buying the product, Mar-Pruf's management had decided that the discounted present value of the whole stream of future contributions to be expected from a customer who was initially sold on the new product would be about $2 for each gallon-per-year of initial sales. In other words: Mar-Pruf "expected" to realize contributions with a present value of $20 from a customer who started buying at a rate of 10 gallons per year, $50 from a customer who started buying at a rate of 25 gallons per year, and so forth.

Mar-Pruf's hesitation about entering the market with this new product arose from the fact that the total cost of installing and debugging the necessary equipment for volume manufacture plus the cost of the required introductory sales effort would amount to about $600,000, so that unless a sales volume of $600,000/$2 = 300,000 gallons per year could be attained, the introduction of the product would result in a net loss. Mar-Pruf's market research had shown that there were about 10,000 firms which could be considered potential customers for the product, so that the break-even point could also be considered as achieving annual sales averaging 30 gallons per firm. Because of the considerable risk involved in the decision, Mar-Pruf's marketing-research department had drawn a sample of 100 of these 10,000 firms in such a way that each firm had an equal chance of being drawn and had then dispatched salesmen to give free samples of the product to these firms and to ask whether they would buy if it were actually placed on the market and if so how much per year. The results of this survey are shown in simplified form in the table below.

Annual purchase rate	Number of firms
0	60
60	10
90	20
120	10

a. Thinking of the sample as consisting of 100 x's drawn from a population of 10,000 x's each of which describes the initial purchase rate of one particular firm, show that

$$\bar{x}_o = \frac{1}{n} \Sigma x = 36,$$

$$s = \sqrt{\frac{1}{n-1} \Sigma (x - \bar{x})^2} = 46.3.$$

b. Letting μ denote the mean of the 10,000 x's in the whole population, obtain formulas for the loss of marketing the product when μ is too low, and for the loss of not marketing it when μ is too high.

c. If Mar-Pruf wishes to limit to .05 the conditional probability of marketing if μ has any value which makes marketing unprofitable, what decision rule should be followed and what decision should be reached?

d. Same as (*c*) except that the conditional probabilities to be limited to .05 are those of failing to market the product if any money could be made by marketing it.

e. Same as (*c*) except that the .05 limit is to apply only for μ's such that Mar-Pruf would lose $100,000 or more by marketing the product.

f. In your opinion, what should Mar-Pruf do?

2. In January, 1957, a number of American railroads were offering a special passenger tariff known as the "Family-Fare Plan." There were some variations in the details from road to road, but basically the tariff provided that if a husband bought a round trip at the regular rate, his wife could buy a round trip at half price and his children could buy their round trips at still lower prices. A single ticket was issued to cover the transportation of the entire family.

There was great controversy among passenger officers of the various roads concerning the effect of the Family-Fare Plan on revenue and profit, and the Grand Western Railroad was seriously considering its abandonment. A good deal of revenue was at stake: sales of Family-Plan tickets amounted to about $4 million per year on the Grand Western, and if the same passengers had been carried at full fare this figure would have been nearly doubled. While the general passenger agent of the Grand Western believed that 90 per cent of the passenger-miles sold under the special tariff would not have been sold at all under the normal tariff, the senior executives of the Grand Western knew that the general passenger agent of another railroad serving exactly the same major cities believed that about 90 per cent of the passenger-miles sold under the special tariff *could* have been sold at regular fares.

The president of the Grand Western, H. B. Jones, was particularly puzzled by the fact that both his own GPA and the GPA of the other road based their contradictory statements on the results of surveys carried out by having ticket agents ask purchasers of Family-Fare tickets whether or not they would have made the same trip if the special rates had not been in effect. Jones was inclined to believe that the samples taken by the two men were too small to be reliable, and since there was no one among the road's personnel who was an expert in such matters he called in a representative of a marketing-research agency specializing in consumer surveys and laid the problem before him. The agency representative answered that both the samples were so large that sampling error as such could not possibly account for more than 1 or 2 of the 80 percentage points of difference and went on to assert that the real difficulty was that reliable answers to a question like the one asked of the ticket buyers could not possibly be obtained through hurried interviews conducted by ticket clerks under unfavorable conditions. Even if the Grand Western sample were extended to a 100 per cent count, there would in his opinion be no more real knowledge than there was before any data were collected. He recommended that the railroad employ his agency to draw a small sample of purchasers of Family-Fare tickets in such a way that every purchaser would have an equal chance of being drawn and then to have the persons in the sample interviewed in their homes by really skilled interviewers.

When asked about the cost of such a survey, the agency representative quoted a price of $1000 for general expenses plus $100 per family in the sample, explaining the high cost per head as due in part to the fees of the skilled interviewers and in part to the time and expense which would be incurred in securing interviews with people selected with equal probabilities among all persons who had traveled on Family-Fare tickets during the preceding year. It seemed to Jones that this obviously implied that a sample large enough to give reliable results would be prohibitive in cost, but the agency representative argued that this was not necessarily true and that in any case a good deal of very useful information could be obtained by taking a very small pilot sample and analyzing its results. Since the total amount of Grand Western revenue at stake was really substantial, Jones finally decided to contract with the marketing-research agency to interview a sample of 50 families at a cost of $6000.

Before taking the sample the agency examined the available data on the values of the individual Family-Fare tickets sold during the previous year and found that the large majority of the tickets were for short trips and actually accounted for only a small part of the total dollar sales; 80 per cent of the dollars came from individual sales of $150 and over. The railroad and the agency quickly agreed that the sample should be drawn exclusively from families who had paid over $150 for their tickets, since it seemed very likely that the behavior of these families alone would determine whether the plan was or was not profitable over all.

The pilot sample was promptly drawn and interviewed with the results shown (in simplified form) in the table below. The figure shown in the column headed "effect of cancellation" was calculated by subtracting the amount which the family *actually* spent on its Family-Fare ticket *from* the amount it *would* have spent traveling on the Grand Western if Family Fares had not been available.

Effect of cancellation	Number of families
−$200	10
− 100	12
0	7
+ 100	16
+ 200	5
	50

When these results were in, Jones was still very unsure about what to do next. It was easy to calculate that the effect of cancellation of the plan on families in the sample would have been a reduction in revenue amounting to $600 in total or $12 per family on the average. Jones also knew that about 20,000 Family-Fare tickets had been sold for amounts of $150 and over in the past year, so that *if* the $12 sample figure held for the entire population, about $240,000 would be lost in one year by abandoning the plan. The road's passenger-train schedules and consists were such that the reduction in passenger-miles traveled would have no effect on train costs, so that this loss of revenue was an out-and-out loss of that much net income.

Jones believed that conditions were changing so rapidly that the entire question would have to be reexamined next year and therefore that there was no sense in projecting profit or loss farther than a year in advance, but he was seriously disturbed about basing his decision on a sample of only 50 families.

a. Thinking of the sample as consisting of 50 x's drawn from a population of 20,000 x's each of which describes the change *in dollars* which cancellation of the plan would produce in some particular family's expenditure on Grand Western tickets, show that

$$\bar{x}_o = \frac{1}{n}\Sigma x = -\$12, \qquad s = \sqrt{\frac{1}{n-1}\Sigma(x-\bar{x})^2} = 133.4.$$

b. Letting μ denote the mean of the population of 20,000 x's, find the break-even value μ_b and obtain formulas for the loss of canceling the plan and for the loss of retaining the plan.

c. Compute the statistical significance of the sample against the null hypothesis that $\mu > 0$ and the plan should therefore be canceled.

d. Same as (*b*) for the null hypothesis that $\mu < 0$ and the plan should therefore be retained.

e. If Jones is to make a final decision about the plan on the basis of the evidence currently available, should he retain the plan or cancel it?

CHAPTER 18

Expected Loss with Normal Sampling

18.1 Conditional Expected Terminal Loss

As we have already pointed out in Section 11.1 of Part Two, the fact that the loss of a wrong decision depends on μ makes it very difficult to think systematically about risk when all that one has in front of one is a curve showing the conditional *probability* of wrong decision for each possible μ. We can get a far better picture of the risks we are running

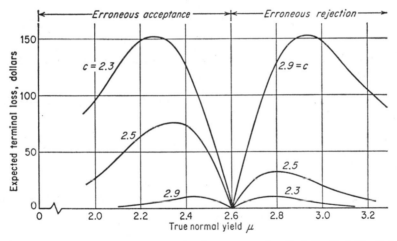

Figure 18.1. Terminal loss under the decision rules (9,2.3), (9,2.5), (9,2.9).

under any given decision rule by plotting a curve of conditional expected *terminal loss* as a function of μ.

The conditional expected terminal loss of a given rule is computed by exactly the same procedure that we described in Section 11.1.1: for any given μ, simply multiply the conditional probability that the rule will lead to a wrong decision by the loss which will result if it does lead to a wrong decision. Thus in the chemical example discussed in the last chapter, the conditional expected terminal loss of the rule (9,2.5) given $\mu = 2.4$ is computed by (1) reading from Figure 17.2 that under this rule

289

the probability of a wrong decision given $\mu = 2.4$ is .37, (2) reading from Figure 17.1 that the loss of a wrong decision given $\mu = 2.4$ is \$200, and (3) multiplying .37 $\times$ \$200 $=$ \$74.

In Figure 18.1 we show curves of conditional expected terminal loss in the chemical example for the three rules with $n = 9$ but various c's whose error characteristics were given in Figure 17.3; and in Figure 18.2 we show similar curves for the rules with various sample sizes whose error characteristics were given in Figure 17.4.   The student will observe that for the reason explained in Section 11.1.2 these curves have the same

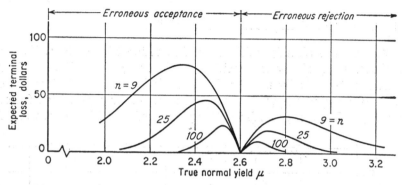

Figure 18.2. Terminal loss under the decision rules (9,2.5), (25,2.54), (100,2.57).

"butterfly" shape as the curves in Figure 11.1.   From these curves the student will also observe that:

    1. By varying c with n fixed, the manufacturer can decrease the conditional expected losses for one kind of wrong decision but only at the cost of increasing the losses for the other kind of wrong decision.

    2. By increasing n and adjusting c accordingly the manufacturer can decrease the conditional expected losses for both kinds of wrong decision, but this of course increases the cost of sampling.

18.2   Unconditional Expected Terminal Loss

Since the risks which the manufacturer may incur under any decision rule depend on the true value of μ, our manufacturer will obviously have been well advised to keep a record of the μ's (true normal yields) of past batches of raw material received from the same supplier who furnished the batch for which a decision rule must now be chosen.   The true μ's of past batches are all known because X content can be accurately measured after the batch has been processed, and we shall suppose that the μ's of the last 100 batches received from this supplier were distributed as shown in Table 18.1.

Table 18.1
Historical Distribution of Normal Yields

Normal yield	Relative frequency
2.0−	0
2.1	.03
2.2	.08
2.3	.18
2.4	.21
2.5	.20
2.6	.17
2.7	.09
2.8	.03
2.9	.01
3.0+	0
	1.00

If now the manufacturer has no reason to believe that there has been any change in the factors causing the variability of the raw material received from this supplier, he can reasonably assign to the *basic random variable* $\tilde{\mu}$ a probability distribution which will very closely resemble the historical frequency distribution of Table 18.1 (cf. the distribution of $\tilde{p}$ in Section 11.2.2); and he can then compute the *unconditional* expected terminal loss of any rule by simply multiplying the probability of each

Table 18.2
Unconditional Expected Terminal Loss
of the Decision Rule (9,2.5)

μ	$P(\mu)$	Terminal Loss Conditional	Terminal Loss Expected
2.0	0	$28	$ 0
2.1	.03	46	1.38
2.2	.08	64	5.12
2.3	.18	75	13.50
2.4	.21	74	15.54
2.5	.20	50	10.00
2.6	.17	0	0
2.7	.09	25	2.25
2.8	.03	32	.96
2.9	.01	28	.28
3.0	0	19	0
	1.00		$49.03

μ by the conditional expected loss given that μ and adding the products. The computations for the rule (9,2.5) are shown in Table 18.2, where we assume that the manufacturer sets his probability distribution exactly equal to the frequency distribution of Table 18.1, without smoothing. The conditional expected losses in Table 18.2 are read from the curve for the rule (9,2.5) in Figure 18.1 or 18.2.   It is left to the student to verify the other unconditional expected terminal losses shown in Table 18.3.

Table 18.3
Unconditional Expected Terminal Loss

Rule	Loss
(9,2.3)	$85.23
(9,2.5)	49.03
(9,2.9)	17.57
(25,2.54)	25.76
(100,2.57)	12.41

The student should observe that with the same sample size $n = 9$, unconditional expected loss is much less with $c = 2.9$ than with $c = 2.5$ or 2.3, and should explain this fact by looking at Figure 18.1 in conjunction with Table 18.1.   He should then explain why terminal loss under the rule (9,2.9) is less than under the rule (25,2.54), even though a sample of 25 is much more "reliable" than a sample of 9.

18.3   Unconditional Expected Total Loss

Although the best critical value c for given sample size n can be found by comparing the unconditional expected *terminal losses* of the c's being considered, we must also take *sampling cost* into consideration if we wish to compare various sample sizes (including $n = 0$, i.e., immediate terminal action without sampling).   To do this we need only add the sampling cost to the unconditional expected terminal loss of each rule, thus obtaining its unconditional expected *total* loss (cf. Section 11.3). Remembering that each measurement in our chemical example costs $2, we leave it to the student to verify the unconditional expected total losses in Table 18.4.

Observe that immediate rejection of the batch—i.e., use of special processing without spending any money on trying to determine its X content—has a substantially lower loss than *any* of the decision rules which we have examined.   Observe also that *if we had computed the expected loss of terminal action without sampling at the outset of our investi-*

Table 18.4
Unconditional Expected Total Loss

Act	Loss
Accept	$163.00
Reject	18.00
(9, 2.3)	103.23
(9, 2.5)	67.03
(9, 2.9)	35.57
(25, 2.54)	75.76
(100, 2.57)	212.41

gation, we would have known at once that *no sample size larger than* $n = 8$ *need be even considered*, since for any n greater than 8 the cost of sampling alone will be at least as great as the *total* loss of optimal immediate terminal action.

Under the distribution of Table 18.2 there is in fact *no* sample size which will pay for itself. *Unless the manufacturer can devise a measuring process which is either cheaper than the present one or more accurate, or both, he should simply give special processing to every batch of raw material received from this supplier.*

18.4   Subjective Distributions of $\tilde{\mu}$

The method which we have just used for evaluating a decision rule or (n, c) pair is easy to apply and leads to "objective" results when the probability distribution of the random variable $\tilde{\mu}$ rests on a solid base of historical relative frequencies. In this respect our chemical-processing example resembled the quality-control example of Chapters 10 and 11. In the store-testing example of Section 17.4, on the contrary, there are obviously *no* historical data bearing on *this particular* package change, and it may seem that the method of analysis described in the first part of this chapter cannot be applied at all.

Before we give up on this problem, however, let us examine the curves of conditional expected terminal loss which are shown in Figure 18.3 for the decision rules (critical values c) whose error characteristics were shown in Figure 17.5. What we see at once is (1) that conditional expected terminal loss with $c = .019 = \mu_b$ is very moderate given *any* true value μ and (2) that use of a c greater than μ_b results in *small reductions* in conditional loss for μ's in a *small interval* to the left of μ_b at the cost of *large increases* in conditional loss for μ's in a *large interval* to the right of μ_b. Use of a c less than μ_b would of course produce the opposite effect, and it is clear at once that

The only conceivable reason for using any c other than μ_b is that *the decision maker attaches much more importance or weight to the way in which the rule will behave if μ is below μ_b than to the way in which it will behave if μ is above μ_b, or vice versa.*

The "weights" in question are of course nothing but *subjective probabilities* which express the manufacturer's "prior" beliefs about the true

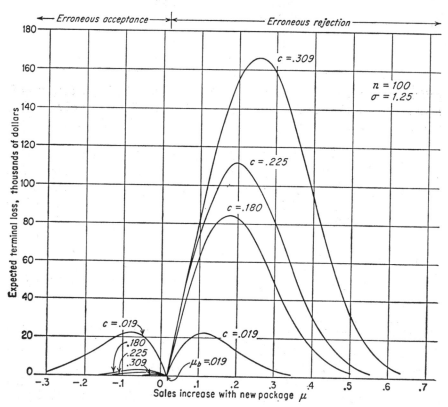

Figure 18.3. Terminal loss under the decision rules (100,.019), (100,.180), (100,.225), (100,.309).

effect μ of the package change; he could give them numerical values by asking himself how he would have bet on μ *before* he knew that the store test had actually resulted in an average increase of $\bar{x}_o = .156$ ounce per store per month in the 100 stores included in the test. Since, however, the basic random variable $\bar{x}$ can have any one of an extremely large number of possible values, it would be very difficult for the manufacturer to assign numerical probabilities to *individual* μ's, and we therefore postpone this step until we introduce a new way of assessing prior distributions in the next chapter.   For the moment we stop with the observation that

> If the losses in any decision problem are *symmetric* in the sense that acceptance when μ is k units below μ_b is neither more nor less serious than rejection when μ is k units above μ_b, then unless the decision maker has *definite reasons* for acting otherwise, he should choose his terminal act in common-sense agreement with the sample evidence: if $\bar{x} > \mu_b$, act as if $\mu > \mu_b$; if $\bar{x} < \mu_b$, act as if $\mu < \mu_b$.

The theory of probability should be reserved for the two situations in which it is really needed:

1. When the sample evidence may be contrary to some really substantial prior evidence and the two must be carefully weighed against each other before choosing a terminal act;

2. When it is necessary to determine the proper size for a sample or to decide whether a sample or another sample should be taken before *any* terminal act is chosen.

PROBLEMS

1. Verify the entry in Table 18.4 for the act "reject without sampling."

2. Verify the entries in Tables 18.3 and 18.4 for the act "use the decision rule (9,2.9)."

3. Graph conditional expected terminal loss for the decision rules (100,25), (100,30), and (100,35) in the Mar-Pruf case (Chapter 17, Problem 1) and decide which of these three rules you would prefer if you had the choice to make.

CHAPTER 19

Normal Prior Distributions; Statistical Significance and Confidence Intervals

We have already seen in Section 13.5 of Part Two that when we are dealing with a basic random variable such as $\tilde{p}$ or $\tilde{\mu}$ which can take on any value whatever (possibly restricted to a certain interval), it is often not only more realistic but actually more convenient to represent the decision maker's beliefs or betting odds by a *continuous* rather than a *discrete* distribution. We shall now see that, provided that the curve representing the distribution is chosen from within a suitable mathematical family of curves, we can use algebraic rather than numerical methods not only to calculate posterior distributions from prior distributions and sample data, as we did in Section 13.5.3, but also to calculate unconditional expected loss and to find optimal sample size.

When the distribution of the sample mean is Normal, the prior distribution must also be Normal if the resulting formulas are to be reasonably simple and easy to use. This does restrict our ability to describe the businessman's prior beliefs mathematically, but we shall see before we are through that in *most* situations this restriction is of absolutely no *practical* importance: the results of an analysis based on a Normal distribution which describes the businessman's beliefs approximately will be virtually identical to the results of a much more laborious analysis based on a distribution which describes his beliefs exactly.

When we first encountered Normal distributions, in Section 15.1, we saw there is actually a whole family of such distributions, any particular member of which is selected by assigning specific numerical values to the *two parameters* of the distribution. At that time we called the two parameters M and S and pointed out that the mean of any Normal distribution was numerically equal to M while the standard deviation of the distribution was numerically equal to S. The choice of the particular Normal distribution which will best describe the decision maker's prior beliefs or betting odds is thus simply a problem of specifying the mean and standard deviation of the distribution, and we shall see in a moment how this can be done. First, however, we must pause to distinguish between the various different Normal distributions and the various different means and standard deviations which may be present in the *same* decision problem.

19.1 Population Distributions, Sampling Distributions, and Distributions of $\tilde{\mu}$

19.1.1 Distribution of the Individual x's in a Population

Any sample consists of a number of individual x's generated by some random process or drawn from some population, and the first of the distributions which the student must be very careful to keep straight is the *frequency distribution of all the individual x's which the process could generate or which are contained in the population*. This distribution may or may not be Normal, as we pointed out at the beginning of Chapter 16; but in *any* case we have been using and shall continue to use the notation

μ: mean of *all* the (actual or potential) individual x's,
σ: standard deviation of *all* the x's.

We also remind the student that the *probability* distribution of a *single* $\tilde{x}$ drawn from a process or population is identical to the *frequency* distribution of *all* the x's which are contained in the population or could be generated by the process.

19.1.2 Distribution of the Sample Mean

The second distribution which the student must distinguish is the *sampling distribution of the mean $\tilde{x}$ of the x's in a sample.* Again this distribution may or may not be Normal, as we pointed out in Section 16.3; but in *any* case we have been using and shall continue to use the notation

$\mathrm{E}(\tilde{x}) = \mu$: expectation of the sample mean,

$\sigma(\tilde{x}) = \dfrac{\sigma}{\sqrt{n}}$: standard deviation of the sample mean.

If the distribution of $\tilde{x}$ can be approximated by a Normal distribution, *then* the approximating Normal distribution has *parameters* which are numerically equal to $\mathrm{E}(\tilde{x})$ and $\sigma(\tilde{x})$.

19.1.3 Distributions of $\tilde{\mu}$

The third and last of the three distributions which the student must carefully distinguish is the *distribution which describes the decision maker's uncertainties about the mean $\tilde{\mu}$ of the sampled process or population*—i.e., which describes the odds at which the decision maker wants to bet concerning the true value of $\tilde{\mu}$. We now introduce the notation

$\mathrm{E}(\tilde{\mu})$: mean of the decision maker's distribution of $\tilde{\mu}$,

$\sigma(\tilde{\mu})$: standard deviation of the decision maker's distribution of $\tilde{\mu}$.

Again these definitions apply *whether or not* the decision maker's betting distribution is Normal—or better, is approximated by a Normal distribution. *If* it is approximated by a Normal distribution, *then* the *parameters* of the approximating distribution will be set numerically equal to $\mathrm{E}(\tilde{\mu})$ and $\sigma(\tilde{\mu})$, and probabilities such as $\mathrm{P}(\tilde{\mu} > \mu)$ can be evaluated by first expressing μ in standard measure as

$$u = \frac{\mu - \mathrm{E}(\tilde{\mu})}{\sigma(\tilde{\mu})}$$

and then using Table III to evaluate

$$\mathrm{P}(\tilde{\mu} > \mu) = \mathrm{P}_{N^\bullet}(\tilde{u} > u).$$

Prior and Posterior Distributions of $\tilde{\mu}$.   One final complication must be introduced into our notation in order to cope with the fact that sample information can convert the decision maker's *prior* distribution of $\tilde{\mu}$ into a different *posterior* distribution of $\tilde{\mu}$. We therefore define

$E_0(\tilde{\mu})$, $\sigma_0(\tilde{\mu})$: mean and standard deviation of the *prior* distribution
of $\tilde{\mu}$,

$E_1(\tilde{\mu})$, $\sigma_1(\tilde{\mu})$: mean and standard deviation of the *posterior* distribution of $\tilde{\mu}$.

The subscripts 0 and 1 refer to the fact that the prior distribution often rests on 0 sample evidence while the posterior distribution rests on the evidence of at least 1 sample. When there is no need to distinguish between prior and posterior distributions because the fact being stated applies to *any* distribution of $\tilde{\mu}$, we shall suppress the subscripts and write simply $\mathrm{E}(\tilde{\mu})$ and $\sigma(\tilde{\mu})$.

19.2   Selection of a Normal Prior Distribution

We are now ready to take up the problem of determining the mean $E_0(\tilde{\mu})$ and the standard deviation $\sigma_0(\tilde{\mu})$ of the decision maker's *prior* distribution of $\tilde{\mu}$. Equivalently, this is the problem of setting the values of the *parameters* of the Normal distribution which will represent or approximate the decision maker's true prior distribution.

19.2.1   *Fitting a Normal Prior Distribution to a Historical Frequency Distribution*

In some situations the evidence on which a prior distribution is to be assessed will consist primarily of a frequency distribution of values actually taken on by the basic random variable in the past. Thus in the chemical-processing example described in Section 17.1, the manufacturer had records of the *true* normal yields μ of 100 batches of raw material previously received from the same supplier and from these records constructed the *historical* frequency distribution of $\tilde{\mu}$ shown in Table 18.1. We can think of the *batches* as generated by a random *superprocess*, not to be confused with the *measuring process* which generates measurements $\tilde{x}$ when applied to any *single* μ generated by the superprocess. What the manufacturer would like to adopt as his prior distribution of the $\tilde{\mu}$ of the *present* batch is the true *long-run* frequency distribution of all the μ's which could potentially be generated by the batch-producing superprocess.

When we plot the actual *historical* frequency distribution of $\tilde{\mu}$ in Figure 19.1 and compare it with a Normal curve, we see that it is close to

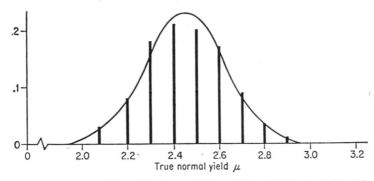

Figure 19.1. Historical distribution of $\tilde{\mu}$ and fitted Normal distribution.

Normal in shape; and therefore it would not be unreasonable for the manufacturer to assume that the *long-run* frequency distribution would be approximately Normal and to adopt as his (prior) *betting distribution* an *estimate* of this long-run frequency distribution. The mean and standard deviation of all the μ's which could potentially be generated by the batch-producing *superprocess* can be estimated in exactly the same way that we estimate the mean and standard deviation of all the *individual* x's which could be generated by an *ordinary* process: we take the mean of the historical μ's as our estimate of the *mean* of all the potential μ's, and we take the quantity s defined in Section 16.7.1 as our estimate of the standard deviation of all the potential μ's. The work is shown in Table 19.1 for the data of Table 18.1: we first calculate $\Sigma\mu = 245.5$ in column 3 and then

$$\bar{\mu} = \frac{1}{n}\Sigma\mu = \frac{1}{100}\,245.5 = 2.455;$$

using this result we calculate $\mu - \bar{\mu}$, $(\mu - \bar{\mu})^2$, $\Sigma(\mu - \bar{\mu})^2 = 2.8875$, and finally

$$s^2 = \frac{1}{n-1} \Sigma(\mu - \bar{\mu})^2 = \frac{1}{99} 2.8875 = .0292,$$

$$s = \sqrt{.0292} = .171.$$

If now the decision maker is satisfied with a Normal approximation to the *long-run frequency* distribution of $\tilde{\mu}$, he will adopt as his *prior bet-*

Table 19.1

(1)	(2)	(3)	(4)	(5)	(6)
μ	Occurrences	(1) × (2)	$\mu - \bar{\mu}$	$(\mu - \bar{\mu})^2$	(2) × (5)
2.1	3	6.3	−.355	.126025	.378075
2.2	8	17.6	−.255	.065025	.520200
2.3	18	41.4	−.155	.024025	.432450
2.4	21	50.4	−.055	.003025	.063525
2.5	20	50.0	+.045	.002025	.040500
2.6	17	44.2	+.145	.021025	.357425
2.7	9	24.3	+.245	.060025	.540225
2.8	3	8.4	+.345	.119025	.357075
2.9	1	2.9	+.445	.198025	.198025
	100	245.5			2.887500

ting distribution of the $\tilde{\mu}$ of the *current* batch the Normal distribution with parameters

$$E_0(\tilde{\mu}) = \bar{\mu} = 2.455, \qquad \sigma_0(\tilde{\mu}) = s = .171,$$

which has been superimposed on the frequency distribution in Figure 19.1.

19.2.2   *Fitting a Normal Prior Distribution to Subjective Judgments*

In many situations a prior distribution must be assessed without the aid of any historical frequencies at all.   Thus in the store-testing example of Section 17.4, the manufacturer had had no experience with package changes that were of the same kind and made under the same conditions as the one he was then considering.   In such situations the *prior* distribution will have to rest entirely on the decision maker's *general* experience and judgment; but one of the reasons an executive is well paid is that he is believed to possess such experience and judgment, and we therefore start by asking the manufacturer to quantify the most essential aspects of his judgment about the new package by answering the two following questions.

1. Name a number $\bar{\mu}$ such that, *before* you knew the outcome of the store test, you would have been as ready to bet that the *true* effect $\tilde{\mu}$

would be *less* than $\hat{\mu}$ as you would have been to bet that $\tilde{\mu}$ would be *greater* than $\hat{\mu}$.

2. Name a number e such that, *before* you knew the outcome of the store test, you would have been as ready to bet that the true effect $\tilde{\mu}$ would be *between* $\hat{\mu} - e$ and $\hat{\mu} + e$ as you would have been to bet that $\tilde{\mu}$ would be *outside* this range.

We shall suppose that the manufacturer answers these questions as follows.

1. I would originally have thought that there was an even chance that the new package would increase sales by at least 1% of my existing volume, i.e., by at least 700,000 ounces per year. Since this amounts to

$$\hat{\mu} = \frac{700,000}{12 \times 400,000} = .146 \text{ ounce per store per month,}$$

I would have been ready to bet at the same odds either that the true $\tilde{\mu}$ would be *above* or that it would be *below* $\hat{\mu}$ as thus determined.

2. Since, however, it is very hard to estimate the effect of an intangible like this package change, I would have thought that there was an even chance that my 700,000-ounce "estimate" was off by at least 1 million ounces per year or by

$$e = \frac{1,000,000}{12 \times 400,000} = .208 \text{ ounce per store per month;}$$

and therefore I would have been willing to bet at the same odds either that the true $\tilde{\mu}$ would be *within* the interval $\hat{\mu} \pm e$ or that it would be *outside* this interval.

Our next step is to find a Normal distribution which agrees with the expressions of the manufacturer's judgment, and we do so by reasoning as follows.

1. Because half of a Normal distribution lies on either side of its mean, we have at once

$$E_0(\tilde{\mu}) = \hat{\mu} = .146,$$

as shown in Figure 19.2.

2. The answer to the second question means that the standard deviation of the distribution must be such that $\frac{1}{2}$ of the area lies between

$$\hat{\mu} - e = .146 - .208 = -.062$$

and

$$\hat{\mu} + e = .146 + .208 = +.354$$

as shown in Figure 19.2. Because a Normal distribution is symmetric, this means that $\frac{1}{4}$ of the area must lie above .354, i.e., that

$$P_0(\tilde{\mu} > .354) = \frac{1}{4}.$$

If we express the value $\mu = .354$ in standard measure as

$$u = \frac{\mu - E_0(\tilde{\mu})}{\sigma_0(\tilde{\mu})} = \frac{.354 - .146}{\sigma_0(\tilde{\mu})},$$

this implies that u must have a value such that $P_{N^\bullet}(\tilde{u} > u) = \frac{1}{4}$.   From Table III we find that this implies $u = .67$, and we can then calculate

$$.67 = \frac{.354 - .146}{\sigma_0(\tilde{\mu})}, \qquad \sigma_0(\tilde{\mu}) = \frac{.354 - .146}{.67} = .310.$$

Finally, we take Figure 19.2 to the manufacturer and ask whether the general shape of this curve is a reasonably accurate description of his prior judgment *in general*, pointing out for example that the curve implies that the manufacturer would have thought it extremely improbable that $\tilde{\mu}$ would increase sales by more than 1.0 ounce per store per

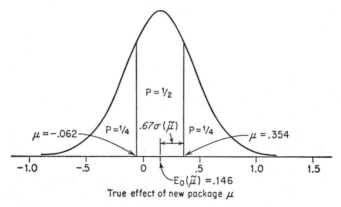

Figure 19.2. Judgmental Normal distribution.

month or reduce them by more than .8 ounce per store per month (corresponding respectively to an increase of 4.8 million and a decrease of 3.8 million ounces in total annual sales). If the manufacturer agrees that such implications of the fitted Normal curve reflect his opinions with reasonable accuracy, then we may go ahead to use this Normal curve as a *practical* expression of his prior distribution of $\tilde{\mu}$.

19.3   The Posterior Distribution When the Prior and Sampling Distributions Are Normal and the Sampling Variance Is Known

We now turn to the problem of determining the *posterior* distribution of the random variable $\tilde{\mu}$ when the *prior* distribution is Normal.   This posterior distribution *could* be derived by an arithmetical procedure identical in principle to the one we used in Chapter 12 to obtain **posterior** distributions of $\tilde{p}$, but the real advantage of assigning a Normal prior distribution to $\tilde{\mu}$ in situations of the kind we are now considering lies in the fact that it makes this heavy numerical work unnecessary.

19.3.1 The Posterior Distribution of $\tilde{\mu}$ When σ Is Known

The following result obtained by use of the calculus will be used continually in the remainder of this course. In any problem where:

1. The prior distribution of $\tilde{\mu}$ is Normal with parameters $E_0(\tilde{\mu})$ and $\sigma_0(\tilde{\mu})$,
2. The sampling distribution of $\tilde{x}$ is Normal with parameters μ and $\sigma(\tilde{x})$,
3. The value of $\sigma(\tilde{x}) = \sigma/\sqrt{n}$ is known,

the posterior distribution of $\tilde{\mu}$ is Normal with parameters given by

$$E_1(\tilde{\mu}) = \frac{E_0(\tilde{\mu})[1/\sigma_0^2(\tilde{\mu})] + \bar{x}[1/\sigma^2(\tilde{x})]}{1/\sigma_0^2(\tilde{\mu}) + 1/\sigma^2(\tilde{x})}$$

$$\frac{1}{\sigma_1^2(\tilde{\mu})} = \frac{1}{\sigma_0^2(\tilde{\mu})} + \frac{1}{\sigma^2(\tilde{x})}$$

Notice that:

1. The posterior mean is a *weighted average* of the prior mean and the sample mean, the weights being the *reciprocals* of the variances of the two distributions.
2. The *reciprocal* of the posterior variance is the *sum* of the reciprocals of the variances of the prior and the sampling distributions.

These convenient results are restricted, it is true, to situations where we "know" the standard deviation σ of the individual members of the process or population from which the sample is drawn. We have, however, already seen (Section 16.7) that situations in which σ can legitimately be treated *as if* it were known even though μ cannot are by no means rare in actual business practice. When costs on profits depend on μ and not on σ, we can treat an estimate s based on a sample of size 25 as if it were the true value of σ even though we cannot treat the $\bar{x}$ of that same sample as if it were the true value of μ.

19.3.2 The Posterior Distribution in the Package-change Example

We have seen in Section 19.2.2 that the manufacturer who must ultimately decide whether or not to adopt a new package might reasonably have assigned to the true effect $\tilde{\mu}$ of the new package a Normal prior betting distribution with parameters

$$E_0(\tilde{\mu}) = .146, \qquad \sigma_0(\tilde{\mu}) = .310.$$

In Section 17.5.3 we saw that the distribution of the result $\tilde{x}$ of the store test was Normal with parameters

$$E(\tilde{x}) = \mu, \qquad \sigma(\tilde{x}) = .125,$$

and in Section 17.4.1 we saw that the test actually resulted in

$$\bar{x} = .157.$$

It follows that *after* the store test the manufacturer must for logical consistency adopt a Normal betting distribution of $\tilde{\mu}$ with parameters

$$E_1(\tilde{\mu}) = \frac{.146 \dfrac{1}{.310^2} + .157 \dfrac{1}{.125^2}}{\dfrac{1}{.310^2} + \dfrac{1}{.125^2}} = .155,$$

$$\frac{1}{\sigma_1^2(\tilde{\mu})} = \frac{1}{.310^2} + \frac{1}{.125^2} = 74.41, \qquad \sigma_1(\tilde{\mu}) = \sqrt{\frac{1}{74.41}} = .116.$$

19.3.3   Quantity of Information

If we compare the manufacturer's prior and posterior distributions in the example we have just discussed, we see that the posterior betting distribution is much closer to agreeing with the sample evidence than with the manufacturer's prior betting distribution. Looking at the three means,

$$E_0(\tilde{\mu}) = .146, \qquad \bar{x} = .157, \qquad E_1(\tilde{\mu}) = .155,$$

we see that $E_1(\tilde{\mu})$ is only .002 unit away from $\bar{x}$ but .009 unit away from $E_0(\tilde{\mu})$. This result is due, of course, to the fact that in computing the weighted average $E_1(\tilde{\mu})$ the weight $1/.125^2 = 64.00$ given to $\bar{x}$ was much greater than the weight $1/.310^2 = 10.41$ given to $E_0(\tilde{\mu})$; and it is natural to think of the disparity between the two weights as a reflection of the fact that the guesstimate $\hat{\mu} = E_0(\tilde{\mu})$ rested on very little solid information about the true effect of the new package whereas the effect $\bar{x}$ actually measured in 100 stores represents a good deal of solid information.

We can acquire a better feeling for the way in which the prior distribution and the sample evidence combine to determine the posterior distribution by thinking of both $E_0(\tilde{\mu})$ and $\bar{x}$ as "estimates" of the true μ and thinking of the weights used in the computation of $E_1(\tilde{\mu})$ as measures of the *"quantity of information"* underlying these estimates. Therefore *provided that $\tilde{x}$ is Normally distributed with known variance* we define

$$I_{\tilde{x}} = \frac{1}{\sigma^2(\tilde{x})} : \text{the quantity of information summarized by } \tilde{x};$$

and *provided that $\tilde{\mu}$ is Normally distributed* we define

$$I_0 = \frac{1}{\sigma_0^2(\tilde{\mu})} : \text{the quantity of information summarized by } E_0(\tilde{\mu});$$

$$I_1 = \frac{1}{\sigma_1^2(\tilde{\mu})} : \text{the quantity of information summarized by } E_1(\tilde{\mu}).$$

Substituting the first two of these new symbols in the formula for $E_1(\tilde{\mu})$ we have

✳
$$E_1(\tilde{\mu}) = \frac{I_0 E_0(\tilde{\mu}) + I_{\bar{x}}\bar{x}}{I_0 + I_{\bar{x}}}$$

and we can say that

> The mean of the posterior distribution of $\tilde{\mu}$ is a weighted average of the prior mean and the sample mean, the weight of each estimate being the quantity of information it summarizes.

Next let us look at the standard deviation of the posterior distribution of our example. It may seem puzzling at first sight that the posterior standard deviation $\sigma_1(\tilde{\mu}) = .116$ came out less than *either* the prior standard deviation $\sigma_0(\tilde{\mu}) = .310$ or the sampling standard deviation $\sigma(\bar{x}) = .125$, but in terms of quantities of information this result is the most obvious common sense. The original formula for $1/\sigma_1^2(\tilde{\mu})$ can be written

✳
$$I_1 = I_0 + I_{\bar{x}}$$

and we can say that

> The total information contained in $E_1(\tilde{\mu})$ is the sum of the information contained in $E_0(\tilde{\mu})$ and the information contained in $\bar{x}$.

Thus I_1 is *necessarily* greater than either I_0 or $I_{\bar{x}}$, and therefore

$$\sigma_1^2(\tilde{\mu}) = \frac{1}{I_1}$$

is *necessarily* less than either $\sigma_0^2(\tilde{\mu})$ or $\sigma^2(\bar{x})$.

19.3.4   *Disregard of Negligible Prior Information*

We saw in Section 19.3.1 that the weight which the manufacturer attached to his prior "estimate" $\hat{\mu} = .146$ ounce per store per month was so slight compared with the weight he attached to the mean $\bar{x} = .155$ obtained from the store test that the prior distribution had only a small effect on the posterior distribution of $\tilde{\mu}$. Suppose now that before the objective evidence was received he had felt still more uncertain about $\tilde{\mu}$; specifically, suppose that he had felt that there was an even chance that his "estimate" $\hat{\mu} = .146$ was wrong by at least .416 ounce per store-month instead of .208, as we assumed in Section 19.2.2. We would then have had $\sigma_0(\tilde{\mu}) = .620$ rather than .310, so that $I_0 = 1/.620^2 = 2.60$; and when this information was combined with $I_{\bar{x}} = 1/.125^2 = 64.00$ to find the posterior distribution we would have obtained

$$\mathrm{E}_1(\tilde{\mu}) = \frac{.146(2.60) + .157(64.00)}{2.60 + 64.00} = .157,$$

$$\sigma_1(\tilde{\mu}) = \sqrt{\frac{1}{2.60 + 64.00}} = .123.$$

The posterior mean $\mathrm{E}_1(\tilde{\mu})$ is the same to three significant figures as the sample mean $\bar{x} = .157$, and the posterior standard deviation $\sigma_1(\tilde{\mu})$ differs by less than 2 per cent from the sampling standard deviation $\sigma(\bar{x})$.

In this case it would have been just as well for all practical purposes if the manufacturer had simply declared that his prior opinions about μ rested on so little real knowledge that he did not want to give them *any weight at all* in comparison with the results of the store test and had simply set

$$\mathrm{E}_1(\tilde{\mu}) = \bar{x} = .157, \qquad \sigma_1(\tilde{\mu}) = \sigma(\bar{x}) = .125.$$

Formally, if the decision maker says that his prior "information" is zero, $I_0 = 0$, the formulas previously given for the parameters of the posterior distribution reduce to

---

$$\begin{aligned} \mathrm{E}_1(\tilde{\mu}) &= \bar{x} \\ \sigma_1(\tilde{\mu}) &= \sigma(\bar{x}) \end{aligned} \qquad \text{when } I_0 = 0$$

In general, it is clear from the way in which the prior and sample informations enter the formulas for the parameters of the posterior distribution that even substantial percentage changes in $\mathrm{E}_0(\tilde{\mu})$ will have little effect on the posterior distribution if I_0 is very small compared to $I_{\bar{x}}$ and that substantial percentage changes in I_0 will have little effect if the largest reasonable value for I_0 is small compared to $I_{\bar{x}}$. In such cases the person responsible for a decision will usually be justified in sparing himself the mental agony required for a careful assessment of $\mathrm{E}_0(\tilde{\mu})$ and $\sigma_0(\tilde{\mu})$ and basing his posterior distribution entirely on the sample according to the reduced formulas given just above. We shall sometimes refer to such a procedure as adopting a Normal prior distribution with infinite standard deviation.†

"*Total Ignorance.*" Let us be careful, however, to treat this process of disregarding evidence which is *negligible in comparison with other evidence* as what it is and not as something nobler than this. Innumerable attempts have been made to treat the use of a prior distribution with $\sigma_0(\tilde{\mu}) = \infty$ as an "objective" expression of "total ignorance."‡ The argument runs that if we know nothing at all about the value of $\tilde{\mu}$, then all values *must* be equally likely; and a Normal prior distribution with $\sigma_0(\tilde{\mu}) = \infty$ in a certain sense assigns equal probability to all values of $\tilde{\mu}$.

The argument is absurd, however, as can easily be seen. If "total ignorance" about $\tilde{\mu}$ implies that all values of $\tilde{\mu}$ are "equally likely," then total ignorance about $\tilde{\mu}^2$ must imply that all values of $\tilde{\mu}^2$ are equally likely. Total ignorance about $\tilde{\mu}$ certainly implies total ignorance about $\tilde{\mu}^2$ and vice versa; but unfortunately it is simply impossible to assign equal probability to all values of $\tilde{\mu}$ and at the same time to assign equal probability to all values of $\tilde{\mu}^2$. Suppose, for example, that we say that it is just as likely that $\tilde{\mu}$ is between 0 and 1 as it is that $\tilde{\mu}$ is between 1 and 2. This necessarily implies that $\tilde{\mu}^2$ is as likely to be between 0 and 1 as it is to be between 1 and 4 and values of $\tilde{\mu}^2$ between 0 and 1 are therefore *three times* as likely on the average as values between 1 and 4.

Thus even if a person responsible for a decision feels himself to be in a state of total ignorance about the value of $\tilde{\mu}$, there is no "objective" way of assigning prior probabilities. He must make up his own mind—he must place his own bets—and when there is no sample evidence available, it is these bets which will be crucial for the decision. *Prior information or prior betting odds can be neglected only when substantial sample evidence is available.*

19.3.5 Nonnormal Prior Distributions

Now that we have seen that the exact *numerical values* of the parameters of the prior distribution are of little importance when $I_{\bar{x}}$ is large, let us look briefly at the effect of the exact *shape* of the prior distribution on the posterior distribution when $I_{\bar{x}}$ is large. In Figure 19.3a we show two contrasting prior distributions which we take as examples:

† Strictly speaking a Normal distribution with infinite standard deviation does not exist because the area under such a curve would be infinite. The values of $E_1(\tilde{\mu})$ and $\sigma_1(\tilde{\mu})$ given by these reduced formulas really describe the *limit* approached by the posterior distribution as $\sigma_0(\tilde{\mu})$ becomes larger and larger.

‡ The assertion that we *should* use such a prior distribution when we are totally ignorant is known as Bayes' postulate. This "postulate" is to be sharply distinguished from Bayes' theorem.

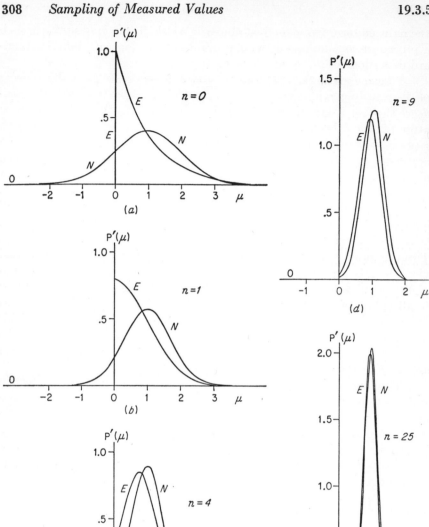

Figure 19.3. Posterior distributions corresponding to Normal and exponential prior distributions.

1. A *Normal* prior distribution with mean $E_0(\tilde{\mu}) = 1$ and standard deviation $\sigma_0(\tilde{\mu}) = 1$.
2. An *exponential* prior distribution with the same mean and standard deviation as the Normal.

The exponential distribution is about as violently nonnormal as any smooth distribution can be: it is J-shaped rather than symmetric, and it actually assigns 0 probability to all negative values of the random variable $\tilde{\mu}$.

In the remaining four graphs of Figure 19.3 we compare the *posterior* distributions corresponding to these two prior distributions after samples of four different sizes have been taken. In all four cases we assume that the observed value of the sample mean $\bar{x} = 1$ and that $\sigma^2(\tilde{x}) = 1/n$; it is only the sample size n that differs from case to case. In Figure 19.3b we see that if the sample consists of just one observation, there is a very substantial difference between the two posterior distributions; and in Figure 19.3c we see that the difference would still be quite large if $n = 4$. By the time $n = 9$, however, the difference is becoming much smaller (Figure 19.3d), and it is very small for $n = 25$ (Figure 19.3e). With a sample of 50 or more the difference would be completely negligible for all practical purposes.

Although Figure 19.3 is only a study of a special case, the general nature of the conclusions derived from it can be proved to hold for *any* prior distribution which is reasonably smooth in the vicinity of the observed sample mean $\bar{x}$:

> If the variance of the decision maker's true prior distribution is large compared with the sampling variance of $\tilde{x}$, he can simplify his calculations with no material loss of accuracy by substituting the mean and variance of his true prior distribution into the formulas which apply to a Normal prior distribution.

19.4 Statistical Significance and Suspension of Judgment

19.4.1 Null Hypotheses and Two-tail Significance

When we originally described the problems facing the manufacturer who must ultimately decide whether or not to adopt a new package (Section 17.4), we assumed that he wanted to reach a terminal decision *immediately*, i.e., on the basis of the 100 store-months of testing which had already been conducted. Actually, however, there was no reason a terminal decision had to be reached at this point; the situation was such that the manufacturer could if he liked "suspend judgment" for the time being and postpone a terminal decision until some *further* store testing had supplied additional information to use in reaching this decision.

If the manufacturer wishes to raise the question of the desirability of additional testing, then his problem is exactly the same in principle as the problem of deciding whether the president of the book club of Section 10.5 should or should not send out another sample mailing before definitely choosing either to publish or not to publish. Following the reasoning described in Section 13.2, statisticians traditionally recommend that in such a situation the question of suspension of judgment should be answered by proceeding as follows.

1. Set up the dummy *null hypothesis* that $\mu = \mu_b$ exactly, i.e., that the new package would increase sales by just enough to break even.

2. Compute the expected value of $\bar{x}$ given that $\mu = \mu_b$. In problems of the type with which we are now dealing, where $E(\bar{x}) = \mu$, this expected value is simply μ_b itself.

3. Compute the "absolute distance" $d_o = |\bar{x}_o - \mu_b|$ between this conditional expected value of $\bar{x}$ and the value $\bar{x}_o$ which was actually observed.

4. Compute the *two-tail statistical significance* of the observed $\bar{x}_o$, i.e., the *conditional* probability, *given* $\mu = \mu_b$, that pure chance would yield an $\bar{x}$ differing from μ_b by *at least* the amount d_o.

5. If this conditional probability is *greater* than some predetermined number α, suspend judgment and collect more information before reaching any terminal decision.

Applying this procedure to the package-change example, where

$$\mu_b = .019, \qquad \bar{x}_o = .157, \qquad \sigma(\bar{x}) = .125,$$

we first compute

$$d_o = |.157 - .019| = .138, \qquad u_o = \frac{.138}{.125} = 1.10,$$

and then obtain for the statistical significance

$$P(\bar{x} \leq \mu_b - d_o | \mu = \mu_b) + P(\bar{x} \geq \mu_b + d_o | \mu = \mu_b)$$
$$= P_{N*}(\bar{u} < -1.10) + P_{N*}(\bar{u} > +1.10) = 2 \times .1357 = .2714.$$

Although the choice of the predetermined number α is in principle a matter of judgment, statisticians traditionally use .05 or .01, virtually never any number higher than .10, so that it is almost certain that a statistician using traditional procedures would say that the evidence of the store test already conducted was insufficient for a terminal decision. Judgment should be suspended until more evidence has been collected.

19.4.2 *Statistical Significance and Posterior Probability*

In itself this traditional procedure for deciding whether or not judgment should be suspended is merely a rule of thumb with no apparent rationale; but we saw in Section 13.6 that a rationale can be found by looking at the relation between "statistical significance" and the (posterior) *probability that a terminal decision made now will turn out to be wrong.* For, as we pointed out in Section 13.6, a decision maker who finds that the posterior probability that $\tilde{\mu} < \mu_b$ is *extremely small* may be well advised in common sense to neglect this very small risk and to go ahead and choose the terminal act which will be better if in fact $\mu > \mu_b$; and vice versa if the probability that $\tilde{\mu} > \mu_b$ is extremely small.

In Figure 19.4 we show two distributions which are conceptually entirely different: the upper one is the *conditional distribution of the*

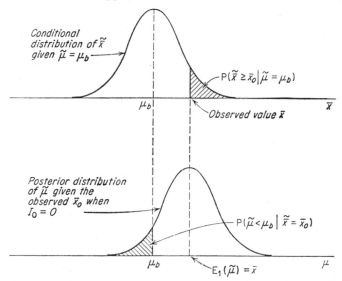

Figure 19.4. Statistical significance and posterior probability.

statistic $\tilde{x}$ *given* $\tilde{\mu} = \mu_b$; the lower one is the *posterior distribution of the basic random variable* $\tilde{\mu}$ *given the observed statistic* $\bar{x}_o$ *and a prior distribution with* $I_0 = 0$—i.e., a prior distribution which assigns "equal probabilities to all values of $\tilde{\mu}$." We saw in Section 19.3.4 that when $I_0 = 0$, the mean $E_1(\tilde{\mu})$ of the posterior distribution of $\tilde{\mu}$ is *numerically equal* to the observed $\bar{x}_o$ and the standard deviation of the posterior distribution of $\tilde{\mu}$ is *numerically equal* to the standard deviation $\sigma(\tilde{x})$ of the conditional distribution of $\tilde{x}$; and from this it follows that the areas of the two shaded tails in the figure are *numerically equal.*

Now the shaded tail in the distribution of $\tilde{\mu}$ represents the *posterior probability* that $\tilde{\mu} < \mu_b$; the shaded tail in the distribution of $\tilde{x}$ represents the conditional probability $P(\tilde{x} \geq \bar{x}_o|\mu = \mu_b)$ which is the *one-tail* significance or *half* the *two-tail* significance of the observed $\bar{x}_o$. We see at once that

Provided that prior information on the basic random variable is negligible in comparison with the information obtained from a Normally distributed sample mean, the posterior probability that $\tilde{\mu}$ is *not* on the same side of μ_b as the observed $\bar{x}_o$ is *numerically equal* to the *one-tail* statistical significance or *half* the *two-tail* significance of the observed $\bar{x}_o$.

In the package-change example, this means that *if* the manufacturer wishes to give no weight at all to his prior opinions concerning the effect of the package change, *then* the posterior probability that $\tilde{\mu}$ is really *below* μ_b would be

$$P(\tilde{\mu} < \mu_b) = P(\tilde{x} \geq \bar{x}_o | \mu = \mu_b) = P(\tilde{x} \geq .157 | \mu = .019)$$
$$= P_{N*}(\tilde{u} > 1.10) = .1357.$$

If, on the other hand, the manufacturer does *not* want to neglect his prior opinions, then as we saw in Section 19.3.2 above, his posterior distribution of $\tilde{\mu}$ is Normal with parameters

$$E_1(\tilde{\mu}) = .155, \qquad \sigma_1(\tilde{\mu}) = .116,$$

and the posterior probability that $\tilde{\mu} < \mu_b$ is

$$P(\tilde{\mu} < \mu_b) = P_{N*}\left(\tilde{u} < \frac{.019 - .155}{.116}\right) = .1210;$$

his prior opinion that $\tilde{\mu}$ had an even chance of being above .146 reinforces the sample evidence $\bar{x}_o = .157$ tending to show that $\tilde{\mu}$ is not below .019.

Now neither .1357 nor .1210 is small enough to make it *obvious* that the manufacturer should go ahead and act as if he were sure that $\tilde{\mu} > \mu_b$; the desirability of collecting more evidence should certainly be *investigated*. We should not, however, jump to the conclusion that further data should definitely be purchased before a terminal decision is reached. We showed in Figure 13.1 and Section 13.3 that the president of the book club should go ahead and publish even though there was probability .134 that this was the wrong terminal act: collection of more evidence was *uneconomical because it could not reduce expected terminal loss by enough to pay for the cost of the sample.* We shall therefore return to the problem of a new store test in the next chapter, after we have learned how to compute expected terminal loss under a Normal distribution.

19.5   Confidence Intervals

If a statistician wishes merely to report what he has learned about some unknown quantity, without trying to give an answer to a specific problem of choice between well-defined terminal acts, then as we saw in Section 13.7.2 he will traditionally make a statement of the form "the unknown μ lies between the number μ_1 and the number μ_2" and he will compute the numbers μ_1 and μ_2 in such a way that in the long run at least a fraction $(1 - \gamma)$ of all statements would be correct. The statement $\mu_1 < \mu < \mu_2$ is called a "confidence interval"; the fraction $(1 - \gamma)$ is called the "confidence coefficient."

19.5.1 Construction of Confidence Intervals

A confidence interval based on a Normally distributed $\bar{x}$ is *constructed* in exactly the same way as an interval based on a binomially distributed $\tilde{r}$. Letting $\bar{x}_o$ denote the value of $\bar{x}$ which has actually been observed, we first look for a number μ_1 such that $P(\bar{x} \geq \bar{x}_o | \mu = \mu_1) = \frac{1}{2}\gamma$. To find it we define

$$u_o = \frac{\bar{x}_o - \mu_1}{\sigma(\bar{x})},$$

then use Table III to find what value u_o must have to make

$$P_{N\cdot}(\tilde{u} > u_o) = \frac{1}{2}\gamma,$$

and then compute

$$\mu_1 = \bar{x}_o - u_o\sigma(\bar{x}).$$

Similarly μ_2 is a number such that $P(\bar{x} \leq \bar{x}_o | \mu = \mu_2) = \frac{1}{2}\gamma$; but the student can readily convince himself that because of the symmetry of the Normal distribution we have no new probabilities to look up: we have at once

$$\mu_2 = \bar{x}_o + u_o\sigma(\bar{x}).$$

19.5.2 Proof of the Essential Property of Confidence Intervals

To see why the method works, suppose that samples are taken repeatedly from the same process or population with true mean μ, and that on every occasion a 95 per cent confidence interval is constructed. By use of Table III we find that to make $P_{N\cdot}(\tilde{u} > u_o) = \frac{1}{2}\gamma = .025$ the quantity u_o must have the value 1.96, so that as each successive $\bar{x}$ is drawn a μ_1 will be computed from the formula

$$\mu_1 = \bar{x} - 1.96\sigma(\bar{x}).$$

From this formula it appears at once that on those occasions where $\bar{x}$ happens to be greater than $\mu + 1.96\sigma(\bar{x})$, μ_1 will be greater than μ and the statement $\mu > \mu_1$ will be wrong. The probability that $\bar{x}$ will actually *be* greater than $\mu + 1.96\sigma(\bar{x})$ is

$$P[\bar{x} > \mu + 1.96\sigma(\bar{x}) | \mu] = P_{N\cdot}(\tilde{u} > 1.96) = \frac{1}{2}\gamma,$$

and therefore in the long run a fraction $\frac{1}{2}\gamma$ of all intervals will err because the *lower* end μ_1 of the confidence interval is actually *above* the true μ. The student can easily reverse this argument to show that the *upper* end μ_2 will be *below* the true μ on a fraction $\frac{1}{2}\gamma$ of all draws, and from this it follows that an error of *one kind or the other* will be made on a fraction γ of all draws. Observe that when a confidence interval is based on a *continuously* distributed $\tilde{x}$, the statistician can be sure that *exactly* γ of all interval statements will be wrong, whereas when intervals are based on a discretely distributed $\tilde{r}$, all that he can be sure of is that *not more than* γ of all statements will be wrong.

19.5.3   *Confidence Intervals and Posterior Probability*

Suppose now that a sample has been taken, that $\bar{x}_o$ has been observed, and that a $(1 - \gamma)$ confidence interval $\mu_1 < \mu < \mu_2$ has been computed by selecting μ_1 and μ_2 such that

$$P(\tilde{\bar{x}} \geq \bar{x}_o | \mu_1) = P(\tilde{\bar{x}} \leq \bar{x}_o | \mu_2) = \tfrac{1}{2}\gamma.$$

If we replace μ_b in Figure 19.4 by μ_1, the line of reasoning in Section 19.4.2 will show us immediately that *if* the decision maker sets $I_0 = 0$, *then* the posterior probability that $\tilde{\mu} < \mu_1$ is exactly $\frac{1}{2}\gamma$; and the student can readily convince himself that the probability that $\tilde{\mu} > \mu_2$ is also $\frac{1}{2}\gamma$. In other words,

> *If* the decision maker wishes to attach no weight whatever to any evidence outside the sample and therefore adopts a *prior* distribution which assigns "equal probabilities to all possible values of $\tilde{\mu}$," *then* the *posterior* probability that $\tilde{\mu}$ lies within a $(1 - \gamma)$ confidence interval is $(1 - \gamma)$.

If on the contrary the decision maker *does* attach some weight to his "prior" information, the posterior probability will *not* be equal to the confidence coefficient.

19.5.4   *Example*

If we wish to construct a 95 per cent confidence interval for the true effect μ of the new package in the example described in Section 17.4, we first compute $\frac{1}{2}\gamma = \frac{1}{2}(.05) = .025$ and then find from Table III that we must set $u_o = 1.96$ to make $P_{N*}(\tilde{u} > u_o) = .025$. Then since by Sections 17.4.1 and 17.5.3

$$\bar{x}_o = .157, \qquad \sigma(\tilde{\bar{x}}) = .125,$$

we can compute

$$\mu_1 = .157 - 1.96 \times .125 = -.088,$$
$$\mu_2 = .157 + 1.96 \times .125 = +.402,$$

and we can state "with 95 per cent confidence" that μ lies between $-.088$ and $+.402$.

To find the *probability* which management should actually assign to the truth of this statement, we make use of the results of Section 19.3.2: the posterior distribution of $\tilde{\mu}$ is Normal with

$$E_1(\tilde{\mu}) = .155, \qquad \sigma_1(\tilde{\mu}) = .116.$$

The probabilities that $\tilde{\mu}$ lies below $-.088$ or above $+.402$ are respectively

$$P(\tilde{\mu} < -.088) = P_{N\bullet}\left(\tilde{\mu} < \frac{-.088 - .155}{.116}\right) = .018,$$

$$P(\tilde{\mu} > +.402) = P_{N\bullet}\left(\tilde{\mu} > \frac{.402 - .155}{.116}\right) = .017,$$

so that the probability that $\tilde{\mu}$ lies *within* the interval from .088 to .402 is actually $1 - .018 - .017 = .965$ rather than .95. The manufacturer's prior opinion that $\tilde{\mu}$ was in the neighborhood of .146 *reinforces* the sample evidence that $\tilde{\mu}$ is in the neighborhood of .157.

PROBLEMS

1. In the Mar-Pruf case (Chapter 17, Problem 1), assume that *before* the sample of 100 interviews was taken management felt (1) that the chances were even that mean sales per customer would be above 50 gallons per year and (2) that the chances were even that mean sales per customer would be between 30 and 70 gallons per year; and assume that management was willing to fill in the details of its prior betting distribution by accepting a Normal distribution which agreed with these two sets of odds. What distribution should management assign to sales after learning the outcome of the 100 interviews?

2. In the Grand Western case (Chapter 17, Problem 2), assume that Jones says that the information he had before the sample of 50 interviews was taken was so vague and self-contradictory that he does not want to give it any weight at all relative to the sample evidence. What distribution should he assign to the true effect of *cancellation* of the Family-Fare Plan after learning the results of the 50 interviews?

3. In the Grand Western case, compute

a. The two-tail significance of the sample outcome.

b. The posterior probability that cancellation of the Family-Fare Plan will increase the railroad's revenue.

c. A 90 per cent confidence interval for the true effect of canceling the plan.

d. The posterior probability that the true effect lies within the confidence interval.

4. In the Mar-Pruf case, compute

a. The two-tail statistical significance of the sample outcome.

b. The posterior probability that average sales will be less than 30 gallons per customer.

c. A 95 per cent confidence interval for average sales per customer.

d. The posterior probability that true sales lie within the confidence interval.

CHAPTER 20

The Economics of Two-action Problems with Linear Profits or Costs and Normal Distributions

20.1 Linear Conditional Profits and Costs

In this chapter we shall see that when the *prior distribution* of $\tilde{\mu}$ and the *sampling distribution* of $\tilde{x}$ are both *Normal with known variance,* very simple formulas can be derived for the complete analysis of any decision problem involving choice between *two acts* whose costs or profits can be expressed by formulas of the type

✳ Cost or profit of act 1 $= K_1 + k_1\mu,$ FIXED COST   VARIABLE COST
✳ Cost or profit of act 2 $= K_2 + k_2\mu.$

Such "linear" two-action problems are extremely common in practical business applications; the student should stop and go back to verify that:

1. In the quality-control example of Section 10.1,
    Cost of acceptance $= \$0 + \$200\ p,$
    Cost of rejection $= \$8 + \$0\ p.$
2. In the book-publishing example of Section 10.5,
    Profit of publishing $= -\$3000 + \$75,000\ p,$
    Profit of not publishing $= \$0 + \$0\ p.$
3. In the new-package problem of Section 17.4,
    Additional profit with new package $= -\$20,000$
    $+ \$1,056,000\ \mu,$
    Additional profit with old package $= \$0 + \$0\ \mu.$

20.2 Expected Profit or Cost

20.2.1 Computation of Expected Profit or Cost

In Section 6.3.1 of Part One of this course we came to a conclusion which can be stated as follows for any problem in which the basic random variable happens to be called $\tilde{\mu}$:

Whenever the conditional profits or costs for *all possible values* of the basic random variable are given by a *linear* formula of the type $K + k\mu$, where K and k are constants, the expected profit or cost is given by the formula

$$K + k\mathrm{E}(\tilde{\mu}).$$

We write $\mathrm{E}(\tilde{\mu})$ without a subscript because the statement applies equally to prior and posterior distributions.

We thus see that in every one of the three examples listed in the previous section we could have found the optimal act under either a prior or the posterior distribution of $\tilde{p}$ or $\tilde{\mu}$ by simply computing $\mathrm{E}(\tilde{p})$ or $\mathrm{E}(\tilde{\mu})$, using this result to compute the expected profits or costs of the two possible acts, and selecting the act with the higher expected profit or the lower expected cost.

20.2.2   Expected Profit in the Package-change Example

Let us complete our analysis of the package-change problem as an example. In Section 19.3.2 we saw that after the store test had been conducted the manufacturer's posterior distribution of $\tilde{\mu}$ was Normal with parameters

$$\mathrm{E}_1(\tilde{\mu}) = .155, \qquad \sigma_1(\tilde{\mu}) = .116.$$

If now the manufacturer wishes to select the optimal terminal act, he has only to compute the expected *additional* profit of adopting the *new* package from the formula

$$-\$20,000 + \$1,056,000\ \mathrm{E}_1(\tilde{\mu}) = \$144,000.$$

Since this is greater than $0 *additional* profit which will be made by retaining the old package, he should adopt the new package *if* he selects *either* package now.

20.3   Expected Opportunity Loss of Optimal Terminal Action

20.3.1   Conditional Opportunity Loss; Break-even Value and Terminal Loss Constant

In Figure 20.1*a* we show a graph of the conditional *profits* in a completely general two-action problem in which the conditional profits of both acts are linear, and in Figure 20.1*b* we show the corresponding conditional *opportunity losses*. If $\mu < \mu_b$, act 1 has the higher profit and therefore 0 opportunity loss, while the opportunity loss of act 2 is the difference between the heights of the two profit lines; if $\mu > \mu_b$, the same statement holds with 1 and 2 interchanged. By a little geometric reason-

ing the student can easily convince himself that, <u>at any point μ on *either*
side of μ_b, the difference between the heights of the two profit lines can be
found by multiplying the absolute *"distance"* $|\mu - \mu_b|$ by the absolute
difference $|k_2 - k_1|$ between the *slopes* of the two profit lines.</u>

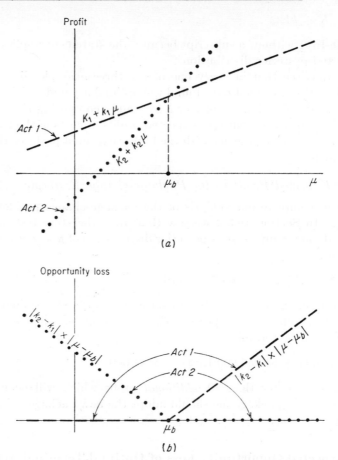

Figure 20.1. **Linear conditional profits and the corresponding conditional
losses.**

The important thing to observe is that <u>the opportunity loss of either
act given any μ depends only on the *break-even value*</u>

$$\text{✻} \quad \mu_b = \frac{K_1 - K_2}{k_2 - k_1} = \frac{K_2 - K_1}{k_1 - k_2}$$

and on what we shall call the *terminal loss constant*

$$\text{✻} \quad k_t = |k_2 - k_1| = |k_1 - k_2|.$$

The student should convince himself that exactly the same thing will be true if we let the lines in Figure 20.1a represent conditional *costs* rather than conditional profits, although in this case the labels "act 1" and "act 2" and the dotted and dashed lines would be interchanged in Figure 20.1b.

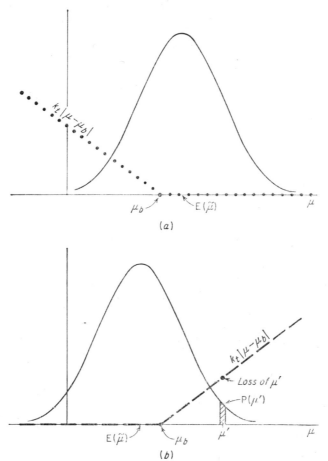

Figure 20.2. Distributions of $\tilde{\mu}$ with conditional terminal loss of the better act under each distribution.

20.3.2   *Computation of the Expected Opportunity Loss*

Having found that for given μ the *conditional* loss of either act in a two-action problem with linear profits or costs depends only on the two constants μ_b and k_t, we are ready to attack the problem of computing *expected* loss when an act is chosen under a Normal distribution of $\tilde{\mu}$. In Figure 20.2a we show such a distribution with mean *greater* than μ_b, in Figure 20.2*b* a distribution with mean *less* than μ_b.   In both figures we also show the conditional losses of *one* of the two acts, and by reviewing Section 20.2.1 the student should convince himself that whether the lines in Figure 20.1*a* represent profits or costs, *the losses graphed in Figure 20.2 are the losses of the* better *act under the corresponding distribution.*

If the probability distributions in Figure 20.2 were *discrete*, we could compute expected opportunity loss in either of the two cases by taking each possible value of μ, multiplying the conditional loss of the act *given* that value by the probability that $\tilde{\mu}$ *has* that value, and adding the products.   Under a *continuous* distribution of $\tilde{\mu}$ we could get an approximate result by cutting the horizontal axis into a large number of narrow brackets (like the one around the point μ' in Figure 20.2*b*), calculating the area under the curve within each bracket (like the shaded area in the figure), multiplying each such area or probability into the conditional loss of the act given the value μ at the mid-point of the bracket, and adding these products.   By making the brackets narrower and narrower, we could come closer and closer to the exact expected loss.

Fortunately we do not actually have to go through this numerical procedure when the distribution of $\tilde{\mu}$ is *Normal*.   If we first compute the two constants k_t and μ_b defined in the previous section and then compute the standardized value

$$ * \qquad D = \frac{|\mu_b - \mathrm{E}(\tilde{\mu})|}{\sigma(\tilde{\mu})} $$

it can be shown by calculus that the expected opportunity loss of the *better* act under uncertainty, or *expected loss of (optimal) terminal action*, is given by the formula

$* \quad$ ELTA $= k_t\sigma(\tilde{\mu})L_{N*}(D)$ *Expected loss of (optimal) terminal action*

where L_{N*} is a function whose value for any D can be found in Table IV at the end of this book.   The same formula applies whether $\mathrm{E}(\tilde{\mu})$ is to the right or to the left of μ_b; what counts is simply the *absolute* distance between $\mathrm{E}(\tilde{\mu})$ and μ_b as expressed in standard measure by the number D.

20.3.3   *Expected Loss of Optimal Terminal Action*

In Section 4.4 of Part One of this course we gave the name "cost of uncertainty" to the expected opportunity loss of the *optimal* terminal act because we were dealing with situations in which nothing could be done about this loss, and it therefore measured the irreducible effect of having to act under uncertainty. Now, however, we are dealing with situations in which something—namely, sampling—*can* be done to reduce uncertainty and with it opportunity loss, and therefore we can no longer call the expected loss of the optimal *terminal* act *the* cost of uncertainty. It is for this reason that we have now introduced the new term

Expected loss of (optimal) terminal action or ELTA: the expected loss of the *optimal terminal* act, i.e., the lowest expected terminal loss which can be achieved *without* acquiring additional information.

Since no amount of additional information can reduce expected opportunity loss below 0, calculation of the ELTA or expected loss of action *without* additional information is a useful first step whenever it is *possible* to obtain more information at a cost. If the ELTA is very small, there is very little that can conceivably be gained by sampling and it may be obvious that the thing to do is to stop worrying and decide now in favor of the terminal act which looks best. If on the contrary the expected loss of this best terminal act is large, the decision maker should clearly make a careful analysis to determine whether he will be better off to buy additional sample information before choosing either terminal act.

20.3.4   ELTA in the Package-change Example

We have already pointed out in Section 19.4.1 that the manufacturer who must *ultimately* decide whether or not to adopt a new package and has had a store test made in order to learn something about the true effect μ of the new package is in no sense obliged to make his final decision *immediately*. He can if he so wishes have some additional store testing done before he definitely chooses one package or the other; and to get a preliminary indication of the desirability of buying such additional information, he can look at the ELTA or loss which he can "expect" to incur if he does *not* buy additional information.

We have already seen in Section 19.3.2 that the manufacturer's *current* distribution of $\tilde{\mu}$ is Normal with parameters

$$E(\tilde{\mu}) = .155, \qquad \sigma(\tilde{\mu}) = .116;$$

we here use neither 0 nor 1 as a subscript because while this distribution is posterior to the store test which has already been conducted it is prior to a new store test which might be conducted. From the formulas given in Section 20.1 for the conditional additional profits of the acts "adopt new package" and "retain old package" we compute

$$\mu_b = \frac{-\$20,000 - \$0}{\$0 - \$1,056,000} = \frac{\$0 - (-\$20,000)}{\$1,056,000 - \$0} = .019,$$
$$k_t = |\$1,056,000 - \$0| = |\$0 - \$1,056,000| = \$1,056,000.$$

We next compute the standardized value

$$D = \frac{|.019 - .155|}{.116} = 1.17,$$

use Table IV to look up

$$L_{N*}(1.17) = .05964,$$

and substitute in the formula in Section 20.3.2 to obtain

$$\text{ELTA} = \$1,056,000 \times .116 \times .05964 \doteq \$7300.$$

Although this expected loss of immediate terminal action is by no means really frightening, it still seems *possible* that further sampling could reduce it by a few thousand dollars, and the manufacturer should certainly take the trouble to find out whether such a reduction is in fact possible.

20.4   Expected Value of the Information to Be Obtained from a Sample

20.4.1   *Determination of Optimal c for Given n*

In Section 11.2.3 we saw that if a decision maker has *arbitrarily fixed the size n* of the sample which he is about to take (or has already taken) but wishes to find the *economically optimal critical value c* to use with that n, he can accomplish his objective by computing *unconditional expected terminal loss* for every possible c and then selecting the c for which this loss is least.   We have also seen, however, in Section 12.4 and again in Section 20.2, that after the sample outcome is known the optimal terminal act can be found by using Bayes' theorem to compute the posterior distribution of the basic random variable $\tilde{p}$ or $\tilde{\mu}$, using this distribution to compute the expected profit, cost, or loss of every possible terminal act, and then selecting the act whose expected *profit* is greatest or whose expected *cost or loss* is least.   This gives us an alternative way of finding the optimal c for the (n,c) decision rule: if we consider *all possible sample outcomes* $\bar{x}$, decide for each one which terminal act is optimal, divide the outcomes into one group for which act 1 is optimal and another for which act 2 is optimal, and let c^* denote the borderline value of $\bar{x}$ for which the two acts are *equally* desirable, we can express our results in the form of a rule:

Sample n and then choose a terminal act according to whether $\bar{x}$ is above or below c^*;

and it is obvious that this c^* is the optimal c for the given n.

Now let us apply this latter method to find a formula for the optimal c in a two-action problem in which (1) the conditional profits or costs of both acts are linear and (2) the prior and sampling distributions are Normal with known variance. From what we said in Section 20.2 about the expected profits or costs of the two acts it follows at once that <u>after a sample has been taken the two acts will be *equally* desirable if $E_1(\tilde{\mu}) = \mu_b$; and therefore we can find c^* by substituting c^* for $\bar{x}$ in the formula given in Section 19.3.1 for $E_1(\tilde{\mu})$</u>, setting this formula equal to μ_b,

$$\frac{E_0(\tilde{\mu})[1/\sigma_0^2(\tilde{\mu})] + c^*[1/\sigma^2(\tilde{x})]}{1/\sigma_0^2(\tilde{\mu}) + 1/\sigma^2(\tilde{x})} = \mu_b,$$

and then solving to obtain

$$c^* = \frac{\mu_b[1/\sigma_0^2(\tilde{\mu}) + 1/\sigma^2(\tilde{x})] - E_0(\tilde{\mu})[1/\sigma_0^2(\tilde{\mu})]}{1/\sigma_0^2(\tilde{x})}.$$

20.4.2 Optimal c for a New Store Test

Regarding the package-change example of Section 17.4, we saw in Section 19.3.2 that after the original store test had been conducted the manufacturer might reasonably have been willing to bet in accordance with a Normal distribution of $\tilde{\mu}$ having mean .155 and standard deviation .116. In Section 20.3.4 we showed that the expected loss of the optimal terminal act or ELTA under this distribution was $7300 and that the manufacturer *might* do well to acquire *additional* sample information before proceeding to choose a terminal act.

Suppose therefore that the manufacturer wishes to consider taking a new sample of size $n = 50$, half as large as the one he has already taken. As regards this *new* sample, the manufacturer's current distribution of $\tilde{\mu}$ is a *prior* distribution whose parameters may be written

$$E_0(\tilde{\mu}) = .155, \qquad \sigma_0(\tilde{\mu}) = .116, \qquad \sigma_0^2(\tilde{\mu}) = .01346.$$

In Section 17.5.3 we saw that $\sigma = 1.25$, so that for a new sample with $n = 50$

$$\sigma^2(\tilde{x}) = \frac{\sigma^2}{n} = \frac{1.25^2}{50} = .03125.$$

The optimal critical value c^* to use in connection with a decision rule based on this new sample will therefore be

$$c^* = \frac{.019\left(\dfrac{1}{.01346} + \dfrac{1}{.03125}\right) - .155\,\dfrac{1}{.01346}}{\dfrac{1}{.03125}} = -.297.$$

If a new store test of size $n = 50$ is conducted, the manufacturer should not reject the new package unless the $\bar{x}$ of the new test is below $-.297$.

Because his current betting distribution with mean $E(\tilde{\mu}) = .155$ *is so favorable to the new package, the result of the new store test should not reverse his opinion unless it is extremely unfavorable to the new package.*

20.4.3   Unconditional Expected Terminal Loss of (n,c*)

The method by which we computed the unconditional expected terminal loss of *any* (n,c) pair in Chapters 11 and 18 was as follows.

1. Construct an error characteristic which shows for every possible μ the probability that the rule will lead to the wrong terminal act.

2. Construct a curve of *conditional* expected terminal loss which shows for every possible μ the product of the probability that the rule will lead to the wrong act times the loss which will be incurred if it does.

3. Calculate *unconditional* expected terminal loss by multiplying the conditional terminal loss given each possible μ by the prior probability that $\tilde{\mu}$ will actually have that value and then adding these products.

Suppose now that in the package-change example we wish to compute the unconditional expected terminal loss of a new store test with arbitrary $n = 50$ but with the $c^* = -.297$ which we have just shown to be optimal for that n. The first two steps in the procedure outlined above could easily be carried out to obtain a curve of conditional expected terminal loss like those already shown for this example in Figure 18.3, but we would come to a new problem when we came to step 3. Because the manufacturer's current distribution of $\tilde{\mu}$ is *continuous* (Normal with mean .155 and standard deviation .116), we cannot literally carry out the computations for every possible value of $\tilde{\mu}$. What we could do would be to divide the μ axis into brackets, calculate the *area* under the *probability* curve within each bracket, multiply each such area or probability into the *height* of the *loss* curve at the mid-point of the bracket, and add the products. As the widths of the brackets were made smaller and smaller, the results of this method of computation would come closer and closer to the true value.

Fortunately we do not actually need to carry out these numerical calculations when the prior distribution is *Normal*. By use of the calculus it can be shown that <u>the unconditional expected terminal loss of a rule with *arbitrary n* but with c^* *optimal for the given n* is</u>

$$✳\quad \text{UETeL}(n) = k_t\sigma_0(\tilde{\mu})L_{N^*}(D_0) - k_t\sigma(\tilde{E}_1)L_{N^*}(D_E)$$

where
$$\sigma^2(\tilde{E}_1) = \sigma_0^2(\tilde{\mu})\,\frac{\sigma_0^2(\tilde{\mu})}{\sigma_0^2(\tilde{\mu}) + \sigma^2(\bar{\tilde{x}})}$$

$$D_E = \frac{|\mu_b - E_0(\tilde{\mu})|}{\sigma(\tilde{E}_1)} \qquad D_0 = \frac{|\mu_b - E_0(\tilde{\mu})|}{\sigma_0(\tilde{\mu})}$$

Here, k_t and μ_b are respectively the terminal loss constant and break-even value defined in Section 20.3.1, and L_{N^*} is the function tabulated in Table IV at the end of this book.†

20.4.4   Expected Value of Sample Information

Inspecting the formula just given for unconditional expected terminal loss under an (n,c^*) decision rule we see that the *first* term on the right, $k_t \sigma_0(\tilde{\mu}) L_{N^*}(D_0)$, is simply the formula for the ELTA, or expected loss of optimal terminal action without sampling, that we encountered in Section 20.3.2; we have added the 0 subscripts to distinguish between $\sigma_0(\tilde{\mu})$ and D_0 on the one hand and $\sigma(\tilde{E}_1)$ and D_E on the other.

The *second* term on the right in the formula for the UETeL of n is thus the *difference* between the expected terminal loss of *immediate* terminal action and the expected terminal loss of terminal action *posterior to taking a sample of size n*. We can therefore think of this second term as measuring the expected value of the information to be obtained from a sample of size n, or more briefly, the *expected value of sample information:*

✳ $\text{EVSI}(n) = k_t \sigma(\tilde{E}_1) L_{N^*}(D_E)$ *Expected value of sample information*

20.4.5   EVSI in the Package-change Example

To evaluate the unconditional terminal loss of the rule $(50, -.297)$, we first recall that the distribution of $\tilde{\mu}$ prior to this *new* test has parameters

$$\text{E}_0(\tilde{\mu}) = .155, \qquad \sigma_0(\tilde{\mu}) = .116, \qquad \sigma_0^2(\tilde{\mu}) = .01346,$$

that the sampling variance will be

$$\sigma^2(\tilde{x}) = .03125,$$

and that the two important economic constants have the values

$$\mu_b = .019, \qquad k_t = \$1,056,000.$$

We can then compute

$$\sigma^2(\tilde{E}_1) = .01346 \, \frac{.01346}{.01346 + .03125} = .00405,$$

$$\sigma(\tilde{E}_1) = \sqrt{.00405} = .0636,$$

† The reason for using the symbol $\sigma(\tilde{E}_1)$ cannot be explained in terms of decision rules; it comes from an alternative method of analyzing sampling problems known as "preposterior" or "extensive-form" analysis, an explanation of which will be found in Robert Schlaifer, "Probability and Statistics for Business Decisions," chap. 34, McGraw-Hill Book Company, Inc., New York, 1959.

$$D_E = \frac{|.019 - .155|}{.0636} \doteq 2.14,$$

$$L_{N^*}(2.14) = .005788,$$

$$\text{EVSI}(50) = \$1,056,000 \times .0636 \times .005788 \doteq \$400.$$

20.5   Expected Net Gain of Sampling

What really counts in a decision about sampling is of course not the EVSI or expected *value* of the sample information *as such* but this amount reduced by the *cost* (or expected cost) of obtaining the information.   Letting

Cost(n) = cost or expected cost of taking a sample of size n,

we define the *expected net gain of sampling* to be

$\text{ENGS}(n) = \text{EVSI}(n) - \text{cost}(n)$ *Expected net gain of sampling*

In the package-change example, assuming that the agency which would conduct the new test would charge the same rates that it charged for the original test, i.e., \$75 per store plus a \$1000 fixed charge for setup and analysis, we would have

Cost(50) = \$1000 + 50 × \$75 = \$4750.

Bringing in the EVSI calculated in the previous section we have for the expected *net* gain of 50 more observations

ENGS(50) = \$400 − \$4750 = −\$4350.

If the manufacturer were forced to choose between immediate terminal action and a new test of size $n = 50$, the latter would be *worse* by \$4350.   Actually, of course, he can make a new test of any size he pleases, and some size other than $n = 50$ *may* have a net gain which is positive. This now looks extremely unlikely, however; the sample will clearly have to be much larger than $n = 50$ if its EVSI is to be large enough to cover even the \$1000 fixed cost of a new test, while on the other hand any test larger than $n = 84$ would have a total sampling cost which was greater than the \$7300 expected loss of terminal action *without* sampling.

20.6   Summary of Relations among Economic Quantities

Quite a number of different economic quantities have now been defined for use in problems involving sampling, and we give here a summary of their definitions.

UETeL(n): unconditional expected *terminal* loss of a decision rule with optimal c but arbitrary n.

UEToL(n): unconditional expected *total* loss of a decision rule with optimal c but arbitrary n.

Cost(n): actual or expected cost of a sample of size n.

These three concepts were introduced in Chapter 11, where we saw that

$$\text{UEToL}(n) = \text{UETeL}(n) + \text{cost}(n).$$

In Chapters 19 and 20 we introduced two new concepts:

ELTA: expected loss of (optimal) terminal action *without* sampling.

EVSI(n): expected value of the information *to be* obtained from a sample.

ENGS(n): expected net gain of sampling.

The last two of these concepts were defined by the relations

$$\text{EVSI}(n) = \text{ELTA} - \text{UETeL}(n).$$
$$\text{ENGS}(n) = \text{EVSI}(n) - \text{cost}(n).$$

From these definitions and the previous definition of unconditional expected total loss it follows that

$$\text{UEToL}(n) = \text{ELTA} - \text{ENGS}(n),$$

a relation which is useful in Normal problems where analysis naturally starts from the convenient formulas

$$\text{ELTA} = k_t \sigma_0(\tilde{\mu}) L_{N^*}(D_0),$$
$$\text{EVSI}(n) = k_t \sigma(\tilde{E}_1) L_{N^*}(D_E).$$

Finally we repeat the definitions involved in evaluating these last two formulas. In any problem where

Profit or cost of act $1 = K_1 + k_1\mu,$
Profit or cost of act $2 = K_2 + k_2\mu,$

we define

$$\mu_b = \frac{K_1 - K_2}{k_2 - k_1} = \frac{K_2 - K_1}{k_1 - k_2},$$

$$k_t = |k_2 - k_1| = |k_1 - k_2|,$$

$$D_0 = \frac{|\mu_b - E_0(\tilde{\mu})|}{\sigma_0(\tilde{\mu})}, \quad \text{std dev known}$$

$$\sigma^2(\tilde{E}_1) = \sigma_0^2(\tilde{\mu}) \frac{\sigma_0^2(\tilde{\mu})}{\sigma_0^2(\tilde{\mu}) + \sigma^2(\tilde{x})},$$

$$D_E = \frac{|\mu_b - E_0(\tilde{\mu})|}{\sigma(\tilde{E}_1)}. \quad \text{std dev expected}$$

PROBLEMS

(1.) In the Mar-Pruf case (Chapter 17, Problem 1),

a. Use your answer to Chapter 19, Problem 1, to show that the expected profits of the acts "market" and "do not market" are respectively $126,400 and $0.

b. Show that whereas *before* the sample was taken the expected loss of terminal action was $90,000, the information obtained from the sample has reduced the ELTA to $3500.

c. Compute the ENGS of a *new* sample of $n = 100$ interviews.

(2.) In the Grand Western case (Chapter 17, Problem 2, and Chapter 19, Problem 2), assuming that Jones wishes to give *no* weight to the opinions he held before the pilot sample was taken,

a. Compute the expected *additional* profit to be obtained by *canceling* the Family-Fare Plan.

b. Compute the ELTA.

c. Compute the ENGS of a *new* sample of 50 interviews.

CHAPTER 21

Optimal Sample Size in Two-action Problems
with Linear Profits or Costs
and Normal Distributions

In any situation where a businessman wishes to take just one (or just one more) sample before reaching a terminal decision, he will wish to find the sample size n^* which yields the greatest possible *net gain,*

$$\text{ENGS}(n) = \text{EVSI}(n) - \text{cost}(n).$$

In this chapter we shall see how n^* can be very easily found in problems which (1) meet the conditions of the last chapter regarding *Normality* and *known variance* of the distributions of $\tilde{\mu}$ and $\tilde{x}$ and *linearity* of *terminal* profits or costs, and (2) involve a *cost of sampling* which is *linear* in n:

$$\text{Cost}(n) = K_s + k_s n.$$

We shall simplify the exposition, however, by first discussing the special case where there is *no fixed element* in sampling cost, $K_s = 0$. After we have seen how to handle this problem it will be a trivial matter to extend our results to the case where there *is* a fixed element $K_s > 0$.

On the assumption that $K_s = 0$, we can write for the expected net gain of a sample of any size

$$\text{ENGS}(n) = k_t \sigma(\tilde{E}_1) L_{N^*}(D_E) - k_s n,$$

where both D_E and $\sigma(\tilde{E}_1)$ depend on the sample size n because D_E depends on $\sigma(\tilde{E}_1)$, $\sigma(\tilde{E}_1)$ depends on $\sigma(\tilde{x})$, and $\sigma(\tilde{x})$ depends on n.

21.1 Behavior of Net Gain as n Increases

21.1.1 The Essential Parameters of the Problem

Our first task is to obtain a picture of the general way in which the $\text{ENGS}(n)$ behaves as n increases. This behavior will of course depend not only on n but also on all the other constants which enter the problem either directly or through the definitions of $\sigma(\tilde{E}_1)$ and D_E. These constants are six in number—μ_b, k_t, k_s, $E_0(\tilde{\mu})$, $\sigma_0(\tilde{\mu})$, and σ—and if the behavior of the ENGS(n) depended on all of them separately, our task would be hopeless.   Fortunately, however, it can be shown that <u>the *essential features* of the way in which ENGS(n) behaves depend only on two combinations of the six constants</u>, one of which we have already encountered:

$$D_0 = \frac{|\mu_b - E_0(\tilde{\mu})|}{\sigma_0(\tilde{\mu})}$$

$$Z_0 = \frac{\sigma_0(\tilde{\mu})}{\sigma} \sqrt[3]{k_t\sigma/k_s}$$

Essential parameters of the problem of sample size

We shall refer to these two quantities as the *essential parameters* of the problem of optimal sample size.

21.1.2   Behavior of ENGS(n) When $D_0 = 0$

<u>D_0 has the value 0 when the mean $E_0(\tilde{\mu})$ of the prior distribution is equal to the break-even value μ_b.</u>   Half the prior probability is on one

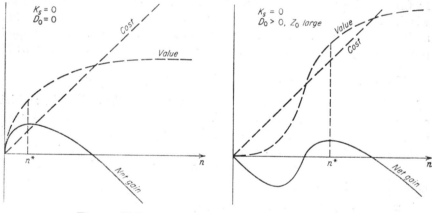

Figure 21.1   **Figure 21.2**

side of μ_b, half on the other; if either of the two terminal acts is chosen *without* sampling, there is an even chance that this act will be the wrong one.   In such a situation even a very small sample will substantially increase the probability of choosing the right act, and accordingly the expected value of the sample information at first increases very rapidly as n increases from 0.   <u>This initial rate at which value increases with n is always greater than the rate at which the variable sampling cost $k_s n$ increases, and therefore net gain = value minus cost always starts by *increasing* with n,</u> as shown in Figure 21.1.   The value of the information has a definite maximum, however,† and therefore increases more and more slowly as n becomes greater, whereas the cost continues indefinitely to increase in strict proportion to n. The result is that there is some value of n beyond which cost increases faster than the value, and at this point *net* gain stops rising and starts to fall. The highest point on the net-gain curve marks the optimal value of n.

21.1.3   Behavior of ENGS(n) When $D_0 > 0$

When $D_0 > 0$ the prior distribution definitely favors one of the two terminal acts and it is very improbable that a really small sample will affect the decision. Accordingly the expected value of sample information starts by increasing very slowly with n. As n becomes large enough

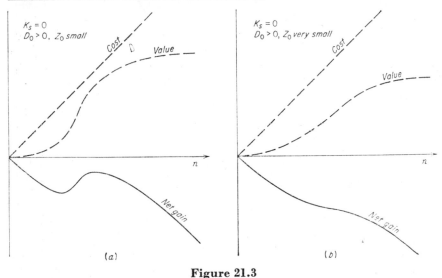

Figure 21.3

for the sample to have a real chance of affecting the decision, the value increases more rapidly; but as the value approaches the value of an infinite sample its rate of increase again becomes small and approaches 0.

Since the variable cost of sampling increases steadily with n from the very beginning, it is not obvious that there will be *any* value of n for which the expected value of the sample is greater than its cost. Whether or not there is such a value can be shown to depend on the relative magnitudes of D_0 and Z_0. If Z_0 *is larger than a certain critical value which depends on* D_0, the net gain will behave as shown in Figure 21.2, first becoming nega-

---

† Recall that, as pointed out in Section 20.4.4, the EVSI is the amount by which sampling can be "expected" to reduce terminal opportunity loss. Since opportunity loss can never be negative, the EVSI can never be greater than the ELTA, or expected loss of optimal terminal action without sampling.

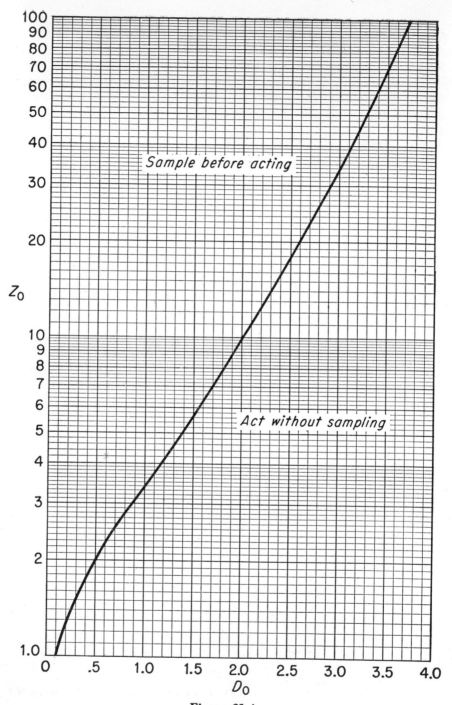

Z_0

Sample before acting

Act without sampling

D_0

Figure 21.4

tive, then rising to some maximum positive value at the optimal value of n, and then falling off to become more and more negative. *If Z_0 is smaller than this critical value*, net gain will behave in one of the ways depicted in Figures 21.3a and b: there may or may not be a peak in the net-gain curve; but even if there is, the top of the peak will represent a *negative* net gain and the best sample size will be no sample at all. The critical value of Z_0 is graphed as a function of D_0 in Figure 21.4.

21.1.4   The Effect of Nonzero K_s

It is now easy to see the effect of a fixed element of sampling cost. Every point on the line showing sampling *cost* in any of the graphs we have just examined will be raised by the amount K_s, the *value* of the sample information will be totally unaffected, and therefore every point on the curve showing *net gain* will be lowered by the amount K_s. In the situations depicted in Figures 21.3a and b no sample is worth its cost even when $K_s = 0$; the same conclusion holds a fortiori when $K_s > 0$. In the situations depicted in Figures 21.1 and 21.2, moving the net-gain curve downward may or may not carry the peak below 0 on the vertical scale, but in either case the change will not affect the value of n at which the peak occurs. If the peak remains above 0 after being lowered by the amount K_s, this lowering has no effect whatever on optimal sample size; it merely diminishes the net gain to be expected from taking a sample of this size. If, however, the peak goes below 0, it will be better to take no sample at all.

21.2   Optimal Sample Size

Having determined the general way in which expected net gain behaves with sample size n, we are ready to take up the problem of finding the exact value of the optimal sample size n^*. We shall follow the same procedure in discussing this problem which we followed in the previous section: we shall first consider the case where there is no fixed element in sampling cost, $K_s = 0$, and we shall then see how our conclusions can very easily be modified to allow for the presence of such a cost.

21.2.1   Optimal Sample Size When $K_s = 0$

The first step in determining optimal sample size when $K_s = 0$ is to determine whether or not there is *any* sample size which will yield a positive net gain. If $D_0 = 0$, so that Figure 21.1 applies, we know immediately that such a sample size exists; if $D_0 > 0$, the question can be quickly settled by the use of Figure 21.4, which will tell us whether we are in the situation of Figure 21.2 or one of the situations depicted in Figure 21.3.

If this preliminary check reveals that sample sizes better than 0 actually exist, i.e. that we are in the situation of Figure 21.1 or 21.2 and not in the situation of Figure 21.3, our next problem is to find the value n^* which corresponds to the peak of the net-gain curve; and since the curve is necessarily flat at its peak, we can do this by finding an algebraic expression for the *slope* of the net-gain curve and then looking for the value or values of n which make this slope 0. If $D_0 = 0$, there will always be one and only one such n, corresponding to the single peak in Figure 21.1. If $D_0 > 0$ and Figure 21.4 tells us that we are in the situation of Figure 21.2, there will be two n's which give zero slope, the smaller one corresponding to the bottom of the dip in the net-gain curve and the larger one to the top of the peak. Since the formula for the slope of the net-gain curve is not a simple one and it requires a good deal of computation to find the n which makes the slope 0 for given Z_0 and D_0, we do not give the formula itself but instead present Chart I, from which the value of n^* can be determined much more easily. This chart shows, not the optimal sample size n^* itself, but the optimal value η^* of the ratio

$$\eta = \frac{n}{(\sqrt[3]{k_t \sigma / k_s})^2}.$$ then page 323 for c^*

The results shown in Figure 21.4 have been taken into account in constructing Chart I, so that it is not actually necessary to consult Figure 21.4 when $D_0 > 0$ in order to determine whether an optimal nonzero sample size exists: if the Z_0 of the problem at hand is to the left of the end of the line for the D_0 of that problem, there is no sample size which will even pay for its variable cost.†

Approximation for Large Z_0. If we examine the shapes of the curves in Chart I we get the impression that every one of the curves tends to become a straight line as Z_0 increases, and it can be proved that this is true. As Z_0 increases, the optimal η for any D_0 is given more and more accurately by the approximate formula

$$\eta^* \doteq \sqrt{\frac{1}{2Z_0}} \, P'_{N^*}(D_0),$$

which plots as a straight line on the kind of grid used for Chart I. This formula can be used to find optimal sample size for values of Z_0 greater than 80, the largest value shown on the chart.‡

† It is this fact which accounts for the abrupt cutoffs in the curves of Chart I. If the curves were extended smoothly to the left, they would give the locations of negative peaks like the one in Figure 21.3a.

‡ As can be seen from the way in which each curve approaches its asymptote, the approximate formula always *overstates* the optimal sample size. The accuracy of the approximation for given D_0 improves as Z_0 increases; for given Z_0 it becomes worse as

21.2.2 Optimal Sample Size When $K_s > 0$

If there is a fixed element of sampling cost K_s as well as a variable element $k_s n$, we will a fortiori act *without* sampling whenever Figure 21.4 or Chart I tells us to do so. If, however, the figure or the chart tells us that we *should* sample, this proves only that the savings expected from a sample of size n^* will cover the *variable* sampling cost $k_s n^*$. We also know, however, that if there *is* any nonzero sample size which will yield a positive net gain, the best such sample size is still n^* as given by Chart I: it was pointed out in Section 21.1.4 above that the effect of adding K_s to the cost of sampling is simply to lower every point on the net-gain curve by the same amount and that the peak in the curve still occurs at the same value of n as it does when $K_s = 0$. Consequently we have only to determine whether the sample size n^* given by Chart I can be expected to produce savings greater than $K_s + k_s n^*$, and this question is quickly settled by evaluating the savings from the formula

$$\text{EVSI} = k_t \sigma(\tilde{E}_1) L_{N^*}(D_E).$$

21.2.3 Example

Returning once more to the package-change problem, for which all the basic constants were collected in Section 20.4.5, let us now find out definitely whether or not a *new* store test should be conducted before any terminal decision is reached. We have as regards the proposed *new* sample

$$E_0(\tilde{\mu}) = .155, \qquad \sigma_0(\tilde{\mu}) = .116, \qquad \sigma_0^2(\tilde{\mu}) = .01346,$$
$$\sigma = 1.25, \qquad \mu_b = .019, \qquad k_t = \$1,056,000,$$
$$K_s = \$1000, \qquad k_s = \$75.$$

We compute the essential parameters

$$D_0 = \frac{|.019 - .155|}{.116} = 1.17,$$

$$Z_0 = \frac{.116}{1.25} \sqrt[3]{\$1,056,000 \times \frac{1.25}{\$75}} = .0928 \times 26.0 = 2.41,$$

and immediately see from Figure 21.4 that *no new sample should be taken*.

Merely to emphasize the fact that the desirability of sampling (or of additional sampling) depends on the costs and losses involved, let us see what conclusion we would have reached in this same example if the amount at stake in the terminal decision had been 10 times as large,

---

D_0 increases. At $Z_0 = 80$ the approximation is excellent for D_0 as large as 3, in which case the error is only about 10 per cent.

i.e., if instead of $k_t = \$1,056,000$ we had had

$$k_t = \$10,560,000.$$

This change in the basic assumptions of the problem leaves the value of D_0 unaltered, but leads to a new

$$Z_0 = \frac{.116}{1.25} \sqrt[3]{\$10,560,000 \times \frac{1.25}{\$75}} = .0928 \times 56.1 = 5.21.$$

Figure 21.4 now shows that a new sample *should* be taken, and therefore we go to Chart I, find 5.21 on the horizontal axis, and over it read $\eta^* = .112$ on the curve for $D_0 = 1.00$ and $\eta^* = .091$ on the curve for $D_0 = 1.20$. Interpolating between these two values we obtain for $D_0 = 1.17$

$$\eta^* = .112 - .7(.112 - .091) = .097,$$
$$n^* = .097 \times 56.1^2 = 305.$$

To check whether a sample of this size will cover the fixed as well as the variable cost of sampling, we compute

$$\sigma^2(\tilde{x}) = \frac{1.25^2}{305} = .00512,$$

$$\sigma^2(\tilde{E}_1) = .01346 \, \frac{.01346}{.01346 + .00512} = .00975,$$

$$\sigma(\tilde{E}_1) = .0993,$$

$$D_E = \frac{|.019 - .155|}{.0993} = 1.37, \qquad L_{N^*}(1.37) = .03916,$$

$$\text{EVSI}(305) = \$10,560,000 \times .0993 \times .03916 \doteq \$41,000,$$
$$\text{Cost}(305) = \$1000 + 305 \times \$75 \doteq \$24,000,$$
$$\text{ENGS}(305) = \$41,000 - \$24,000 = \$17,000.$$

A new store test of size $n^* = 305$ *would* have been indicated *if* the amount at stake in the decision had been 10 times as large as it actually was.

21.3 Effect of Nonoptimal Sample Size

Some interesting general results concerning the unnecessary loss which results from taking a sample of nonoptimal size can be given for the special case where there is no fixed element K_s in sampling cost and where the optimum sample size is not zero. In this case numerical investigations have shown that *the ratio*

Expected total loss with sample of arbitrary size n

Expected total loss with sample of optimal size n^*

is less than

$$\frac{1}{2}\left(\frac{n}{n^*} + \frac{n^*}{n}\right)$$

for all D_0 and Z_0.

This limiting value is graphed in Figure 21.5, and it is immediately apparent that a *moderate* error in sample size is of no *practical importance whatever*—a sample which is 10 per cent above or below optimum cannot increase expected total loss by as much as $\frac{6}{10}$ of 1 per cent; a sample which is 20 per cent above or below optimum cannot increase expected total loss by more than 2.5 per cent.   What is more, even these very low maximum effects are actually approached only when Z_0 is very large;

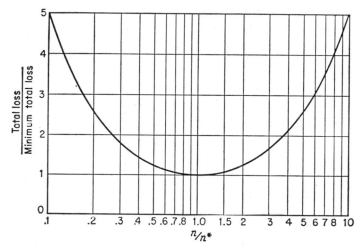

Figure 21.5. Effect of nonoptimal sample size.

for values of Z_0 which occur in common practice the effect of nonoptimal sample size is very substantially less than the limit given by Figure 21.5. Observe on the other hand that *substantial* departures from optimal sample size may have *really serious effects:* a sample which is half or twice what it ought to be may increase expected total loss by as much as 25 per cent, and expected total loss may be more than doubled if the sample is a fourth or four times the optimal size.

21.4   Optimum Sample Size When the Assumptions of This Chapter Are Violated

The only two-action problems for which it is possible to devise a really simple method of determining optimal sample size are those in which all the assumptions underlying the results of this chapter are met and which can therefore be solved by the methods derived in this chapter. Violation of any of these assumptions usually means that the only absolutely sure way of finding the exact optimal sample size is actually to evaluate expected total loss for each of a large number of different sizes. Our assumption that the terminal and sampling costs are linear is very close to exact in the great majority of the two-action problems which arise in practical business situations, but it is often necessary to decide on a sample size in situations where our assumptions about the distributions of $\tilde{\mu}$ and $\tilde{x}$ are seriously violated in one or more of the following respects:

1. The prior distribution of $\tilde{\mu}$ is not Normal;
2. The sampling distribution of $\tilde{x}$ is not Normal;
3. The population or process variance σ^2 is not known.

Even if we do have to resort to numerical evaluation of a number of different sample sizes in such situations, it would help a great deal to have some indication of the general range of n's within which the optimum probably lies; and it naturally occurs to us that we may be able to obtain such an indication by applying the methods of this chapter even though we cannot hope that they will yield the *exact* optimum. We shall now test this idea by trying it out on the quality-control example of Section 10.1; we shall see that the conditions of that problem violate the assumptions of the present chapter in all three of the ways listed above and that every one of the violations is severe.

21.4.1 The Prior Distribution

In Section 11.2.2 we saw that the basic random variable of this problem was the long-run fraction defective $\tilde{p}$ which the operator's setup would generate, and we assumed that on the basis of experience with previous setups made by this operator the manufacturer assigned to the $\tilde{p}$ of the current setup the probability distribution shown in the first two columns of Table 21.1 and graphed in Figure 21.6. Inspection of the graph shows

Table 21.1

p	$P_0(p)$	$p\,P_0(p)$	$p - E_0(\tilde{p})$	$[p - E_0(\tilde{p})]^2$	$[p - E_0(\tilde{p})]^2\,P_0(p)$
.01	.7	.007	$-.042$	.001764	.001235
.05	.1	.005	$-.002$	.000004	.000000
.15	.1	.015	$+.098$	.009604	.000960
.25	.1	.025	$+.198$	.039204	.003920
	1.0	.052			.006115

at a glance that we cannot possibly think of the operator as a super-process producing *Normally distributed* p's; the situation is totally different in this respect from the nearly Normally distributed "normal yields" graphed in Figure 19.1 for the chemical-processing example.

There is thus no long-run *Normal* frequency distribution of $\tilde{p}$ to *estimate*, but just to see what will happen we shall simply *replace* the true distribution of $\tilde{p}$ by a Normal distribution with the *same mean and variance*. In column 3 of Table 21.1 the mean of the true distribution is calculated to be .052, and in the remainder of the table the variance

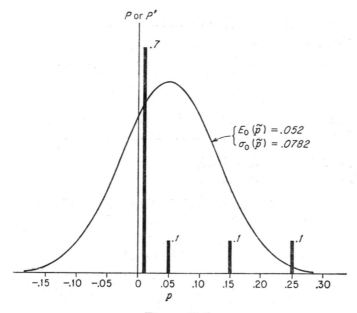

Figure 21.6

is calculated to be .006115. We shall proceed *as if* the prior distribution of $\tilde{p}$ were *Normal* with parameters

$$\mathrm{E}_0(\tilde{p}) = .052, \qquad \sigma_0(\tilde{p}) = \sqrt{.006115} = .0782.$$

This "fitted" Normal distribution is superimposed on the true distribution of $\tilde{p}$, and the student will observe that the "fit" is about as poor as it could be. It actually assigns probability greater than $\frac{1}{4}$ to *negative* values of $\tilde{p}$, which are of course completely impossible.

21.4.2   The Sampling Distribution

The variance of the *individual* x's which could be generated by a Bernoulli process is

$$\sigma^2 = p(1 - p),$$

as we saw in Section 14.5, and we see at once that σ is an *unknown* quantity depending on the unknown basic random variable $\tilde{p}$, rather than a known quantity as we assumed in deriving the results obtained earlier in this chapter. In order to apply these results we shall, however, have to assume *some* fixed value for σ; and again just to see what happens, we shall treat σ *as if* it were known to have the value which it *would in fact* have if $\tilde{p}$ were equal to its *prior expected value* $E_0(\tilde{p})$. We proceed, in other words, by computing

$$\sigma^{*2} = E_0(p)[1 - E_0(\tilde{p})] = .052 \times .948 = .0493,$$
$$\sigma^* = \sqrt{.0493} = .222,$$

and proceeding as if this were the fixed, known value of σ.

21.4.3   The Normal Approximation to Optimal Sample Size

We are now ready to find the "Normal approximation" to the true optimal sample size in this problem. It was shown in Section 10.1 that

$$p_b = .040, \qquad k_t = \$200,$$
$$K_s = \$.25, \qquad k_s = \$.02,$$

and from these exact constants and the "approximate" constant σ^* computed in the previous section we can compute the essential parameters

$$D_0 = \frac{|p_b - E_0(\tilde{p})|}{\sigma_0(\tilde{p})} = \frac{|.040 - .052|}{.0782} = .15,$$

$$Z_0 = \frac{\sigma_0(\tilde{p})}{\sigma^*} \sqrt{\frac{k_t \sigma^*}{k_s}} = \frac{.0782}{.222} \sqrt[3]{\frac{\$200 \times .222}{\$.02}} = .352 \times 13.05 = 4.59.$$

Above $Z_0 = 4.59$ in Chart I we read $\eta^* = .170$ for $D_0 = .1$ and $\eta^* = .172$ for $D_0 = .2$. Interpolating for $D_0 = .15$ we obtain

$$\eta^* = .171,$$
$$n^* = .171 \times 13.05^2 = 29.$$

21.4.4   The Accuracy of the Approximation

The *exact* optimal sample size for this problem has already been computed by brute-force numerical methods in Section 11.3.2, where we worked out a curve of *expected total loss* for all n's from 0 to 56 and found that the one with the lowest expected total loss was $n = 27$. The *exact* loss of this *true* optimum was \$1.21; the *exact* loss of the sample size $n = 29$ derived by the Normal *approximation* to n^* is \$1.22, or less than 1 per cent greater.

We can also compare the two sample sizes in terms of the *expected net gain of sampling*. In Section 11.2.2 we saw that the *exact* ELTA or expected loss of optimal action *without* sampling is $4.20. Since the net gain of sampling is the amount by which sampling reduces expected *total* loss, we can compute

$$\text{ENGS}(27) = \$4.20 - \$1.21 = \$2.99,$$
$$\text{ENGS}(29) = \$4.20 - \$1.22 = \$2.98.$$

Looked at in this way, the exact ENGS of the approximate optimum is only $\frac{1}{3}$ per cent below the exact ENGS of the true optimum.

It is hard to prove anything *in general* about the results which the Normal approximation to optimal sample size will give in violently non-Normal problems, but many *numerical examples* have been tried and in almost every one the results were very good indeed. In problems where a good deal is at stake, however, it will be well to use the Normal optimum only as a starting point and then use exact methods to trace out expected total loss in the neighborhood of this point.

PROBLEMS

1. In the Mar-Pruf case (Problem 1 of Chapters 17, 19, and 20),
   a. Show that the values of the essential parameters for determining whether a *new* sample should be taken are

   $$D_0 = 1.38, \qquad Z_0 = 3.29.$$

   b. Show that no new sample should be taken, assuming that $k_s = \$25$.

2. In the Grand Western case (Problem 2 of Chapters 17, 19, and 20), assume that Jones is willing to take one more sample if this is desirable, but no more than one.
   a. Decide whether a *new* sample should be taken and, if so, how large it should be.
   b. If a new sample should be taken, compute the EVSI and ENGS of a sample of optimal size.
   c. Compute expected total loss with a new sample of optimal size.

Tables

Table I: Cumulative Binomial Distribution $\qquad n = 1$

$$P_b(\tilde{r} \geq r | n, p)$$

$n = 1$

P R	01	02	03	04	05	06	07	08	09	10
1	0100	0200	0300	0400	0500	0600	0700	0800	0900	1000

P R	11	12	13	14	15	16	17	18	19	20
1	1100	1200	1300	1400	1500	1600	1700	1800	1900	2000

P R	21	22	23	24	25	26	27	28	29	30
1	2100	2200	2300	2400	2500	2600	2700	2800	2900	3000

P R	31	32	33	34	35	36	37	38	39	40
1	3100	3200	3300	3400	3500	3600	3700	3800	3900	4000

P R	41	42	43	44	45	46	47	48	49	50
1	4100	4200	4300	4400	4500	4600	4700	4800	4900	5000

$n = 2$

P R	01	02	03	04	05	06	07	08	09	10
1	0199	0396	0591	0784	0975	1164	1351	1536	1719	1900
2	0001	0004	0009	0016	0025	0036	0049	0064	0081	0100

P R	11	12	13	14	15	16	17	18	19	20
1	2079	2256	2431	2604	2775	2944	3111	3276	3439	3600
2	0121	0144	0169	0196	0225	0256	0289	0324	0361	0400

P R	21	22	23	24	25	26	27	28	29	30
1	3759	3916	4071	4224	4375	4524	4671	4816	4959	5100
2	0441	0484	0529	0576	0625	0676	0729	0784	0841	0900

P R	31	32	33	34	35	36	37	38	39	40
1	5239	5376	5511	5644	5775	5904	6031	6156	6279	6400
2	0961	1024	1089	1156	1225	1296	1369	1444	1521	1600

P R	41	42	43	44	45	46	47	48	49	50
1	6519	6636	6751	6864	6975	7084	7191	7296	7399	7500
2	1681	1764	1849	1936	2025	2116	2209	2304	2401	2500

$n = 3$

P R	01	02	03	04	05	06	07	08	09	10
1	0297	0588	0873	1153	1426	1694	1956	2213	2464	2710
2	0003	0012	0026	0047	0073	0104	0140	0182	0228	0280
3				0001	0001	0002	0003	0005	0007	0010

P R	11	12	13	14	15	16	17	18	19	20
1	2950	3185	3415	3639	3859	4073	4282	4486	4686	4880
2	0336	0397	0463	0533	0608	0686	0769	0855	0946	1040
3	0013	0017	0022	0027	0034	0041	0049	0058	0069	0080

P R	21	22	23	24	25	26	27	28	29	30
1	5070	5254	5435	5610	5781	5948	6110	6268	6421	6570
2	1138	1239	1344	1452	1563	1676	1793	1913	2035	2160
3	0093	0106	0122	0138	0156	0176	0197	0220	0244	0270

n = 3

P	31	32	33	34	35	36	37	38	39	40
R
1	6715	6856	6992	7125	7254	7379	7500	7617	7730	7840
2	2287	2417	2548	2682	2818	2955	3094	3235	3.377	3520
3	0298	0328	0359	0393	0429	0467	0507	0549	0593	0640

P	41	42	43	44	45	46	47	48	49	50
R
1	7946	8049	8148	8244	8336	8425	8511	8594	8673	8750
2	3665	3810	3957	4104	4253	4401	4551	4700	4850	5000
3	0689	0741	0795	0852	0911	0973	1038	1106	1176	1250

n = 4

P	01	02	03	04	05	06	07	08	09	10
R
1	0394	0776	1147	1507	1855	2193	2519	2836	3143	3439
2	0006	0023	0052	0091	0140	0199	0267	0344	0430	0523
3			0001	0002	0005	0008	0013	0019	0027	0037
4									0001	0001

P	11	12	13	14	15	16	17	18	19	20
R
1	3726	4003	4271	4530	4780	5021	5254	5479	5695	5904
2	0624	0732	0847	0968	1095	1228	1366	1509	1656	1808
3	0049	0063	0079	0098	0120	0144	0171	0202	0235	0272
4	0001	0002	0003	0004	0005	0007	0008	0010	0013	0016

P	21	22	23	24	25	26	27	28	29	30
R
1	6105	6298	6485	6664	6836	7001	7160	7313	7459	7599
2	1963	2122	2285	2450	2617	2787	2959	3132	3307	3483
3	0312	0356	0403	0453	0508	0566	0628	0694	0763	0837
4	0019	0023	0028	0033	0039	0046	0053	0061	0071	0081

P	31	32	33	34	35	36	37	38	39	40
R
1	7733	7862	7985	8103	8215	8322	8425	8522	8615	8704
2	3660	3837	4015	4193	4370	4547	4724	4900	5075	5248
3	0915	0996	1082	1171	1265	1362	1464	1589	1679	1792
4	0092	0105	0119	0134	0150	0168	0187	0209	0231	0256

P	41	42	43	44	45	46	47	48	49	50
R
1	8788	8868	8944	9017	9085	9150	9211	9269	9323	9375
2	5420	5590	5759	5926	6090	6252	6412	6569	6724	6875
3	1909	2030	2155	2283	2415	2550	2689	2831	2977	3125
4	0283	0311	0342	0375	0410	0448	0488	0531	0576	0625

n = 5

P	01	02	03	04	05	06	07	08	09	10
R
1	0490	0961	1413	1846.	2262	2661	3043	3409	3760	4095
2	0010	0038	0085	0148	0226	0319	0425	0544	0674	0815
3		0001	0003	0006	0012	0020	0031	0045	0063	0086
4						0001	0001	0002	0003	0005

P	11	12	13	14	15	16	17	18	19	20
R
1	4416	4723	5016	5296	5563	5818	6061	6293	6513	6723
2	0965	1125	1292	1467	1648	1835	2027	2224	2424	2627
3	0112	0143	0179	0220	0266	0318	0375	0437	0505	0579
4	0007	0009	0013	0017	0022	0029	0036	0045	0055	0067
5				0001	0001	0001	0001	0002	0002	0003

P	21	22	23	24	25	26	27	28	29	30
R
1	6923	7113	7293	7464	7627	7781	7927	8065	8196	8319
2	2833	3041	3251	3461	3672	3883	4093	4303	4511	4718
3	0659	0744	0836	0933	1035	1143	1257	1376	1501	1631
4	0081	0097	0114	0134	0156	0181	0208	0238	0272	0308
5	0004	0005	0006	0008	0010	0012	0014	0017	0021	0024

Table I: Cumulative Binomial Distribution

n = 5

P	31	32	33	34	35	36	37	38	39	40
R										
1	8436	8546	8650	8748	8840	8926	9008	9084	9155	9222
2	4923	5125	5325	5522	5716	5906	6093	6276	6455	6630
3	1766	1905	2050	2199	2352	2509	2670	2835	3003	3174
4	0347	0390	0436	0486	0540	0598	0660	0726	0796	0870
5	0029	0034	0039	0045	0053	0060	0069	0079	0090	0102

P	41	42	43	44	45	46	47	48	49	50
R										
1	9285	9344	9398	9449	9497	9541	9582	9620	9655	9688
2	6801	6967	7129	7286	7438	7585	7728	7865	7998	8125
3	3349	3525	3705	3886	4069	4253	4439	4625	4813	5000
4	0949	1033	1121	1214	1312	1415	1522	1635	1753	1875
5	0116	0131	0147	0165	0185	0206	0229	0255	0282	0313

n = 6

P	01	02	03	04	05	06	07	08	09	10
R										
1	0585	1142	1670	2172	2649	3101	3530	3936	4321	4686
2	0015	0057	0125	0216	0328	0459	0608	0773	0952	1143
3		0002	0005	0012	0022	0038	0058	0085	0118	0159
4					0001	0002	0003	0005	0008	0013
5										0001

P	11	12	13	14	15	16	17	18	19	20
R										
1	5030	5356	5664	5954	6229	6487	6731	6960	7176	7379
2	1345	1556	1776	2003	2235	2472	2713	2956	3201	3446
3	0206	0261	0324	0395	0473	0560	0655	0759	0870	0989
4	0018	0025	0034	0045	0059	0075	0094	0116	0141	0170
5	0001	0001	0002	0003	0004	0005	0007	0010	0013	0016
6										0001

P	21	22	23	24	25	26	27	28	29	30
R										
1	7569	7748	7916	8073	8220	8358	8487	8607	8719	8824
2	3692	3937	4180	4422	4661	4896	5128	5356	5580	5798
3	1115	1250	1391	1539	1694	1856	2023	2196	2374	2557
4	0202	0239	0280	0326	0376	0431	0492	0557	0628	0705
5	0020	0025	0031	0038	0046	0056	0067	0079	0093	0109
6	0001	0001	0001	0002	0002	0003	0004	0005	0006	0007

P	31	32	33	34	35	36	37	38	39	40
R										
1	8921	9011	9095	9173	9246	9313	9375	9432	9485	9533
2	6012	6220	6422	6619	6809	6994	7172	7343	7508	7667
3	2744	2936	3130	3328	3529	3732	3937	4143	4350	4557
4	0787	0875	0969	1069	1174	1286	1404	1527	1657	1792
5	0127	0148	0170	0195	0223	0254	0288	0325	0365	0410
6	0009	0011	0013	0015	0018	0022	0026	0030	0035	0041

P	41	42	43	44	45	46	47	48	49	50
R										
1	9578	9619	9657	9692	9723	9752	9778	9802	9824	9844
2	7819	7965	8105	8238	8364	8485	8599	8707	8810	8906
3	4764	4971	5177	5382	5585	5786	5985	6180	6373	6563
4	1933	2080	2232	2390	2553	2721	2893	3070	3252	3438
5	0458	0510	0566	0627	0692	0762	0837	0917	1003	1094
6	0048	0055	0063	0073	0083	0095	0108	0122	0138	0156

n = 7

P	01	02	03	04	05	06	07	08	09	10
R										
1	0679	1319	1920	2486	3017	3515	3983	4422	4832	5217
2	0020	0079	0171	0294	0444	0618	0813	1026	1255	1497
3		0003	0009	0020	0038	0063	0097	0140	0193	0257
4				0001	0002	0004	0007	0012	0018	0027
5								0001	0001	0002

P	11	12	13	14	15	16	17	18	19	20
R										
1	5577	5913	6227	6521	6794	7049	7286	7507	7712	7903
2	1750	2012	2281	2556	2834	3115	3396	3677	3956	4233
3	0331	0416	0513	0620	0738	0866	1005	1154	1313	1480
4	0039	0054	0072	0094	0121	0153	0189	0231	0279	0333
5	0003	0004	0006	0009	0012	0017	0022	0029	0037	0047
6					0001	0001	0001	0002	0003	0004

P	21	22	23	24	25	26	27	28	29	30
R										
1	8080	8243	8395	8535	8665	8785	8895	8997	9090	9176
2	4506	4775	5040	5298	5551	5796	6035	6266	6490	6706
3	1657	1841	2033	2231	2436	2646	2861	3081	3304	3529
4	0394	0461	0536	0617	0706	0802	0905	1016	1134	1260
5	0058	0072	0088	0107	0129	0153	0181	0213	0248	0288
6	0005	0006	0008	0011	0013	0017	0021	0026	0031	0038
7					0001	0001	0001	0001	0002	0002

P	31	32	33	34	35	36	37	38	39	40
R										
1	9255	9328	9394	9454	9510	9560	9606	9648	9686	9720
2	6914	7113	7304	7487	7662	7828	7987	8137	8279	8414
3	3757	3987	4217	4447	4677	4906	5134	5359	5581	5801
4	1394	1534	1682	1837	1998	2167	2341	2521	2707	2898
5	0332	0380	0434	0492	0556	0625	0701	0782	0869	0963
6	0046	0055	0065	0077	0090	0105	0123	0142	0164	0188
7	0003	0003	0004	0005	0006	0008	0009	0011	0014	0016

P	41	42	43	44	45	46	47	48	49	50
R										
1	9751	9779	9805	9827	9848	9866	9883	9897	9910	9922
2	8541	8660	8772	8877	8976	9068	9153	9233	9307	9375
3	6017	6229	6436	6638	6836	7027	7213	7393	7567	7734
4	3094	3294	3498	3706	3917	4131	4346	4563	4781	5000
5	1063	1169	1282	1402	1529	1663	1803	1951	2105	2266
6	0216	0246	0279	0316	0357	0402	0451	0504	0562	0625
7	0019	0023	0027	0032	0037	0044	0051	0059	0068	0078

$$n = 8$$

P	01	02	03	04	05	06	07	08	09	10
R										
1	0773	1492	2163	2786	3366	3904	4404	4868	5297	5695
2	0027	0103	0223	0381	0572	0792	1035	1298	1577	1869
3	0001	0004	0013	0031	0058	0096	0147	0211	0289	0381
4			0001	0002	0004	0007	0013	0022	0034	0050
5							0001	0001	0003	0004

P	11	12	13	14	15	16	17	18	19	20
R										
1	6063	6404	6718	7008	7275	7521	7748	7956	8147	8322
2	2171	2480	2794	3111	3428	3744	4057	4366	4670	4967
3	0487	0608	0743	0891	1052	1226	1412	1608	1815	2031
4	0071	0097	0129	0168	0214	0267	0328	0397	0476	0563
5	0007	0010	0015	0021	0029	0038	0050	0065	0083	0104
6		0001	0001	0002	0002	0003	0005	0007	0009	0012
7									0001	0001

P	21	22	23	24	25	26	27	28	29	30
R										
1	8483	8630	8764	8887	8999	9101	9194	9278	9354	9424
2	5257	5538	5811	6075	6329	6573	6807	7031	7244	7447
3	2255	2486	2724	2967	3215	3465	3718	3973	4228	4482
4	0659	0765	0880	1004	1138	1281	1433	1594	1763	1941
5	0129	0158	0191	0230	0273	0322	0377	0438	0505	0580
6	0016	0021	0027	0034	0042	0052	0064	0078	0094	0113
7	0001	0002	0002	0003	0004	0005	0006	0008	0010	0013
8									0001	0001

P	31	32	33	34	35	36	37	38	39	40
R										
1	9486	9543	9594	9640	9681	9719	9752	9782	9808	9832
2	7640	7822	7994	8156	8309	8452	8586	8711	8828	8936
3	4736	4987	5236	5481	5722	5958	6189	6415	6634	6846
4	2126	2319	2519	2724	2936	3153	3374	3599	3828	4059
5	0661	0750	0846	0949	1061	1180	1307	1443	1586	1737
6	0134	0159	0187	0218	0253	0293	0336	0385	0439	0498
7	0016	0020	0024	0030	0036	0043	0051	0061	0072	0085
8	0001	0001	0001	0002	0002	0003	0004	0004	0005	0007

P	41	42	43	44	45	46	47	48	49	50
R										
1	9853	9872	9889	9903	9916	9928	9938	9947	9954	9961
2	9037	9130	9216	9295	9368	9435	9496	9552	9602	9648
3	7052	7250	7440	7624	7799	7966	8125	8276	8419	8555
4	4292	4527	4762	4996	5230	5463	5694	5922	6146	6367
5	1895	2062	2235	2416	2604	2798	2999	3205	3416	3633
6	0563	0634	0711	0794	0885	0982	1086	1198	1318	1445
7	0100	0117	0136	0157	0181	0208	0239	0272	0310	0352
8	0008	0010	0012	0014	0017	0020	0024	0028	0033	0039

$n = 9$

P	01	02	03	04	05	06	07	08	09	10
R										
1	0865	1663	2398	3075	3698	4270	4796	5278	5721	6126
2	0034	0131	0282	0478	0712	0978	1271	1583	1912	2252
3	0001	0006	0020	0045	0084	0138	0209	0298	0405	0530
4			0001	0003	0006	0013	0023	0037	0057	0083
5						0001	0002	0003	0005	0009
6										0001

P	11	12	13	14	15	16	17	18	19	20
R										
1	6496	6835	7145	7427	7684	7918	8131	8324	8499	8658
2	2599	2951	3304	3657	4005	4348	4685	5012	5330	5638
3	0672	0833	1009	1202	1409	1629	1861	2105	2357	2618
4	0117	0158	0209	0269	0339	0420	0512	0615	0730	0856
5	0014	0021	0030	0041	0056	0075	0098	0125	0158	0196
6	0001	0002	0003	0004	0006	0009	0013	0017	0023	0031
7						0001	0001	0002	0002	0003

P	21	22	23	24	25	26	27	28	29	30
R										
1	8801	8931	9048	9154	9249	9335	9411	9480	9542	9596
2	5934	6218	6491	6750	6997	7230	7452	7660	7856	8040
3	2885	3158	3434	3713	3993	4273	4552	4829	5102	5372
4	0994	1144	1304	1475	1657	1849	2050	2260	2478	2703
5	0240	0291	0350	0416	0489	0571	0662	0762	0870	0988
6	0040	0051	0065	0081	0100	0122	0149	0179	0213	0253
7	0004	0006	0008	0010	0013	0017	0022	0028	0035	0043
8			0001	0001	0001	0001	0002	0003	0003	0004

P	31	32	33	34	35	36	37	38	39	40
R										
1	9645	9689	9728	9762	9793	9820	9844	9865	9883	9899
2	8212	8372	8522	8661	8789	8908	9017	9118	9210	9295
3	5636	5894	6146	6390	6627	6856	7076	7287	7489	7682
4	2935	3173	3415	3662	3911	4163	4416	4669	4922	5174
5	1115	1252	1398	1553	1717	1890	2072	2262	2460	2666
6	0298	0348	0404	0467	0536	0612	0696	0787	0886	0994
7	0053	0064	0078	0094	0112	0133	0157	0184	0215	0250
8	0006	0007	0009	0011	0014	0017	0021	0026	0031	0038
9				0001	0001	0001	0001	0002	0002	0003

P	41	42	43	44	45	46	47	48	49	50
R										
1	9913	9926	9936	9946	9954	9961	9967	9972	9977	9980
2	9372	9442	9505	9563	9615	9662	9704	9741	9775	9805
3	7866	8039	8204	8359	8505	8642	8769	8889	8999	9102
4	5424	5670	5913	6152	6386	6614	6836	7052	7260	7461
5	2878	3097	3322	3551	3786	4024	4265	4509	4754	5000
6	1109	1233	1366	1508	1658	1817	1985	2161	2346	2539
7	0290	0334	0383	0437	0498	0564	0637	0717	0804	0898
8	0046	0055	0065	0077	0091	0107	0125	0145	0169	0195
9	0003	0004	0005	0006	0008	0009	0011	0014	0016	0020

n = 10

P	01	02	03	04	05	06	07	08	09	10
R										
1	0956	1829	2626	3352	4013	4614	5160	5656	6106	6513
2	0043	0162	0345	0582	0861	1176	1517	1879	2254	2639
3	0001	0009	0028	0062	0115	0188	0283	0401	0540	0702
4			0001	0004	0010	0020	0036	0058	0088	0128
5					0001	0002	0003	0006	0010	0016
6									0001	0001

P	11	12	13	14	15	16	17	18	19	20
R										
1	6882	7215	7516	7787	8031	8251	8448	8626	8784	8926
2	3028	3417	3804	4184	4557	4920	5270	5608	5932	6242
3	0884	1087	1308	1545	1798	2064	2341	2628	2922	3222
4	0178	0239	0313	0400	0500	0614	0741	0883	1039	1209
5	0025	0037	0053	0073	0099	0130	0168	0213	0266	0328
6	0003	0004	0006	0010	0014	0020	0027	0037	0049	0064
7			0001	0001	0001	0002	0003	0004	0006	0009
8									0001	0001

P	21	22	23	24	25	26	27	28	29	30
R										
1	9053	9166	9267	9357	9437	9508	9570	9626	9674	9718
2	6536	6815	7079	7327	7560	7778	7981	8170	8345	8507
3	3526	3831	4137	4442	4744	5042	5335	5622	5901	6172
4	1391	1587	1794	2012	2241	2479	2726	2979	3239	3504
5	0399	0479	0569	0670	0781	0904	1037	1181	1337	1503
6	0082	0104	0130	0161	0197	0239	0287	0342	0404	0473
7	0012	0016	0021	0027	0035	0045	0056	0070	0087	0106
8	0001	0002	0002	0003	0004	0006	0007	0010	0012	0016
9							0001	0001	0001	0001

P	31	32	33	34	35	36	37	38	39	40
R										
1	9755	9789	9818	9843	9865	9885	9902	9916	9929	9940
2	8656	8794	8920	9035	9140	9236	9323	9402	9473	9536
3	6434	6687	6930	7162	7384	7595	7794	7983	8160	8327
4	3772	4044	4316	4589	4862	5132	5400	5664	5923	6177
5	1679	1867	2064	2270	2485	2708	2939	3177	3420	3669
6	0551	0637	0732	0836	0949	1072	1205	1348	1500	1662
7	0129	0155	0185	0220	0260	0305	0356	0413	0477	0548
8	0020	0025	0032	0039	0048	0059	0071	0086	0103	0123
9	0002	0003	0003	0004	0005	0007	0009	0011	0014	0017
10								0001	0001	0001

P	41	42	43	44	45	46	47	48	49	50
R										
1	9949	9957	9964	9970	9975	9979	9983	9986	9988	9990
2	9594	9645	9691	9731	9767	9799	9827	9852	9874	9893
3	8483	8628	8764	8889	9004	9111	9209	9298	9379	9453
4	6425	6665	6898	7123	7340	7547	7745	7933	8112	8281
5	3922	4178	4436	4696	4956	5216	5474	5730	5982	6230
6	1834	2016	2207	2407	2616	2832	3057	3288	3526	3770
7	0626	0712	0806	0908	1020	1141	1271	1410	1560	1719
8	0146	0172	0202	0236	0274	0317	0366	0420	0480	0547
9	0021	0025	0031	0037	0045	0054	0065	0077	0091	0107
10	0001	0002	0002	0003	0003	0004	0005	0006	0008	0010

n = 11

P	01	02	03	04	05	06	07	08	09	10
R										
1	1047	1993	2847	3618	4312	4937	5499	6004	6456	6862
2	0052	0195	0413	0692	1019	1382	1772	2181	2601	3026
3	0002	0012	0037	0083	0152	0248	0370	0519	0695	0896
4			0002	0007	0016	0030	0053	0085	0129	0185
5					0001	0003	0005	0010	0017	0028
6								0001	0002	0003

P	11	12	13	14	15	16	17	18	19	20
R
1	7225	7549	7839	8097	8327	8531	8712	8873	9015	9141
2	3452	3873	4286	4689	5078	5453	5811	6151	6474	6779
3	1120	1366	1632	1915	2212	2521	2839	3164	3494	3826
4	0256	0341	0442	0560	0694	0846	1013	1197	1397	1611
5	0042	0061	0087	0119	0159	0207	0266	0334	0413	0504
6	0005	0008	0012	0018	0027	0037	0051	0068	0090	0117
7		0001	0001	0002	0003	0005	0007	0010	0014	0020
8							0001	0001	0002	0002

P	21	22	23	24	25	26	27	28	29	30
R
1	9252	9350	9436	9511	9578	9636	9686	9730	9769	9802
2	7065	7333	7582	7814	8029	8227	8410	8577	8730	8870
3	4158	4488	4814	5134	5448	5753	6049	6335	6610	6873
4	1840	2081	2333	2596	2867	3146	3430	3719	4011	4304
5	0607	0723	0851	0992	1146	1313	1493	1685	1888	2103
6	0148	0186	0231	0283	0343	0412	0490	0577	0674	0782
7	0027	0035	0046	0059	0076	0095	0119	0146	0179	0216
8	0003	0005	0007	0009	0012	0016	0021	0027	0034	0043
9			0001	0001	0001	0002	0002	0003	0004	0006

P	31	32	33	34	35	36	37	38	39	40
R
1	9831	9856	9878	9896	9912	9926	9938	9948	9956	9964
2	8997	9112	9216	9310	9394	9470	9537	9597	9650	9698
3	7123	7361	7587	7799	7999	8186	8360	8522	8672	8811
4	4598	4890	5179	5464	5744	6019	6286	6545	6796	7037
5	2328	2563	2807	3059	3317	3581	3850	4122	4397	4672
6	0901	1031	1171	1324	1487	1661	1847	2043	2249	2465
7	0260	0309	0366	0430	0501	0581	0670	0768	0876	0994
8	0054	0067	0082	0101	0122	0148	0177	0210	0249	0293
9	0008	0010	0013	0016	0020	0026	0032	0039	0048	0059
10	0001	0001	0001	0002	0002	0003	0004	0005	0006	0007

P	41	42	43	44	45	46	47	48	49	50
R
1	9970	9975	9979	9983	9986	9989	9991	9992	9994	9995
2	9739	9776	9808	9836	9861	9882	9900	9916	9930	9941
3	8938	9055	9162	9260	9348	9428	9499	9564	9622	9673
4	7269	7490	7700	7900	8089	8266	8433	8588	8733	8867
5	4948	5223	5495	5764	6029	6288	6541	6787	7026	7256
6	2690	2924	3166	3414	3669	3929	4193	4460	4729	5000
7	1121	1260	1408	1568	1738	1919	2110	2312	2523	2744
8	0343	0399	0461	0532	0610	0696	0791	0895	1009	1133
9	0072	0087	0104	0125	0148	0175	0206	0241	0282	0327
10	0009	0012	0014	0018	0022	0027	0033	0040	0049	0059
11	0001	0001	0001	0001	0002	0002	0002	0003	0004	0005

$n = 12$

P	01	02	03	04	05	06	07	08	09	10
R
1	1136	2153	3062	3873	4596	5241	5814	6323	6775	7176
2	0062	0231	0486	0809	1184	1595	2033	2487	2948	3410
3	0002	0015	0048	0107	0196	0316	0468	0652	0866	1109
4		0001	0003	0010	0022	0043	0075	0120	0180	0256
5				0001	0002	0004	0009	0016	0027	0043
6							0001	0002	0003	0005
7										0001

P	11	12	13	14	15	16	17	18	19	20
R
1	7530	7843	8120	8363	8578	8766	8931	9076	9202	9313
2	3867	4314	4748	5166	5565	5945	6304	6641	6957	7251
3	1377	1667	1977	2303	2642	2990	3344	3702	4060	4417
4	0351	0464	0597	0750	0922	1114	1324	1552	1795	2054
5	0065	0095	0133	0181	0239	0310	0393	0489	0600	0726
6	0009	0014	0022	0033	0046	0065	0088	0116	0151	0194
7	0001	0002	0003	0004	0007	0010	0015	0021	0029	0039
8					0001	0001	0002	0003	0004	0006
9										0001

P	21	22	23	24	25	26	27	28	29	30
R
1	9409	9493	9566	9629	9683	9730	9771	9806	9836	9862
2	7524	7776	8009	8222	8416	8594	8755	8900	9032	9150
3	4768	5114	5450	5778	6093	6397	6687	6963	7225	7472
4	2326	2610	2904	3205	3512	3824	4137	4452	4765	5075
5	0866	1021	1192	1377	1576	1790	2016	2254	2504	2763
6	0245	0304	0374	0453	0544	0646	0760	0887	1026	1178
7	0052	0068	0089	0113	0143	0178	0219	0267	0322	0386
8	0008	0011	0016	0021	0028	0036	0047	0060	0076	0095
9	0001	0001	0002	0003	0004	0005	0007	0010	0013	0017
10						0001	0001	0001	0002	0002

P	31	32	33	34	35	36	37	38	39	40
R
1	9884	9902	9918	9932	9943	9953	9961	9968	9973	9978
2	9256	9350	9435	9509	9576	9634	9685	9730	9770	9804
3	7704	7922	8124	8313	8487	8648	8795	8931	9054	9166
4	5381	5681	5973	6258	6533	6799	7053	7296	7528	7747
5	3032	3308	3590	3876	4167	4459	4751	5043	5332	5618
6	1343	1521	1711	1913	2127	2352	2588	2833	3087	3348
7	0458	0540	0632	0734	0846	0970	1106	1253	1411	1582
8	0118	0144	0176	0213	0255	0304	0359	0422	0493	0573
9	0022	0028	0036	0045	0056	0070	0086	0104	0127	0153
10	0003	0004	0005	0007	0008	0011	0014	0018	0022	0028
11				0001	0001	0001	0001	0002	0002	0003

P	41	42	43	44	45	46	47	48	49	50
R
1	9982	9986	9988	9990	9992	9994	9995	9996	9997	9998
2	9834	9860	9882	9901	9917	9931	9943	9953	9961	9968
3	9267	9358	9440	9513	9579	9637	9688	9733	9773	9807
4	7953	8147	8329	8498	8655	8801	8934	9057	9168	9270
5	5899	6175	6443	6704	6956	7198	7430	7652	7862	8062
6	3616	3889	4167	4448	4731	5014	5297	5577	5855	6128
7	1765	1959	2164	2380	2607	2843	3089	3343	3604	3872
8	0662	0760	0869	0988	1117	1258	1411	1575	1751	1930
9	0183	0218	0258	0304	0356	0415	0481	0555	0638	0730
10	0035	0043	0053	0065	0079	0095	0114	0137	0163	0193
11	0004	0005	0007	0009	0011	0014	0017	0021	0026	0032
12				0001	0001	0001	0001	0001	0002	0002

$n = 13$

P	01	02	03	04	05	06	07	08	09	10
R
1	1225	2310	3270	4118	4867	5526	6107	6617	7065	7458
2	0072	0270	0564	0932	1354	1814	2298	2794	3293	3787
3	0003	0020	0062	0135	0245	0392	0578	0799	1054	1339
4		0001	0005	0014	0031	0060	0103	0163	0243	0342
5				0001	0003	0007	0013	0024	0041	0065
6						0001	0001	0003	0005	0009
7									0001	0001

P	11	12	13	14	15	16	17	18	19	20
R
1	7802	8102	8364	8592	8791	8963	9113	9242	9354	9450
2	4270	4738	5186	5614	6017	6396	6751	7080	7384	7664
3	1651	1985	2337	2704	3080	3463	3848	4231	4611	4983
4	0464	0609	0776	0967	1180	1414	1667	1939	2226	2527
5	0097	0139	0193	0260	0342	0438	0551	0681	0827	0991
6	0015	0024	0036	0053	0075	0104	0139	0183	0237	0300
7	0002	0003	0005	0008	0013	0019	0027	0038	0052	0070
8			0001	0001	0002	0003	0004	0006	0009	0012
9								0001	0001	0002

P	21	22	23	24	25	26	27	28	29	30
R										
1	9533	9604	9666	9718	9762	9800	9833	9860	9883	9903
2	7920	8154	8367	8559	8733	8889	9029	9154	9265	9363
3	5347	5699	6039	6364	6674	6968	7245	7505	7749	7975
4	2839	3161	3489	3822	4157	4493	4826	5155	5478	5794
5	1173	1371	1585	1816	2060	2319	2589	2870	3160	3457
6	0375	0462	0562	0675	0802	0944	1099	1270	1455	1654
7	0093	0120	0154	0195	0243	0299	0365	0440	0527	0624
8	0017	0024	0032	0043	0056	0073	0093	0118	0147	0182
9	0002	0004	0005	0007	0010	0013	0018	0024	0031	0040
10			0001	0001	0001	0002	0003	0004	0005	0007
11									0001	0001

P	31	32	33	34	35	36	37	38	39	40
R										
1	9920	9934	9945	9955	9963	9970	9975	9980	9984	9987
2	9450	9527	9594	9653	9704	9749	9787	9821	9849	9874
3	8185	8379	8557	8720	8868	9003	9125	9235	9333	9421
4	6101	6398	6683	6957	7217	7464	7698	7917	8123	8314
5	3760	4067	4376	4686	4995	5301	5603	5899	6188	6470
6	1867	2093	2331	2581	2841	3111	3388	3673	3962	4256
7	0733	0854	0988	1135	1295	1468	1654	1853	2065	2288
8	0223	0271	0326	0390	0462	0544	0635	0738	0851	0977
9	0052	0065	0082	0102	0126	0154	0187	0225	0270	0321
10	0009	0012	0015	0020	0025	0032	0040	0051	0063	0078
11	0001	0001	0002	0003	0003	0005	0006	0008	0010	0013
12							0001	0001	0001	0001

P	41	42	43	44	45	46	47	48	49	50
R										
1	9990	9992	9993	9995	9996	9997	9997	9998	9998	9999
2	9895	9912	9928	9940	9951	9960	9967	9974	9979	9983
3	9499	9569	9630	9684	9731	9772	9808	9838	9865	9888
4	8492	8656	8807	8945	9071	9185	9288	9381	9464	9539
5	6742	7003	7254	7493	7721	7935	8137	8326	8502	8666
6	4552	4849	5146	5441	5732	6019	6299	6573	6838	7095
7	2524	2770	3025	3290	3563	3842	4127	4415	4707	5000
8	1114	1264	1426	1600	1788	1988	2200	2424	2659	2905
9	0379	0446	0520	0605	0698	0803	0918	1045	1183	1334
10	0096	0117	0141	0170	0203	0242	0287	0338	0396	0461
11	0017	0021	0027	0033	0041	0051	0063	0077	0093	0112
12	0002	0002	0003	0004	0005	0007	0009	0011	0014	0017
13							0001	0001	0001	0001

n = 14

P	01	02	03	04	05	06	07	08	09	10
R										
1	1313	2464	3472	4353	5123	5795	6380	6888	7330	7712
2	0084	0310	0645	1059	1530	2037	2564	3100	3632	4154
3	0003	0025	0077	0167	0301	0478	0698	0958	1255	1584
4		0001	0006	0019	0042	0080	0136	0214	0315	0441
5				0002	0004	0010	0020	0035	0059	0092
6						0001	0002	0004	0008	0015
7									0001	0002

P	11	12	13	14	15	16	17	18	19	20
R										
1	8044	8330	8577	8789	8972	9129	9264	9379	9477	9560
2	4658	5141	5599	6031	6433	6807	7152	7469	7758	8021
3	1939	2315	2708	3111	3521	3932	4341	4744	5138	5519
4	0594	0774	0979	1210	1465	1742	2038	2351	2679	3018
5	0137	0196	0269	0359	0467	0594	0741	0907	1093	1298
6	0024	0038	0057	0082	0115	0157	0209	0273	0349	0439
7	0003	0006	0009	0015	0022	0032	0046	0064	0087	0116
8		0001	0001	0002	0003	0005	0008	0012	0017	0024
9						0001	0001	0002	0003	0004

P R	21	22	23	24	25	26	27	28	29	30
1	9631	9691	9742	9786	9822	9852	9878	9899	9917	9932
2	8259	8473	8665	8837	8990	9126	9246	9352	9444	9525
3	5887	6239	6574	6891	7189	7467	7727	7967	8188	8392
4	3366	3719	4076	4432	4787	5136	5479	5813	6137	6448
5	1523	1765	2023	2297	2585	2884	3193	3509	3832	4158
6	0543	0662	0797	0949	1117	1301	1502	1718	1949	2195
7	0152	0196	0248	0310	0383	0467	0563	0673	0796	0933
8	0033	0045	0060	0079	0103	0132	0167	0208	0257	0315
9	0006	0008	0011	0016	0022	0029	0038	0050	0065	0083
10	0001	0001	0002	0002	0003	0005	0007	0009	0012	0017
11						0001	0001	0001	0002	0002

P R	31	32	33	34	35	36	37	38	39	40
1	9945	9955	9963	9970	9976	9981	9984	9988	9990	9992
2	9596	9657	9710	9756	9795	9828	9857	9881	9902	9919
3	8577	8746	8899	9037	9161	9271	9370	9457	9534	9602
4	6747	7032	7301	7556	7795	8018	8226	8418	8595	8757
5	4486	4813	5138	5458	5773	6080	6378	6666	6943	7207
6	2454	2724	3006	3297	3595	3899	4208	4519	4831	5141
7	1084	1250	1431	1626	1836	2059	2296	2545	2805	3075
8	0381	0458	0545	0643	0753	0876	1012	1162	1325	1501
9	0105	0131	0163	0200	0243	0294	0353	0420	0497	0583
10	0022	0029	0037	0048	0060	0076	0095	0117	0144	0175
11	0003	0005	0006	0008	0011	0014	0019	0024	0031	0039
12		0001	0001	0001	0001	0002	0003	0003	0005	0006
13										0001

P R	41	42	43	44	45	46	47	48	49	50
1	9994	9995	9996	9997	9998	9998	9999	9999	9999	9999
2	9934	9946	9956	9964	9971	9977	9981	9985	9988	9991
3	9661	9713	9758	9797	9830	9858	9883	9903	9921	9935
4	8905	9039	9161	9270	9368	9455	9532	9601	9661	9713
5	7459	7697	7922	8132	8328	8510	8678	8833	8974	9102
6	5450	5754	6052	6344	6627	6900	7163	7415	7654	7880
7	3355	3643	3937	4236	4539	4843	5148	5451	5751	6047
8	1692	1896	2113	2344	2586	2840	3105	3380	3663	3953
9	0680	0789	0910	1043	1189	1348	1520	1707	1906	2120
10	0212	0255	0304	0361	0426	0500	0583	0677	0782	0898
11	0049	0061	0076	0093	0114	0139	0168	0202	0241	0287
12	0008	0010	0013	0017	0022	0027	0034	0042	0053	0065
13	0001	0001	0001	0002	0003	0003	0004	0006	0007	0009
14										0001

$n = 15$

P R	01	02	03	04	05	06	07	08	09	10
1	1399	2614	3667	4579	5367	6047	6633	7137	7570	7941
2	0096	0353	0730	1191	1710	2262	2832	3403	3965	4510
3	0004	0030	0094	0203	0362	0571	0829	1130	1469	1841
4		0002	0008	0024	0055	0104	0175	0273	0399	0556
5			0001	0002	0006	0014	0028	0050	0082	0127
6					0001	0001	0003	0007	0013	0022
7								0001	0002	0003

P R	11	12	13	14	15	16	17	18	19	20
1	8259	8530	8762	8959	9126	9269	9389	9490	9576	9648
2	5031	5524	5987	6417	6814	7179	7511	7813	8085	8329
3	2238	2654	3084	3520	3958	4392	4819	5234	5635	6020
4	0742	0959	1204	1476	1773	2092	2429	2782	3146	3518
5	0187	0265	0361	0478	0617	0778	0961	1167	1394	1642
6	0037	0057	0084	0121	0168	0227	0300	0387	0490	0611
7	0006	0010	0015	0024	0036	0052	0074	0102	0137	0181
8	0001	0001	0002	0004	0006	0010	0014	0021	0030	0042
9					0001	0001	0002	0003	0005	0008
10									0001	0001

Table I: Cumulative Binomial Distribution $n = 15$

P	21	22	23	24	25	26	27	28	29	30
R										
1	9709	9759	9802	9837	9866	9891	9911	9928	9941	9953
2	8547	8741	8913	9065	9198	9315	9417	9505	9581	9647
3	6385	6731	7055	7358	7639	7899	8137	8355	8553	8732
4	3895	4274	4650	5022	5387	5742	6086	6416	6732	7031
5	1910	2195	2495	2810	3135	3469	3810	4154	4500	4845
6	0748	0905	1079	1272	1484	1713	1958	2220	2495	2784
7	0234	0298	0374	0463	0566	0684	0817	0965	1130	1311
8	0058	0078	0104	0135	0173	0219	0274	0338	0413	0500
9	0011	0016	0023	0031	0042	0056	0073	0094	0121	0152
10	0002	0003	0004	0006	0008	0011	0015	0021	0028	0037
11			0001	0001	0001	0002	0002	0003	0005	0007
12									0001	0001

P	31	32	33	34	35	36	37	38	39	40
R										
1	9962	9969	9975	9980	9984	9988	9990	9992	9994	9995
2	9704	9752	9794	9829	9858	9883	9904	9922	9936	9948
3	8893	9038	9167	9281	9383	9472	9550	9618	9678	9729
4	7314	7580	7829	8060	8273	8469	8649	8813	8961	9095
5	5187	5523	5852	6171	6481	6778	7062	7332	7587	7827
6	3084	3393	3709	4032	4357	4684	5011	5335	5654	5968
7	1509	1722	1951	2194	2452	2722	3003	3295	3595	3902
8	0599	0711	0837	0977	1132	1302	1487	1687	1902	2131
9	0190	0236	0289	0351	0422	0504	0597	0702	0820	0950
10	0048	0062	0079	0099	0124	0154	0190	0232	0281	0338
11	0009	0012	0016	0022	0028	0037	0047	0059	0075	0093
12	0001	0002	0003	0004	0005	0006	0009	0011	0015	0019
13					0001	0001	0001	0002	0002	0003

P	41	42	43	44	45	46	47	48	49	50
R										
1	9996	9997	9998	9998	9999	9999	9999	9999	10000	10000
2	9958	9966	9973	9979	9983	9987	9990	9992	9994	9995
3	9773	9811	9843	9870	9893	9913	9929	9943	9954	9963
4	9215	9322	9417	9502	9576	9641	9697	9746	9788	9824
5	8052	8261	8454	8633	8796	8945	9080	9201	9310	9408
6	6274	6570	6856	7131	7392	7641	7875	8095	8301	8491
7	4214	4530	4847	5164	5478	5799	6095	6394	6684	6964
8	2374	2630	2898	3176	3465	3762	4065	4374	4686	5000
9	1095	1254	1427	1615	1818	2034	2265	2510	2767	3036
10	0404	0479	0565	0661	0769	0890	1024	1171	1333	1509
11	0116	0143	0174	0211	0255	0305	0363	0430	0506	0592
12	0025	0032	0040	0051	0063	0079	0097	0119	0145	0176
13	0004	0005	0007	0009	0011	0014	0018	0023	0029	0037
14			0001	0001	0001	0002	0002	0003	0004	0005

$n = 16$

P	01	02	03	04	05	06	07	08	09	10
R										
1	1485	2762	3857	4796	5599	6284	6869	7366	7789	8147
2	0109	0399	0818	1327	1892	2489	3098	3701	4289	4853
3	0005	0037	0113	0242	0429	0673	0969	1311	1694	2108
4		0002	0011	0032	0070	0132	0221	0342	0496	0684
5			0001	0003	0009	0019	0038	0068	0111	0170
6						0001	0002	0005	0010	0019	0033
7							0001	0001	0003	0005
8										0001

P	11	12	13	14	15	16	17	18	19	20
R										
1	8450	8707	8923	9105	9257	9386	9493	9582	9657	9719
2	5386	5885	6347	6773	7161	7513	7830	8115	8368	8593
3	2545	2999	3461	3926	4386	4838	5277	5698	6101	6482
4	0907	1162	1448	1763	2101	2460	2836	3223	3619	4019
5	0248	0348	0471	0618	0791	0988	1211	1458	1727	2018
6	0053	0082	0120	0171	0235	0315	0412	0527	0662	0817
7	0009	0015	0024	0038	0056	0080	0112	0153	0204	0267
8	0001	0002	0004	0007	0011	0016	0024	0036	0051	0070
9			0001	0001	0002	0003	0004	0007	0010	0015
10							0001	0001	0002	0002

P	21	22	23	24	25	26	27	28	29	30
R										
1	9770	9812	9847	9876	9900	9919	9935	9948	9958	9967
2	8791	8965	9117	9250	9365	9465	9550	9623	9686	9739
3	6839	7173	7483	7768	8029	8267	8482	8677	8851	9006
4	4418	4814	5203	5583	5950	6303	6640	6959	7260	7541
5	2327	2652	2991	3341	3698	4060	4425	4788	5147	5501
6	0992	1188	1405	1641	1897	2169	2458	2761	3077	3402
7	0342	0432	0536	0657	0796	0951	1125	1317	1526	1753
8	0095	0127	0166	0214	0271	0340	0420	0514	0621	0744
9	0021	0030	0041	0056	0075	0098	0127	0163	0206	0257
10	0004	0006	0008	0012	0016	0023	0031	0041	0055	0071
11	0001	0001	0001	0002	0003	0004	0006	0008	0011	0016
12						0001	0001	0001	0002	0003

P	31	32	33	34	35	36	37	38	39	40
R										
1	9974	9979	9984	9987	9990	9992	9994	9995	9996	9997
2	9822	9854	9880	9902	9921	9936	9948	9959	9967	9967
3	9144	9266	9374	9467	9549	9620	9681	9734	9778	9817
4	7804	8047	8270	8475	8661	8830	8982	9119	9241	9349
5	5846	6181	6504	6813	7108	7387	7649	7895	8123	8334
6	3736	4074	4416	4759	5100	5438	5770	6094	6408	6712
7	1997	2257	2531	2819	3119	3428	3746	4070	4398	4728
8	0881	1035	1205	1391	1594	1813	2048	2298	2562	2839
9	0317	0388	0470	0564	0671	0791	0926	1076	1242	1423
10	0092	0117	0148	0185	0229	0280	0341	0411	0491	0583
11	0021	0028	0037	0048	0062	0079	0100	0125	0155	0191
12	0004	0005	0007	0010	0013	0017	0023	0030	0038	0049
13		0001	0001	0001	0002	0003	0004	0005	0007	0009
14								0001	0001	0001

P	41	42	43	44	45	46	47	48	49	50
R										
1	9998	9998	9999	9999	9999	9999	10000	10000	10000	10000
2	9974	9979	9984	9987	9990	9992	9994	9995	9997	9997
3	9849	9876	9899	9918	9934	9947	9958	9966	9973	9979
4	9444	9527	9600	9664	9719	9766	9806	9840	9869	9894
5	8529	8707	8869	9015	9147	9265	9370	9463	9544	9616
6	7003	7280	7543	7792	8024	8241	8441	8626	8795	8949
7	5058	5387	5711	6029	6340	6641	6932	7210	7476	7728
8	3128	3428	3736	4051	4371	4694	5019	5343	5665	5982
9	1619	1832	2060	2302	2559	2829	3111	3405	3707	4018
10	0687	0805	0936	1081	1241	1416	1607	1814	2036	2272
11	0234	0284	0342	0409	0486	0574	0674	0786	0911	1051
12	0062	0078	0098	0121	0149	0183	0222	0268	0322	0384
13	0012	0016	0021	0027	0035	0044	0055	0069	0086	0106
14	0002	0002	0003	0004	0006	0007	0010	0013	0016	0021
15					0001	0001	0001	0001	0002	0003

$$n = 17$$

P	01	02	03	04	05	06	07	08	09	10
R										
1	1571	2907	4042	5004	5819	6507	7088	7577	7988	8332
2	0123	0446	0909	1465	2078	2717	3362	3995	4604	5182
3	0006	0044	0134	0286	0503	0782	1118	1503	1927	2382
4		0003	0014	0040	0088	0164	0273	0419	0603	0826
5			0001	0004	0012	0026	0051	0089	0145	0221
6					0001	0003	0007	0015	0027	0047
7							0001	0002	0004	0008
8										0001

P	11	12	13	14	15	16	17	18	19	20
R										
1	8621	8862	9063	9230	9369	9484	9579	9657	9722	9775
2	5723	6223	6682	7099	7475	7813	8113	8379	8613	8818
3	2858	3345	3836	4324	4802	5266	5711	6133	6532	6904
4	1087	1383	1710	2065	2444	2841	3251	3669	4091	4511
5	0321	0446	0598	0778	0987	1224	1487	1775	2087	2418
6	0075	0114	0166	0234	0319	0423	0548	0695	0864	1057
7	0014	0023	0037	0056	0083	0118	0163	0220	0291	0377
8	0002	0004	0007	0011	0017	0027	0039	0057	0080	0109
9		0001	0001	0002	0003	0005	0008	0012	0018	0026
10					0001	0001	0002	0003	0005
11										0001

P R	21	22	23	24	25	26	27	28	29	30
1	9818	9854	9882	9906	9925	9940	9953	9962	9970	9977
2	8996	9152	9285	9400	9499	9583	9654	9714	9765	9807
3	7249	7567	7859	8123	8363	8578	8771	8942	9093	9226
4	4927	5333	5728	6107	6470	6814	7137	7440	7721	7981
5	2766	3128	3500	3879	4261	4643	5023	5396	5760	6113
6	1273	1510	1770	2049	2347	2661	2989	3329	3677	4032
7	0479	0598	0736	0894	1071	1268	1485	1721	1976	2248
8	0147	0194	0251	0320	0402	0499	0611	0739	0884	1046
9	0037	0051	0070	0094	0124	0161	0206	0261	0326	0403
10	0007	0011	0016	0022	0031	0042	0057	0075	0098	0127
11	0001	0002	0003	0004	0006	0009	0013	0018	0024	0032
12				0001	0001	0002	0002	0003	0005	0007
13									0001	0001

P R	31	32	33	34	35	36	37	38	39	40
1	9982	9986	9989	9991	9993	9995	9996	9997	9998	9998
2	9843	9872	9896	9917	9933	9946	9957	9966	9973	9979
3	9343	9444	9532	9608	9673	9728	9775	9815	9849	9877
4	8219	8437	8634	8812	8972	9115	9241	9353	9450	9536
5	6453	6778	7087	7378	7652	7906	8142	8360	8559	8740
6	4390	4749	5105	5458	5803	6139	6465	6778	7077	7361
7	2536	2838	3153	3479	3812	4152	4495	4839	5182	5522
8	1227	1426	1642	1877	2128	2395	2676	2971	3278	3595
9	0492	0595	0712	0845	0994	1159	1341	1541	1757	1989
10	0162	0204	0254	0314	0383	0464	0557	0664	0784	0919
11	0043	0057	0074	0095	0120	0151	0189	0234	0286	0348
12	0009	0013	0017	0023	0030	0040	0051	0066	0084	0106
13	0002	0002	0003	0004	0006	0008	0011	0015	0019	0025
14				0001	0001	0001	0002	0002	0003	0005
15										0001

P R	41	42	43	44	45	46	47	48	49	50
1	9999	9999	9999	9999	10000	10000	10000	10000	10000	10000
2	9984	9987	9990	9992	9994	9996	9997	9998	9998	9999
3	9900	9920	9935	9948	9959	9968	9975	9980	9985	9988
4	9610	9674	9729	9776	9816	9849	9877	9901	9920	9936
5	8904	9051	9183	9301	9404	9495	9575	9644	9704	9755
6	7628	7879	8113	8330	8529	8712	8878	9028	9162	9283
7	5856	6182	6499	6805	7098	7377	7641	7890	8122	8338
8	3920	4250	4585	4921	5257	5590	5918	6239	6552	6855
9	2238	2502	2780	3072	3374	3687	4008	4335	4667	5000
10	1070	1236	1419	1618	1834	2066	2314	2577	2855	3145
11	0420	0503	0597	0705	0826	0962	1112	1279	1462	1662
12	0133	0165	0203	0248	0301	0363	0434	0517	0611	0717
13	0033	0042	0054	0069	0086	0108	0134	0165	0202	0245
14	0006	0008	0011	0014	0019	0024	0031	0040	0050	0064
15	0001	0001	0002	0002	0003	0004	0005	0007	0009	0012
16							0001	0001	0001	0001

$n = 18$

P R	01	02	03	04	05	06	07	08	09	10
1	1655	3049	4220	5204	6028	6717	7292	7771	8169	8499
2	0138	0495	1003	1607	2265	2945	3622	4281	4909	5497
3	0007	0052	0157	0333	0581	0898	1275	1702	2168	2662
4		0004	0018	0050	0109	0201	0333	0506	0723	0982
5			0002	0006	0015	0034	0067	0116	0186	0282
6				0001	0002	0005	0010	0021	0038	0064
7							0001	0003	0006	0012
8									0001	0002

P R	11	12	13	14	15	16	17	18	19	20
1	8773	8998	9185	9338	9464	9566	9651	9719	9775	9820
2	6042	6540	6992	7398	7759	8080	8362	8609	8824	9009
3	3173	3690	4206	4713	5203	5673	6119	6538	6927	7287
4	1282	1618	1986	2382	2798	3229	3669	4112	4554	4990
5	0405	0558	0743	0959	1206	1482	1787	2116	2467	2836

P / R	11	12	13	14	15	16	17	18	19	20
6	0102	0154	0222	0310	0419	0551	0708	0889	1097	1329
7	0021	0034	0054	0081	0118	0167	0229	0306	0400	0513
8	0003	0006	0011	0017	0027	0041	0060	0086	0120	0163
9		0001	0002	0003	0005	0008	0013	0020	0029	0043
10					0001	0001	0002	0004	0006	0009
11								0001	0001	0002

P / R	21	22	23	24	25	26	27	28	29	30
1	9856	9886	9909	9928	9944	9956	9965	9973	9979	9984
2	9169	9306	9423	9522	9605	9676	9735	9784	9824	9858
3	7616	7916	8187	8430	8647	8839	9009	9158	9288	9400
4	5414	5825	6218	6591	6943	7272	7578	7860	8119	8354
5	3220	3613	4012	4414	4813	5208	5594	5968	6329	6673
6	1586	1866	2168	2488	2825	3176	3538	3907	4281	4656
7	0645	0799	0974	1171	1390	1630	1891	2171	2469	2783
8	0217	0283	0363	0458	0569	0699	0847	1014	1200	1407
9	0060	0083	0112	0148	0193	0249	0316	0395	0488	0596
10	0014	0020	0028	0039	0054	0073	0097	0127	0164	0210
11	0003	0004	0006	0009	0012	0018	0025	0034	0046	0061
12		0001	0001	0002	0002	0003	0005	0007	0010	0014
13						0001	0001	0001	0002	0003

P / R	31	32	33	34	35	36	37	38	39	40
1	9987	9990	9993	9994	9996	9997	9998	9998	9999	9999
2	9886	9908	9927	9942	9954	9964	9972	9978	9983	9987
3	9498	9581	9652	9713	9764	9807	9843	9873	9897	9918
4	8568	8759	8931	9083	9217	9335	9439	9528	9606	9672
5	7001	7309	7598	7866	8114	8341	8549	8737	8907	9058
6	5029	5398	5759	6111	6450	6776	7086	7379	7655	7912
7	3111	3450	3797	4151	4509	4867	5224	5576	5921	6257
8	1633	1878	2141	2421	2717	3027	3349	3681	4021	4366
9	0720	0861	1019	1196	1391	1604	1835	2084	2350	2632
10	0264	0329	0405	0494	0597	0714	0847	0997	1163	1347
11	0080	0104	0133	0169	0212	0264	0325	0397	0480	0576
12	0020	0027	0036	0047	0062	0080	0102	0130	0163	0203
13	0004	0005	0008	0011	0014	0019	0026	0034	0044	0058
14	0001	0001	0001	0002	0003	0004	0005	0007	0010	0013
15						0001	0001	0001	0002	0002

P / R	41	42	43	44	45	46	47	48	49	50
1	9999	9999	10000	10000	10000	10000	10000	10000	10000	10000
2	9990	9992	9994	9996	9997	9998	9998	9999	9999	9999
3	9934	9948	9959	9968	9975	9981	9985	9989	9991	9993
4	9729	9777	9818	9852	9880	9904	9923	9939	9952	9962
5	9193	9313	9418	9510	9589	9658	9717	9767	9810	9846
6	8151	8372	8573	8757	8923	9072	9205	9324	9428	9519
7	6582	6895	7193	7476	7742	7991	8222	8436	8632	8811
8	4713	5062	5406	5750	6085	6412	6728	7032	7322	7597
9	2928	3236	3556	3885	4222	4562	4906	5249	5591	5927
10	1549	1768	2004	2258	2527	2812	3110	3421	3742	4073
11	0686	0811	0951	1107	1280	1470	1677	1902	2144	2403
12	0250	0307	0372	0449	0537	0638	0753	0883	1028	1189
13	0074	0094	0118	0147	0183	0225	0275	0334	0402	0481
14	0017	0022	0029	0038	0049	0063	0079	0100	0125	0154
15	0003	0004	0006	0007	0010	0013	0017	0023	0029	0038
16		0001	0001	0001	0001	0002	0003	0004	0005	0007
17									0001	0001

n = 19

P / R	01	02	03	04	05	06	07	08	09	10
1	1738	3188	4394	5396	6226	6914	7481	7949	8334	8649
2	0153	0546	1100	1751	2453	3171	3879	4560	5202	5797
3	0009	0061	0183	0384	0665	1021	1439	1908	2415	2946
4		0005	0022	0061	0132	0243	0398	0602	0853	1150
5			0002	0007	0020	0044	0085	0147	0235	0352
6				0001	0002	0006	0014	0029	0051	0086
7						0001	0002	0004	0009	0017
8								0001	0001	0003

Table I: Cumulative Binomial Distribution   n = 19

P\R	11	12	13	14	15	16	17	18	19	20
1	8908	9119	9291	9431	9544	9636	9710	9770	9818	9856
2	6342	6835	7277	7669	8015	8318	8581	8809	9004	9171
3	3488	4032	4568	5089	5587	6059	6500	6910	7287	7631
4	1490	1867	2275	2708	3159	3620	4085	4549	5005	5449
5	0502	0685	0904	1158	1444	1762	2107	2476	2864	3267
6	0135	0202	0290	0401	0537	0700	0891	1110	1357	1631
7	0030	0048	0076	0113	0163	0228	0310	0411	0532	0676
8	0005	0009	0016	0026	0041	0061	0089	0126	0173	0233
9	0001	0002	0003	0005	0008	0014	0021	0032	0047	0067
10				0001	0001	0002	0004	0007	0010	0016
11							0001	0001	0002	0003

P\R	21	22	23	24	25	26	27	28	29	30
1	9887	9911	9930	9946	9958	9967	9975	9981	9985	9989
2	9313	9434	9535	9619	9690	9749	9797	9837	9869	9896
3	7942	8222	8471	8692	8887	9057	9205	9333	9443	9538
4	5877	6285	6671	7032	7369	7680	7965	8224	8458	8668
5	3681	4100	4520	4936	5346	5744	6129	6498	6848	7178
6	1929	2251	2592	2950	3322	3705	4093	4484	4875	5261
7	0843	1034	1248	1487	1749	2032	2336	2657	2995	3345
8	0307	0396	0503	0629	0775	0941	1129	1338	1568	1820
9	0093	0127	0169	0222	0287	0366	0459	0568	0694	0839
10	0023	0034	0047	0066	0089	0119	0156	0202	0258	0326
11	0005	0007	0011	0016	0023	0032	0044	0060	0080	0105
12	0001	0001	0002	0003	0005	0007	0010	0015	0021	0028
13				0001	0001	0001	0002	0003	0004	0006
14									0001	0001

P\R	31	32	33	34	35	36	37	38	39	40
1	9991	9993	9995	9996	9997	9998	9998	9999	9999	9999
2	9917	9935	9949	9960	9969	9976	9981	9986	9989	9992
3	9618	9686	9743	9791	9830	9863	9890	9913	9931	9945
4	8856	9022	9169	9297	9409	9505	9588	9659	9719	9770
5	7486	7773	8037	8280	8500	8699	8878	9038	9179	9304
6	5641	6010	6366	6707	7032	7339	7627	7895	8143	8371
7	3705	4073	4445	4818	5188	5554	5913	6261	6597	6919
8	2091	2381	2688	3010	3344	3690	4043	4401	4762	5122
9	1003	1186	1389	1612	1855	2116	2395	2691	3002	3325
10	0405	0499	0608	0733	0875	1035	1213	1410	1626	1861
11	0137	0176	0223	0280	0347	0426	0518	0625	0747	0885
12	0038	0051	0068	0089	0114	0146	0185	0231	0287	0352
13	0009	0012	0017	0023	0031	0041	0054	0070	0091	0116
14	0002	0002	0003	0005	0007	0009	0013	0017	0023	0031
15			0001	0001	0001	0002	0002	0003	0005	0006
16									0001	0001

P\R	41	42	43	44	45	46	47	48	49	50
1	10000	10000	10000	10000	10000	10000	10000	10000	10000	10000
2	9994	9995	9996	9997	9998	9999	9999	9999	9999	10000
3	9957	9967	9974	9980	9985	9988	9991	9993	9995	9996
4	9813	9849	9878	9903	9923	9939	9952	9963	9971	9978
5	9413	9508	9590	9660	9720	9771	9814	9850	9879	9904
6	8579	8767	8937	9088	9223	9342	9446	9537	9615	9682
7	7226	7515	7787	8039	8273	8488	8684	8862	9022	9165
8	5480	5832	6176	6509	6831	7138	7430	7706	7964	8204
9	3660	4003	4353	4706	5060	5413	5762	6105	6439	6762
10	2114	2385	2672	2974	3290	3617	3954	4299	4648	5000
11	1040	1213	1404	1613	1841	2087	2351	2631	2928	3238
12	0429	0518	0621	0738	0871	1021	1187	1372	1575	1796
13	0146	0183	0227	0280	0342	0415	0500	0597	0709	0835
14	0040	0052	0067	0086	0109	0137	0171	0212	0261	0318
15	0009	0012	0016	0021	0028	0036	0046	0060	0076	0096
16	0001	0002	0003	0004	0005	0007	0010	0013	0017	0022
17				0001	0001	0001	0001	0001	0002	0003	0004

Table I: Cumulative Binomial Distribution

n = 20

P	01	02	03	04	05	06	07	08	09	10
R										
1	1821	3324	4562	5580	6415	7099	7658	8113	8484	8784
2	0169	0599	1198	1897	2642	3395	4131	4831	5484	6083
3	0010	0071	0210	0439	0755	1150	1610	2121	2666	3231
4		0006	0027	0074	0159	0290	0471	0706	0993	1330
5			0003	0010	0026	0056	0107	0183	0290	0432
6				0001	0003	0009	0019	0038	0068	0113
7						0001	0003	0006	0013	0024
8								0001	0002	0004
9										0001

P	11	12	13	14	15	16	17	18	19	20
R										
1	9028	9224	9383	9510	9612	9694	9759	9811	9852	9885
2	6624	7109	7539	7916	8244	8529	8773	8982	9159	9308
3	3802	4369	4920	5450	5951	6420	6854	7252	7614	7939
4	1710	2127	2573	3041	3523	4010	4496	4974	5439	5886
5	0610	0827	1083	1375	1702	2059	2443	2849	3271	3704
6	0175	0260	0370	0507	0673	0870	1098	1356	1643	1958
7	0041	0067	0103	0153	0219	0304	0409	0537	0689	0867
8	0008	0014	0024	0038	0059	0088	0127	0177	0241	0321
9	0001	0002	0005	0008	0013	0021	0033	0049	0071	0100
10			0001	0001	0002	0004	0007	0011	0017	0026
11							0001	0001	0002	0004	0006
12									0001	0001

P	21	22	23	24	25	26	27	28	29	30
R										
1	9910	9931	9946	9959	9968	9976	9982	9986	9989	9992
2	9434	9539	9626	9698	9757	9805	9845	9877	9903	9924
3	8230	8488	8716	8915	9087	9237	9365	9474	9567	9645
4	6310	6711	7085	7431	7748	8038	8300	8534	8744	8929
5	4142	4580	5014	5439	5852	6248	6625	6981	7315	7625
6	2297	2657	3035	3427	3828	4235	4643	5048	5447	5836
7	1071	1301	1557	1838	2142	2467	2810	3169	3540	3920
8	0419	0536	0675	0835	1018	1225	1455	1707	1982	2277
9	0138	0186	0246	0320	0409	0515	0640	0784	0948	1133
10	0038	0054	0075	0103	0139	0183	0238	0305	0385	0480
11	0009	0013	0019	0028	0039	0055	0074	0100	0132	0171
12	0002	0003	0004	0006	0009	0014	0019	0027	0038	0051
13			0001	0001	0002	0003	0004	0006	0009	0013
14							0001	0001	0002	0003

P	31	32	33	34	35	36	37	38	39	40
R										
1	9994	9996	9997	9998	9998	9999	9999	9999	9999	10000
2	9940	9953	9964	9972	9979	9984	9988	9991	9993	9995
3	9711	9765	9811	9848	9879	9904	9924	9940	9953	9964
4	9092	9235	9358	9465	9556	9634	9700	9755	9802	9840
5	7911	8173	8411	8626	8818	8989	9141	9274	9390	9490
6	6213	6574	6917	7243	7546	7829	8090	8329	8547	8744
7	4305	4693	5079	5460	5834	6197	6547	6882	7200	7500
8	2591	2922	3268	3624	3990	4361	4735	5108	5478	5841
9	1340	1568	1818	2087	2376	2683	3005	3341	3688	4044
10	0591	0719	0866	1032	1218	1424	1650	1897	2163	2447
11	0220	0279	0350	0434	0532	0645	0775	0923	1090	1275
12	0069	0091	0119	0154	0196	0247	0308	0381	0466	0565
13	0018	0025	0034	0045	0060	0079	0102	0132	0167	0210
14	0004	0006	0008	0011	0015	0021	0028	0037	0049	0065
15	0001	0001	0001	0002	0003	0004	0006	0009	0012	0016
16						0001	0001	0002	0002	0003

P	41	42	43	44	45	46	47	48	49	50
R										
1	10000	10000	10000	10000	10000	10000	10000	10000	10000	10000
2	9996	9997	9998	9998	9999	9999	9999	9999	10000	10000
3	9972	9979	9984	9988	9991	9993	9995	9996	9997	9998
4	9872	9898	9920	9937	9951	9962	9971	9977	9983	9987
5	9577	9651	9714	9767	9811	9848	9879	9904	9924	9941

R \ P	41	42	43	44	45	46	47	48	49	50
6	8921	9078	9217	9340	9447	9539	9619	9687	9745	9793
7	7780	8041	8281	8501	8701	8881	9042	9186	9312	9423
8	6196	6539	6868	7183	7480	7759	8020	8261	8482	8684
9	4406	4771	5136	5499	5857	6207	6546	6873	7186	7483
10	2748	3064	3394	3736	4086	4443	4804	5166	5525	5881
11	1480	1705	1949	2212	2493	2791	3104	3432	3771	4119
12	0679	0810	0958	1123	1308	1511	1734	1977	2238	2517
13	0262	0324	0397	0482	0580	0694	0823	0969	1133	1316
14	0084	0107	0136	0172	0214	0265	0326	0397	0480	0577
15	0022	0029	0038	0050	0064	0083	0105	0133	0166	0207
16	0004	0006	0008	0011	0015	0020	0027	0035	0046	0059
17	0001	0001	0001	0002	0003	0004	0005	0007	0010	0013
18						0001	0001	0001	0001	0002

$n = 50$

R \ P	01	02	03	04	05	06	07	08	09	10
1	3950	6358	7819	8701	9231	9547	9734	9845	9910	9948
2	0894	2642	4447	5995	7206	8100	8735	9173	9468	9662
3	0138	0784	1892	3233	4595	5838	6892	7740	8395	8883
4	0016	0178	0628	1391	2396	3527	4673	5747	6697	7497
5	0001	0032	0168	0490	1036	1794	2710	3710	4723	5688
6		0005	0037	0144	0378	0776	1350	2081	2928	3839
7		0001	0007	0036	0118	0289	0583	1019	1596	2298
8			0001	0008	0032	0094	0220	0438	0768	1221
9				0001	0008	0027	0073	0167	0328	0579
10					0002	0007	0022	0056	0125	0245
11						0002	0006	0017	0043	0094
12						0001	0005	0013	0032
13								0001	0004	0010
14									0001	0003
15										0001

R \ P	11	12	13	14	15	16	17	18	19	20
1	9971	9983	9991	9995	9997	9998	9999	10000	10000	10000
2	9788	9869	9920	9951	9971	9983	9990	9994	9997	9998
3	9237	9487	9661	9779	9858	9910	9944	9965	9979	9987
4	8146	8655	9042	9330	9540	9688	9792	9863	9912	9943
5	6562	7320	7956	8472	8879	9192	9428	9601	9726	9815
6	4760	5647	6463	7186	7806	8323	8741	9071	9327	9520
7	3091	3935	4789	5616	6387	7081	7686	8199	8624	8966
8	1793	2467	3217	4010	4812	5594	6328	6996	7587	8096
9	0932	1392	1955	2605	3319	4071	4832	5576	6280	6927
10	0435	0708	1074	1537	2089	2718	3403	4122	4849	5563
11	0183	0325	0535	0824	1199	1661	2203	2813	3473	4164
12	0069	0135	0242	0402	0628	0929	1309	1768	2300	2893
13	0024	0051	0100	0179	0301	0475	0714	1022	1405	1861
14	0008	0018	0037	0073	0132	0223	0357	0544	0791	1106
15	0002	0006	0013	0027	0053	0096	0164	0266	0411	0607
16	0001	0002	0004	0009	0019	0038	0070	0120	0197	0308
17			0001	0003	0007	0014	0027	0050	0087	0144
18				0001	0002	0005	0010	0019	0036	0063
19					0001	0001	0003	0007	0013	0025
20							0001	0002	0005	0009
21								0001	0002	0003
22										0001

R \ P	21	22	23	24	25	26	27	28	29	30
1	10000	10000	10000	10000	10000	10000	10000	10000	10000	10000
2	9999	9999	10000	10000	10000	10000	10000	10000	10000	10000
3	9992	9995	9997	9998	9999	10000	10000	10000	10000	10000
4	9964	9978	9986	9992	9995	9997	9998	9999	9999	10000
5	9877	9919	9948	9967	9979	9987	9992	9995	9997	9998
6	9663	9767	9841	9893	9930	9954	9970	9981	9988	9993
7	9236	9445	9603	9720	9806	9868	9911	9941	9961	9975
8	8523	8874	9156	9377	9547	9676	9772	9842	9892	9927
9	7505	8009	8437	8794	9084	9316	9497	9635	9740	9817
10	6241	6870	7436	7934	8363	8724	9021	9260	9450	9598

P	21	22	23	24	25	26	27	28	29	30
R										
11	4864	5552	6210	6822	7378	7871	8299	8663	8965	9211
12	3533	4201	4878	5544	6184	6782	7329	7817	8244	8610
13	2383	2963	3585	4233	4890	5539	6163	6749	7287	7771
14	1490	1942	2456	3023	3630	4261	4901	5534	6145	6721
15	0862	1181	1565	2013	2519	3075	3669	4286	4912	5532
16	0462	0665	0926	1247	1631	2075	2575	3121	3703	4308
17	0229	0347	0508	0718	0983	1306	1689	2130	2623	3161
18	0105	0168	0259	0384	0551	0766	1034	1359	1741	2178
19	0045	0075	0122	0191	0287	0418	0590	0809	1080	1406
20	0018	0031	0054	0088	0139	0212	0314	0449	0626	0848
21	0006	0012	0022	0038	0063	0100	0155	0232	0338	0478
22	0002	0004	0008	0015	0026	0044	0071	0112	0170	0251
23	0001	0001	0003	0006	0010	0018	0031	0050	0080	0123
24			0001	0002	0004	0007	0012	0021	0035	0056
25				0001	0001	0002	0004	0008	0014	0024
26						0001	0002	0003	0005	0009
27								0001	0002	0003
28									0001	0001

P	31	32	33	34	35	36	37	38	39	40
R										
1	10000	10000	10000	10000	10000	10000	10000	10000	10000	10000
2	10000	10000	10000	10000	10000	10000	10000	10000	10000	10000
3	10000	10000	10000	10000	10000	10000	10000	10000	10000	10000
4	10000	10000	10000	10000	10000	10000	10000	10000	10000	10000
5	9999	9999	10000	10000	10000	10000	10000	10000	10000	10000
6	9997	9997	9998	9999	9999	10000	10000	10000	10000	10000
7	9984	9990	9994	9996	9998	9999	9999	10000	10000	10000
8	9952	9969	9980	9987	9992	9995	9997	9998	9999	9999
9	9874	9914	9942	9962	9975	9984	9990	9994	9996	9998
10	9710	9794	9856	9901	9933	9955	9971	9981	9988	9992
11	9409	9563	9683	9773	9840	9889	9924	9949	9966	9978
12	8916	9168	9371	9533	9658	9753	9825	9878	9916	9943
13	8197	8564	8873	9130	9339	9505	9635	9736	9811	9867
14	7253	7732	8157	8524	8837	9097	9310	9481	9616	9730
15	6131	6698	7223	7699	8122	8491	8805	9069	9286	9460
16	4922	5530	6120	6679	7199	7672	8094	8462	8779	9045
17	3734	4328	4931	5530	6111	6664	7179	7649	8070	8439
18	2666	3197	3760	4346	4940	5531	6105	6653	7164	7631
19	1786	2220	2703	3227	3784	4362	4949	5533	6101	6644
20	1121	1447	1826	2257	2736	3255	3805	4376	4957	5535
21	0657	0882	1156	1482	1861	2289	2764	3278	3824	4390
22	0360	0503	0685	0912	1187	1513	1890	2317	2788	3299
23	0184	0267	0379	0525	0710	0938	1214	1540	1916	2340
24	0087	0133	0196	0282	0396	0544	0730	0960	1236	1562
25	0039	0061	0094	0141	0207	0295	0411	0560	0748	0978
26	0016	0026	0042	0066	0100	0149	0216	0305	0423	0573
27	0006	0011	0018	0029	0045	0070	0106	0155	0223	0314
28	0002	0004	0007	0012	0019	0031	0048	0074	0110	0160
29	0001	0001	0002	0004	0007	0012	0020	0032	0050	0076
30			0001	0002	0003	0005	0008	0013	0021	0034
31					0001	0002	0003	0005	0008	0014
32						0001	0001	0002	0003	0005
33								0001	0001	0002
34										0001

P	41	42	43	44	45	46	47	48	49	50
R										
1	10000	10000	10000	10000	10000	10000	10000	10000	10000	10000
2	10000	10000	10000	10000	10000	10000	10000	10000	10000	10000
3	10000	10000	10000	10000	10000	10000	10000	10000	10000	10000
4	10000	10000	10000	10000	10000	10000	10000	10000	10000	10000
5	10000	10000	10000	10000	10000	10000	10000	10000	10000	10000
6	10000	10000	10000	10000	10000	10000	10000	10000	10000	10000
7	10000	10000	10000	10000	10000	10000	10000	10000	10000	10000
8	10000	10000	10000	10000	10000	10000	10000	10000	10000	10000
9	9999	9999	10000	10000	10000	10000	10000	10000	10000	10000
10	9995	9997	9998	9999	9999	10000	10000	10000	10000	10000
11	9986	9991	9994	9997	9998	9999	9999	10000	10000	10000
12	9962	9975	9984	9990	9994	9996	9998	9999	9999	10000
13	9908	9938	9958	9973	9982	9989	9993	9996	9997	9998
14	9799	9858	9902	9933	9955	9970	9981	9988	9992	9995
15	9599	9707	9789	9851	9896	9929	9952	9968	9980	9987

P R	41	42	43	44	45	46	47	48	49	50
16	9265	9443	9585	9696	9780	9844	9892	9926	9950	9967
17	8757	9025	9248	9429	9573	9687	9774	9839	9888	9923
18	8051	8421	8740	9010	9235	9418	9565	9680	9769	9836
19	7152	7617	8037	8406	8727	8998	9225	9410	9559	9675
20	6099	6638	7143	7608	8026	8396	8718	8991	9219	9405
21	4965	5539	6099	6635	7138	7602	8020	8391	8713	8987
22	3840	4402	4973	5543	6100	6634	7137	7599	8018	8389
23	2809	3316	3854	4412	4981	5548	6104	6636	7138	7601
24	1936	2359	2826	3331	3866	4422	4989	5554	6109	6641
25	1255	1580	1953	2375	2840	3343	3876	4431	4996	5561
26	0762	0992	1269	1593	1966	2386	2850	3352	3885	4439
27	0432	0584	0772	1003	1279	1603	1975	2395	2858	3359
28	0229	0320	0439	0591	0780	1010	1286	1609	1981	2399
29	0113	0164	0233	0325	0444	0595	0784	1013	1289	1611
30	0052	0078	0115	0166	0235	0327	0446	0596	0784	1013
31	0022	0034	0053	0079	0116	0167	0236	0327	0445	0595
32	0009	0014	0022	0035	0053	0079	0116	0166	0234	0325
33	0003	0005	0009	0014	0022	0035	0053	0078	0114	0164
34	0001	0002	0003	0005	0009	0014	0022	0034	0052	0077
35		0001	0001	0002	0003	0005	0008	0014	0021	0033
36				0001	0001	0002	0003	0005	0008	0013
37						0001	0001	0002	0003	0005
38								0001	0001	0002

n = 100

P R	01	02	03	04	05	06	07	08	09	10
1	6340	8674	9524	9831	9941	9979	9993	9998	9999	10000
2	2642	5967	8054	9128	9629	9848	9940	9977	9991	9997
3	0794	3233	5802	7679	8817	9434	9742	9887	9952	9981
4	0184	1410	3528	5705	7422	8570	9256	9633	9827	9922
5	0034	0508	1821	3711	5640	7232	8368	9097	9526	9763
6	0005	0155	0808	2116	3840	5593	7086	8201	8955	9424
7	0001	0041	0312	1064	2340	3936	5557	6968	8060	8828
8		0009	0106	0475	1280	2517	4012	5529	6872	7939
9		0002	0032	0190	0631	1463	2660	4074	5506	6791
10			0009	0068	0282	0775	1620	2780	4125	5487
11			0002	0022	0115	0376	0908	1757	2882	4168
12				0007	0043	0168	0469	1028	1876	2970
13				0002	0015	0069	0224	0559	1138	1982
14					0005	0026	0099	0282	0645	1239
15					0001	0009	0041	0133	0341	0726
16						0003	0016	0058	0169	0399
17						0001	0006	0024	0078	0206
18							0002	0009	0034	0100
19							0001	0003	0014	0046
20								0001	0005	0020
21									0002	0008
22									0001	0003
23										0001

P R	11	12	13	14	15	16	17	18	19	20
1	10000	10000	10000	10000	10000	10000	10000	10000	10000	10000
2	9999	10000	10000	10000	10000	10000	10000	10000	10000	10000
3	9992	9997	9999	10000	10000	10000	10000	10000	10000	10000
4	9966	9985	9994	9998	9999	10000	10000	10000	10000	10000
5	9886	9947	9977	9990	9996	9998	9999	10000	10000	10000
6	9698	9848	9926	9966	9984	9993	9997	9999	10000	10000
7	9328	9633	9808	9903	9953	9978	9990	9996	9998	9999
8	8715	9239	9569	9766	9878	9939	9970	9986	9994	9997
9	7835	8614	9155	9508	9725	9853	9924	9962	9982	9991
10	6722	7743	8523	9078	9449	9684	9826	9908	9953	9977
11	5471	6663	7663	8440	9006	9393	9644	9800	9891	9943
12	4206	5458	6611	7591	8365	8939	9340	9605	9773	9874
13	3046	4239	5446	6566	7527	8297	8876	9289	9567	9747
14	2076	3114	4268	5436	6526	7469	8234	8819	9241	9531
15	1330	2160	3173	4294	5428	6490	7417	8177	8765	9196
16	0802	1414	2236	3227	4317	5420	6458	7370	8125	8715
17	0456	0874	1492	2305	3275	4338	5414	6429	7327	8077
18	0244	0511	0942	1563	2367	3319	4357	5408	6403	7288
19	0123	0282	0564	1006	1628	2424	3359	4374	5403	6379
20	0059	0147	0319	0614	1065	1689	2477	3395	4391	5398

R	11	12	13	14	15	16	17	18	19	20
21	0026	0073	0172	0356	0663	1121	1745	2525	3429	4405
22	0011	0034	0088	0196	0393	0710	1174	1797	2570	3460
23	0005	0015	0042	0103	0221	0428	0754	1223	1846	2611
24	0002	0006	0020	0051	0119	0246	0462	0796	1270	1891
25	0001	0003	0009	0024	0061	0135	0271	0496	0837	1314
26		0001	0004	0011	0030	0071	0151	0295	0528	0875
27			0001	0005	0014	0035	0081	0168	0318	0558
28			0001	0002	0006	0017	0041	0091	0184	0342
29				0001	0003	0008	0020	0048	0102	0200
30					0001	0003	0009	0024	0054	0112
31						0001	0004	0011	0027	0061
32						0001	0002	0005	0013	0031
33							0001	0002	0006	0016
34								0001	0003	0007
35									0001	0003
36										0001
37										0001

R	21	22	23	24	25	26	27	28	29	30
1	10000	10000	10000	10000	10000	10000	10000	10000	10000	10000
2	10000	10000	10000	10000	10000	10000	10000	10000	10000	10000
3	10000	10000	10000	10000	10000	10000	10000	10000	10000	10000
4	10000	10000	10000	10000	10000	10000	10000	10000	10000	10000
5	10000	10000	10000	10000	10000	10000	10000	10000	10000	10000
6	10000	10000	10000	10000	10000	10000	10000	10000	10000	10000
7	10000	10000	10000	10000	10000	10000	10000	10000	10000	10000
8	9999	10000	10000	10000	10000	10000	10000	10000	10000	10000
9	9996	9998	9999	10000	10000	10000	10000	10000	10000	10000
10	9989	9995	9998	9999	10000	10000	10000	10000	10000	10000
11	9971	9986	9993	9997	9999	9999	10000	10000	10000	10000
12	9933	9965	9983	9992	9996	9998	9999	10000	10000	10000
13	9857	9922	9959	9979	9990	9995	9998	9999	10000	10000
14	9721	9840	9911	9953	9975	9988	9994	9997	9999	9999
15	9496	9695	9823	9900	9946	9972	9986	9993	9997	9998
16	9153	9462	9671	9806	9889	9939	9967	9983	9992	9996
17	8668	9112	9430	9647	9789	9878	9932	9963	9981	9990
18	8032	8625	9074	9399	9624	9773	9867	9925	9959	9978
19	7252	7991	8585	9038	9370	9601	9757	9856	9918	9955
20	6358	7220	7953	8547	9005	9342	9580	9741	9846	9911
21	5394	6338	7189	7918	8512	8973	9316	9560	9726	9835
22	4419	5391	6320	7162	7886	8479	8943	9291	9540	9712
23	3488	4432	5388	6304	7136	7856	8448	8915	9267	9521
24	2649	3514	4444	5386	6289	7113	7828	8420	8889	9245
25	1933	2684	3539	4455	5383	6276	7091	7802	8393	8864
26	1355	1972	2717	3561	4465	5381	6263	7071	7778	8369
27	0911	1393	2009	2748	3583	4475	5380	6252	7053	7756
28	0588	0945	1429	2043	2776	3602	4484	5378	6242	7036
29	0364	0616	0978	1463	2075	2803	3621	4493	5377	6232
30	0216	0386	0643	1009	1495	2105	2828	3638	4501	5377
31	0123	0232	0406	0669	1038	1526	2134	2851	3654	4509
32	0067	0134	0247	0427	0693	1065	1554	2160	2873	3669
33	0035	0074	0144	0262	0446	0717	1091	1580	2184	2893
34	0018	0039	0081	0154	0276	0465	0739	1116	1605	2207
35	0009	0020	0044	0087	0164	0290	0482	0760	1139	1629
36	0004	0010	0023	0048	0094	0174	0303	0499	0780	1161
37	0002	0005	0011	0025	0052	0101	0183	0316	0515	0799
38	0001	0002	0005	0013	0027	0056	0107	0193	0328	0530
39		0001	0002	0006	0014	0030	0060	0113	0201	0340
40			0001	0003	0007	0015	0032	0064	0119	0210
41				0001	0003	0008	0017	0035	0068	0125
42					0001	0004	0008	0018	0037	0072
43						0001	0004	0009	0020	0040
44						0001	0002	0005	0010	0021
45							0001	0002	0005	0011
46								0001	0002	0005
47									0001	0003
48										0001
49										0001

Table I: Cumulative Binomial Distribution — n = 100

P R	31	32	33	34	35	36	37	38	39	40
1	10000	10000	10000	10000	10000	10000	10000	10000	10000	10000
2	10000	10000	10000	10000	10000	10000	10000	10000	10000	10000
3	10000	10000	10000	10000	10000	10000	10000	10000	10000	10000
4	10000	10000	10000	10000	10000	10000	10000	10000	10000	10000
5	10000	10000	10000	10000	10000	10000	10000	10000	10000	10000
6	10000	10000	10000	10000	10000	10000	10000	10000	10000	10000
7	10000	10000	10000	10000	10000	10000	10000	10000	10000	10000
8	10000	10000	10000	10000	10000	10000	10000	10000	10000	10000
9	10000	10000	10000	10000	10000	10000	10000	10000	10000	10000
10	10000	10000	10000	100.00	10000	10000	10000	10000	10000	10000
11	10000	10000	10000	10000	10000	10000	10000	10000	10000	10000
12	10000	10000	10000	10000	10000	10000	10000	10000	10000	10000
13	10000	10000	10000	10000	10000	10000	10000	10000	10000	10000
14	10000	10000	10000	10000	10000	10000	10000	10000	10000	10000
15	9999	10000	10000	10000	10000	10000	10000	10000	10000	10000
16	9998	9999	10000	10000	10000	10000	10000	10000	10000	10000
17	9995	9998	9999	10000	10000	10000	10000	10000	10000	10000
18	9989	9995	9997	9999	9999	10000	10000	10000	10000	10000
19	9976	9988	9994	9997	9999	9999	10000	10000	10000	10000
20	9950	9973	9986	9993	9997	9998	9999	10000	10000	10000
21	9904	9946	9971	9985	9992	9996	9998	9999	10000	10000
22	9825	9898	9942	9968	9983	9991	9996	9998	9999	10000
23	9698	9816	9891	9938	9966	9982	9991	9995	9998	9999
24	9504	9685	9806	9885	9934	9963	9980	9990	9995	9997
25	9224	9487	9672	9797	9879	9930	9961	9979	9989	9994
26	8841	9204	9471	9660	9789	9873	9926	9958	9977	9988
27	8346	8820	9185	9456	9649	9780	9867	9922	9956	9976
28	7736	8325	8800	9168	9442	9638	9773	9862	9919	9954
29	7021	7717	8305	8781	9152	9429	9628	9765	9857	9916
30	6224	7007	7699	8287	8764	9137	9417	9618	9759	9852
31	5376	6216	6994	7684	8270	8748	9123	9405	9610	9752
32	4516	5376	6209	6982	7669	8254	8733	9110	9395	9602
33	3683	4523	5375	6203	6971	7656	8240	8720	9098	9385
34	2912	3696	4530	5375	6197	6961	7643	8227	8708	9087
35	2229	2929	3708	4536	5376	6192	6953	7632	8216	8697
36	1650	2249	2946	3720	4542	5376	6188	6945	7623	8205
37	1181	1671	2268	2961	3731	4547	5377	6184	6938	7614
38	0816	1200	1690	2285	2976	3741	4553	5377	6181	6932
39	0545	0833	1218	1708	2301	2989	3750	4558	5378	6178
40	0351	0558	0849	1235	1724	2316	3001	3759	4562	5379
41	0218	0361	0571	0863	1250	1739	2330	3012	3767	4567
42	0131	0226	0371	0583	0877	1265	1753	2343	3023	3775
43	0075	0136	0233	0380	0594	0889	1278	1766	2355	3033
44	0042	0079	0141	0240	0389	0605	0901	1290	1778	2365
45	0023	0044	0082	0146	0246	0397	0614	0911	1301	1789
46	0012	0024	0046	0085	0150	0252	0405	0623	0921	1311
47	0006	0012	0025	0048	0088	0154	0257	0411	0631	0930
48	0003	0006	0013	0026	0050	0091	0158	0262	0417	0638
49	0001	0003	0007	0014	0027	0052	0094	0162	0267	0423
50	0001	0001	0003	0007	0015	0029	0054	0096	0165	0271
51		0001	0002	0003	0007	0015	0030	0055	0098	0168
52		0001	0001	0002	0004	0008	0016	0030	0056	0100
53				0001	0002	0004	0008	0016	0031	0058
54					0001	0002	0004	0008	0017	0032
55						0001	0002	0004	0009	0017
56							0001	0002	0004	0009
57								0001	0002	0004
58									0001	0002
59										0001

P	41	42	43	44	45	46	47	48	49	50
R										
1	10000	10000	10000	10000	10000	10000	10000	10000	10000	10000
2	10000	10000	10000	10000	10000	10000	10000	10000	10000	10000
3	10000	10000	10000	10000	10000	10000	10000	10000	10000	10000
4	10000	10000	10000	10000	10000	10000	10000	10000	10000	10000
5	10000	10000	10000	10000	10000	10000	10000	10000	10000	10000
6	10000	10000	10000	10000	10000	10000	10000	10000	10000	10000
7	10000	10000	10000	10000	10000	10000	10000	10000	10000	10000
8	10000	10000	10000	10000	10000	10000	10000	10000	10000	10000
9	10000	10000	10000	10000	10000	10000	10000	10000	10000	10000
10	10000	10000	10000	10000	10000	10000	10000	10000	10000	10000
11	10000	10000	10000	10000	10000	10000	10000	10000	10000	10000
12	10000	10000	10000	10000	10000	10000	10000	10000	10000	10000
13	10000	10000	10000	10000	10000	10000	10000	10000	10000	10000
14	10000	10000	10000	10000	10000	10000	10000	10000	10000	10000
15	10000	10000	10000	10000	10000	10000	10000	10000	10000	10000
16	10000	10000	10000	10000	10000	10000	10000	10000	10000	10000
17	10000	10000	10000	10000	10000	10000	10000	10000	10000	10000
18	10000	10000	10000	10000	10000	10000	10000	10000	10000	10000
19	10000	10000	10000	10000	10000	10000	10000	10000	10000	10000
20	10000	10000	10000	10000	10000	10000	10000	10000	10000	10000
21	10000	10000	10000	10000	10000	10000	10000	10000	10000	10000
22	10000	10000	10000	10000	10000	10000	10000	10000	10000	10000
23	10000	10000	10000	10000	10000	10000	10000	10000	10000	10000
24	9999	9999	10000	10000	10000	10000	10000	10000	10000	10000
25	9997	9999	9999	10000	10000	10000	10000	10000	10000	10000
26	9994	9997	9999	9999	10000	10000	10000	10000	10000	10000
27	9987	9994	9997	9998	9999	10000	10000	10000	10000	10000
28	9975	9987	9993	9997	9998	9999	10000	10000	10000	10000
29	9952	9974	9986	9993	9996	9998	9999	10000	10000	10000
30	9913	9950	9972	9985	9992	9996	9998	9999	10000	10000
31	9848	9910	9948	9971	9985	9992	9996	9998	9999	10000
32	9746	9844	9907	9947	9970	9984	9992	9996	9998	9999
33	9594	9741	9840	9905	9945	9969	9984	9991	9996	9998
34	9376	9587	9736	9837	9902	9944	9969	9983	9991	9996
35	9078	9368	9581	9732	9834	9900	9942	9968	9983	9991
36	8687	9069	9361	9576	9728	9831	9899	9941	9967	9982
37	8196	8678	9061	9355	9571	9724	9829	9897	9941	9967
38	7606	8188	8670	9054	9349	9567	9721	9827	9896	9940
39	6927	7599	8181	8663	9049	9345	9563	9719	9825	9895
40	6176	6922	7594	8174	8657	9044	9341	9561	9717	9824
41	5380	6174	6919	7589	8169	8653	9040	9338	9558	9716
42	4571	5382	6173	6916	7585	8165	8649	9037	9335	9557
43	3782	4576	5383	6173	6913	7582	8162	8646	9035	9334
44	3041	3788	4580	5385	6172	6912	7580	8160	8645	9033
45	2375	3049	3794	4583	5387	6173	6911	7579	8159	8644
46	1799	2384	3057	3799	4587	5389	6173	6911	7579	8159
47	1320	1807	2391	3063	3804	4590	5391	6174	6912	7579
48	0938	1328	1815	2398	3069	3809	4593	5393	6176	6914
49	0644	0944	1335	1822	2404	3074	3813	4596	5395	6178
50	0428	0650	0950	1341	1827	2409	3078	3816	4599	5398
51	0275	0432	0655	0955	1346	1832	2413	3082	3819	4602
52	0170	0278	0436	0659	0960	1350	1836	2417	3084	3822
53	0102	0172	0280	0439	0662	0963	1353	1838	2419	3086
54	0059	0103	0174	0282	0441	0664	0965	1355	1840	2421
55	0033	0059	0104	0175	0284	0443	0666	0967	1356	1841
56	0017	0033	0060	0105	0176	0285	0444	0667	0967	1356
57	0009	0018	0034	0061	0106	0177	0286	0444	0667	0967
58	0004	0009	0018	0034	0061	0106	0177	0286	0444	0666
59	0002	0005	0009	0018	0034	0061	0106	0177	0285	0443
60	0001	0002	0005	0009	0018	0034	0061	0106	0177	0284
61		0001	0002	0005	0009	0018	0034	0061	0106	0176
62			0001	0002	0005	0009	0018	0034	0061	0105
63				0001	0002	0005	0009	0018	0034	0060
64					0001	0002	0005	0009	0018	0033
65						0001	0002	0005	0009	0018
66							0001	0002	0004	0009
67								0001	0002	0004
68									0001	0002
69										0001

Table II

Unit Normal Probability Distribution
$$P'_N*(u)$$

u	.00	.01	.02	.03	.04	.05	.06	.07	.08	.09
.0	.3989	.3989	.3989	.3988	.3986	.3984	.3982	.3980	.3977	.3973
.1	.3970	.3965	.3961	.3956	.3951	.3945	.3939	.3932	.3925	.3918
.2	.3910	.3902	.3894	.3885	.3876	.3867	.3857	.3847	.3836	.3825
.3	.3814	.3802	.3790	.3778	.3765	.3752	.3739	.3725	.3712	.3697
.4	.3683	.3668	.3653	.3637	.3621	.3605	.3589	.3572	.3555	.3538
.5	.3521	.3503	.3485	.3467	.3448	.3429	.3410	.3391	.3372	.3352
.6	.3332	.3312	.3292	.3271	.3251	.3230	.3209	.3187	.3166	.3144
.7	.3123	.3101	.3079	.3056	.3034	.3011	.2989	.2966	.2943	.2920
.8	.2897	.2874	.2850	.2827	.2803	.2780	.2756	.2732	.2709	.2685
.9	.2661	.2637	.2613	.2589	.2565	.2541	.2516	.2492	.2468	.2444
1.0	.2420	.2396	.2371	.2347	.2323	.2299	.2275	.2251	.2227	.2203
1.1	.2179	.2155	.2131	.2107	.2083	.2059	.2036	.2012	.1989	.1965
1.2	.1942	.1919	.1895	.1872	.1849	.1826	.1804	.1781	.1758	.1736
1.3	.1714	.1691	.1669	.1647	.1626	.1604	.1582	.1561	.1539	.1518
1.4	.1497	.1476	.1456	.1435	.1415	.1394	.1374	.1354	.1334	.1315
1.5	.1295	.1276	.1257	.1238	.1219	.1200	.1182	.1163	.1145	.1127
1.6	.1109	.1092	.1074	.1057	.1040	.1023	.1006	.09893	.09728	.09566
1.7	.09405	.09246	.09089	.08933	.08780	.08628	.08478	.08329	.08183	.08038
1.8	.07895	.07754	.07614	.07477	.07341	.07206	.07074	.06943	.06814	.06687
1.9	.06562	.06438	.06316	.06195	.06077	.05959	.05844	.05730	.05618	.05508
2.0	.05399	.05292	.05186	.05082	.04980	.04879	.04780	.04682	.04586	.04491
2.1	.04398	.04307	.04217	.04128	.04041	.03955	.03871	.03788	.03706	.03626
2.2	.03547	.03470	.03394	.03319	.03246	.03174	.03103	.03034	.02965	.02898
2.3	.02833	.02768	.02705	.02643	.02582	.02522	.02463	.02406	.02349	.02294
2.4	.02239	.02186	.02134	.02083	.02033	.01984	.01936	.01888	.01842	.01797

x	.00	.01	.02	.03	.04	.05	.06	.07	.08	.09
2.5	.01753	.01709	.01667	.01625	.01585	.01545	.01506	.01468	.01431	.01394
2.6	.01358	.01323	.01289	.01256	.01223	.01191	.01160	.01130	.01100	.01071
2.7	.01042	.01014	$.0^{2}9871$	$.0^{2}9606$	$.0^{2}9347$	$.0^{2}9094$	$.0^{2}8846$	$.0^{2}8605$	$.0^{2}8370$	$.0^{2}8140$
2.8	$.0^{2}7915$	$.0^{2}7697$	$.0^{2}7483$	$.0^{2}7274$	$.0^{2}7071$	$.0^{2}6873$	$.0^{2}6679$	$.0^{2}6491$	$.0^{2}6307$	$.0^{2}6127$
2.9	$.0^{2}5953$	$.0^{2}5782$	$.0^{2}5616$	$.0^{2}5454$	$.0^{2}5296$	$.0^{2}5143$	$.0^{2}4993$	$.0^{2}4847$	$.0^{2}4705$	$.0^{2}4567$
3.0	$.0^{2}4432$	$.0^{2}4301$	$.0^{2}4173$	$.0^{2}4049$	$.0^{2}3928$	$.0^{2}3810$	$.0^{2}3695$	$.0^{2}3584$	$.0^{2}3475$	$.0^{2}3370$
3.1	$.0^{2}3267$	$.0^{2}3167$	$.0^{2}3070$	$.0^{2}2975$	$.0^{2}2884$	$.0^{2}2794$	$.0^{2}2707$	$.0^{2}2623$	$.0^{2}2541$	$.0^{2}2461$
3.2	$.0^{2}2384$	$.0^{2}2309$	$.0^{2}2236$	$.0^{2}2165$	$.0^{2}2096$	$.0^{2}2029$	$.0^{2}1964$	$.0^{2}1901$	$.0^{2}1840$	$.0^{2}1780$
3.3	$.0^{2}1723$	$.0^{2}1667$	$.0^{2}1612$	$.0^{2}1560$	$.0^{2}1508$	$.0^{2}1459$	$.0^{2}1411$	$.0^{2}1364$	$.0^{2}1319$	$.0^{2}1275$
3.4	$.0^{2}1232$	$.0^{2}1191$	$.0^{2}1151$	$.0^{2}1112$	$.0^{2}1075$	$.0^{2}1038$	$.0^{2}1003$	$.0^{3}9689$	$.0^{3}9358$	$.0^{3}9037$
3.5	$.0^{3}8727$	$.0^{3}8426$	$.0^{3}8135$	$.0^{3}7853$	$.0^{3}7581$	$.0^{3}7317$	$.0^{3}7061$	$.0^{3}6814$	$.0^{3}6575$	$.0^{3}6343$
3.6	$.0^{3}6119$	$.0^{3}5902$	$.0^{3}5693$	$.0^{3}5490$	$.0^{3}5294$	$.0^{3}5105$	$.0^{3}4921$	$.0^{3}4744$	$.0^{3}4573$	$.0^{3}4408$
3.7	$.0^{3}4248$	$.0^{3}4093$	$.0^{3}3944$	$.0^{3}3800$	$.0^{3}3661$	$.0^{3}3526$	$.0^{3}3396$	$.0^{3}3271$	$.0^{3}3149$	$.0^{3}3032$
3.8	$.0^{3}2919$	$.0^{3}2810$	$.0^{3}2705$	$.0^{3}2604$	$.0^{3}2506$	$.0^{3}2411$	$.0^{3}2320$	$.0^{3}2232$	$.0^{3}2147$	$.0^{3}2065$
3.9	$.0^{3}1987$	$.0^{3}1910$	$.0^{3}1837$	$.0^{3}1766$	$.0^{3}1698$	$.0^{3}1633$	$.0^{3}1569$	$.0^{3}1508$	$.0^{3}1449$	$.0^{3}1393$
4.0	$.0^{3}1338$	$.0^{3}1286$	$.0^{3}1235$	$.0^{3}1186$	$.0^{3}1140$	$.0^{3}1094$	$.0^{3}1051$	$.0^{3}1009$	$.0^{4}9687$	$.0^{4}9299$
4.1	$.0^{4}8926$	$.0^{4}8567$	$.0^{4}8222$	$.0^{4}7890$	$.0^{4}7570$	$.0^{4}7263$	$.0^{4}6967$	$.0^{4}6683$	$.0^{4}6410$	$.0^{4}6147$
4.2	$.0^{4}5894$	$.0^{4}5652$	$.0^{4}5418$	$.0^{4}5194$	$.0^{4}4979$	$.0^{4}4772$	$.0^{4}4573$	$.0^{4}4382$	$.0^{4}4199$	$.0^{4}4023$
4.3	$.0^{4}3854$	$.0^{4}3691$	$.0^{4}3535$	$.0^{4}3386$	$.0^{4}3242$	$.0^{4}3104$	$.0^{4}2972$	$.0^{4}2845$	$.0^{4}2723$	$.0^{4}2606$
4.4	$.0^{4}2494$	$.0^{4}2387$	$.0^{4}2284$	$.0^{4}2185$	$.0^{4}2090$	$.0^{4}1999$	$.0^{4}1912$	$.0^{4}1829$	$.0^{4}1749$	$.0^{4}1672$
4.5	$.0^{4}1598$	$.0^{4}1528$	$.0^{4}1461$	$.0^{4}1396$	$.0^{4}1334$	$.0^{4}1275$	$.0^{4}1218$	$.0^{4}1164$	$.0^{4}1112$	$.0^{4}1062$
4.6	$.0^{4}1014$	$.0^{5}9684$	$.0^{5}9248$	$.0^{5}8830$	$.0^{5}8430$	$.0^{5}8047$	$.0^{5}7681$	$.0^{5}7331$	$.0^{5}6996$	$.0^{5}6676$
4.7	$.0^{5}6370$	$.0^{5}6077$	$.0^{5}5797$	$.0^{5}5530$	$.0^{5}5274$	$.0^{5}5030$	$.0^{5}4796$	$.0^{5}4573$	$.0^{5}4360$	$.0^{5}4156$
4.8	$.0^{5}3961$	$.0^{5}3775$	$.0^{5}3598$	$.0^{5}3428$	$.0^{5}3267$	$.0^{5}3112$	$.0^{5}2965$	$.0^{5}2824$	$.0^{5}2690$	$.0^{5}2561$
4.9	$.0^{5}2439$	$.0^{5}2322$	$.0^{5}2211$	$.0^{5}2105$	$.0^{5}2003$	$.0^{5}1907$	$.0^{5}1814$	$.0^{5}1727$	$.0^{5}1643$	$.0^{5}1563$

Example: $P'_{N*}(3.57) = P'_{N*}(-3.57) = .0^{3}6814 = .0006814$

Reproduced by permission from A. Hald, "Statistical Tables and Formulas," John Wiley & Sons, Inc., New York, 1952.

Table III
Cumulative Unit Normal Distribution
$$P_{N^*}(\tilde{u} > u)$$

u	.00	.01	.02	.03	.04	.05	.06	.07	.08	.09
0	.5000	.4960	.4920	.4880	.4840	.4801	.4761	.4721	.4681	.4641
.1	.4602	.4562	.4522	.4483	.4443	.4404	.4364	.4325	.4286	.4247
.2	.4207	.4168	.4129	.4090	.4052	.4013	.3974	.3936	.3897	.3859
.3	.3821	.3783	.3745	.3707	.3669	.3632	.3594	.3557	.3520	.3483
.4	.3446	.3409	.3372	.3336	.3300	.3264	.3228	.3192	.3156	.3121
.5	.3085	.3050	.3015	.2981	.2946	.2912	.2877	.2843	.2810	.2776
.6	.2743	.2709	.2676	.2643	.2611	.2578	.2546	.2514	.2483	.2451
.7	.2420	.2389	.2358	.2327	.2297	.2266	.2236	.2206	.2177	.2148
.8	.2119	.2090	.2061	.2033	.2005	.1977	.1949	.1922	.1894	.1867
.9	.1841	.1814	.1788	.1762	.1736	.1711	.1685	.1660	.1635	.1611
1.0	.1587	.1562	.1539	.1515	.1492	.1469	.1446	.1423	.1401	.1379
1.1	.1357	.1335	.1314	.1292	.1271	.1251	.1230	.1210	.1190	.1170
1.2	.1151	.1131	.1112	.1093	.1075	.1056	.1038	.1020	.1003	.09853
1.3	.09680	.09510	.09342	.09176	.09012	.08851	.08691	.08534	.08379	.08226
1.4	.08076	.07927	.07780	.07636	.07493	.07353	.07215	.07078	.06944	.06811
1.5	.06681	.06552	.06426	.06301	.06178	.06057	.05938	.05821	.05705	.05592
1.6	.05480	.05370	.05262	.05155	.05050	.04947	.04846	.04746	.04648	.04551
1.7	.04457	.04363	.04272	.04182	.04093	.04006	.03920	.03836	.03754	.03673
1.8	.03593	.03515	.03438	.03362	.03288	.03216	.03144	.03074	.03005	.02938
1.9	.02872	.02807	.02743	.02680	.02619	.02559	.02500	.02442	.02385	.02330
2.0	.02275	.02222	.02169	.02118	.02068	.02018	.01970	.01923	.01876	.01831
2.1	.01786	.01743	.01700	.01659	.01618	.01578	.01539	.01500	.01463	.01426
2.2	.01390	.01355	.01321	.01287	.01255	.01222	.01191	.01160	.01130	.01101
2.3	.01072	.01044	.01017	$.0^2 9903$	$.0^2 9642$	$.0^2 9387$	$.0^2 9137$	$.0^2 8894$	$.0^2 8656$	$.0^2 8424$
2.4	$.0^2 8198$	$.0^2 7976$	$.0^2 7760$	$.0^2 7549$	$.0^2 7344$	$.0^2 7143$	$.0^2 6947$	$.0^2 6756$	$.0^2 6569$	$.0^2 6387$

u	0	1	2	3	4	5	6	7	8	9
2.5	$.0^{2}6210$	$.0^{2}6037$	$.0^{2}5868$	$.0^{2}5703$	$.0^{2}5543$	$.0^{2}5386$	$.0^{2}5234$	$.0^{2}5085$	$.0^{2}4940$	$.0^{2}4799$
2.6	$.0^{2}4661$	$.0^{2}4527$	$.0^{2}4396$	$.0^{2}4269$	$.0^{2}4145$	$.0^{2}4025$	$.0^{2}3907$	$.0^{2}3793$	$.0^{2}3681$	$.0^{2}3573$
2.7	$.0^{2}3467$	$.0^{2}3364$	$.0^{2}3264$	$.0^{2}3167$	$.0^{2}3072$	$.0^{2}2980$	$.0^{2}2890$	$.0^{2}2803$	$.0^{2}2718$	$.0^{2}2635$
2.8	$.0^{2}2555$	$.0^{2}2477$	$.0^{2}2401$	$.0^{2}2327$	$.0^{2}2256$	$.0^{2}2186$	$.0^{2}2118$	$.0^{2}2052$	$.0^{2}1988$	$.0^{2}1926$
2.9	$.0^{2}1866$	$.0^{2}1807$	$.0^{2}1750$	$.0^{2}1695$	$.0^{2}1641$	$.0^{2}1589$	$.0^{2}1538$	$.0^{2}1489$	$.0^{2}1441$	$.0^{2}1395$
3.0	$.0^{2}1350$	$.0^{2}1306$	$.0^{2}1264$	$.0^{2}1223$	$.0^{2}1183$	$.0^{2}1144$	$.0^{2}1107$	$.0^{2}1070$	$.0^{2}1035$	$.0^{2}1001$
3.1	$.0^{3}9676$	$.0^{3}9354$	$.0^{3}9043$	$.0^{3}8740$	$.0^{3}8447$	$.0^{3}8164$	$.0^{3}7888$	$.0^{3}7622$	$.0^{3}7364$	$.0^{3}7114$
3.2	$.0^{3}6871$	$.0^{3}6637$	$.0^{3}6410$	$.0^{3}6190$	$.0^{3}5976$	$.0^{3}5770$	$.0^{3}5571$	$.0^{3}5377$	$.0^{3}5190$	$.0^{3}5009$
3.3	$.0^{3}4834$	$.0^{3}4665$	$.0^{3}4501$	$.0^{3}4342$	$.0^{3}4189$	$.0^{3}4041$	$.0^{3}3897$	$.0^{3}3758$	$.0^{3}3624$	$.0^{3}3495$
3.4	$.0^{3}3369$	$.0^{3}3248$	$.0^{3}3131$	$.0^{3}3018$	$.0^{3}2909$	$.0^{3}2803$	$.0^{3}2701$	$.0^{3}2602$	$.0^{3}2507$	$.0^{3}2415$
3.5	$.0^{3}2326$	$.0^{3}2241$	$.0^{3}2158$	$.0^{3}2078$	$.0^{3}2001$	$.0^{3}1926$	$.0^{3}1854$	$.0^{3}1785$	$.0^{3}1718$	$.0^{3}1653$
3.6	$.0^{3}1591$	$.0^{3}1531$	$.0^{3}1473$	$.0^{3}1417$	$.0^{3}1363$	$.0^{3}1311$	$.0^{3}1261$	$.0^{3}1213$	$.0^{3}1166$	$.0^{3}1121$
3.7	$.0^{3}1078$	$.0^{3}1036$	$.0^{4}9961$	$.0^{4}9574$	$.0^{4}9201$	$.0^{4}8842$	$.0^{4}8162$	$.0^{4}8162$	$.0^{4}7841$	$.0^{4}7532$
3.8	$.0^{4}7235$	$.0^{4}6948$	$.0^{4}6673$	$.0^{4}6407$	$.0^{4}6152$	$.0^{4}5906$	$.0^{4}5669$	$.0^{4}5442$	$.0^{4}5223$	$.0^{4}5012$
3.9	$.0^{4}4810$	$.0^{4}4615$	$.0^{4}4427$	$.0^{4}4247$	$.0^{4}4074$	$.0^{4}3908$	$.0^{4}3747$	$.0^{4}3594$	$.0^{4}3446$	$.0^{4}3304$
4.0	$.0^{4}3167$	$.0^{4}3036$	$.0^{4}2910$	$.0^{4}2789$	$.0^{4}2673$	$.0^{4}2561$	$.0^{4}2454$	$.0^{4}2351$	$.0^{4}2252$	$.0^{4}2157$
4.1	$.0^{4}2066$	$.0^{4}1978$	$.0^{4}1894$	$.0^{4}1814$	$.0^{4}1737$	$.0^{4}1662$	$.0^{4}1591$	$.0^{4}1523$	$.0^{4}1458$	$.0^{4}1395$
4.2	$.0^{4}1335$	$.0^{4}1277$	$.0^{4}1222$	$.0^{4}1168$	$.0^{4}1118$	$.0^{4}1069$	$.0^{4}1022$	$.0^{5}9774$	$.0^{5}9345$	$.0^{5}8934$
4.3	$.0^{5}8540$	$.0^{5}8163$	$.0^{5}7801$	$.0^{5}7455$	$.0^{5}7124$	$.0^{5}6807$	$.0^{5}6503$	$.0^{5}6212$	$.0^{5}5934$	$.0^{5}5668$
4.4	$.0^{5}5413$	$.0^{5}5169$	$.0^{5}4935$	$.0^{5}4712$	$.0^{5}4498$	$.0^{5}4294$	$.0^{5}4098$	$.0^{5}3911$	$.0^{5}3732$	$.0^{5}3561$
4.5	$.0^{5}3398$	$.0^{5}3241$	$.0^{5}3092$	$.0^{5}2949$	$.0^{5}2813$	$.0^{5}2682$	$.0^{5}2558$	$.0^{5}2439$	$.0^{5}2325$	$.0^{5}2216$
4.6	$.0^{5}2112$	$.0^{5}2013$	$.0^{5}1919$	$.0^{5}1828$	$.0^{5}1742$	$.0^{5}1660$	$.0^{5}1581$	$.0^{5}1506$	$.0^{5}1434$	$.0^{5}1366$
4.7	$.0^{5}1301$	$.0^{5}1239$	$.0^{5}1179$	$.0^{5}1123$	$.0^{5}1069$	$.0^{5}1017$	$.0^{5}9680$	$.0^{5}9211$	$.0^{5}8765$	$.0^{5}8339$
4.8	$.0^{6}7933$	$.0^{6}7547$	$.0^{6}7178$	$.0^{6}6827$	$.0^{6}6492$	$.0^{6}6173$	$.0^{6}5869$	$.0^{6}5580$	$.0^{6}5304$	$.0^{6}5042$
4.9	$.0^{6}4792$	$.0^{6}4554$	$.0^{6}4327$	$.0^{6}4111$	$.0^{6}3906$	$.0^{6}3711$	$.0^{6}3525$	$.0^{6}3348$	$.0^{6}3179$	$.0^{6}3019$

Examples: $P_{N*}(\bar{u} > 3.57) = P_{N*}(\bar{u} < -3.57) = .0^{3}1785 = .0001785$

$P_{N*}(\bar{u} < 3.57) = P_{N*}(\bar{u} > -3.57) = 1 - .0^{3}1785 = .9998215$

Reproduced by permission from A. Hald, "Statistical Tables and Formulas," John Wiley & Sons, Inc., New York, 1952.

Table IV
Unit Normal Loss Integral
$$L_{N*}(u) = P'_{N*}(u) - u\,P_{N*}(\bar{u} > u)$$

u	.00	.01	.02	.03	.04	.05	.06	.07	.08	.09
.0	.3989	.3940	.3890	.3841	.3793	.3744	.3697	.3649	.3602	.3556
.1	.3509	.3464	.3418	.3373	.3328	.3284	.3240	.3197	.3154	.3111
.2	.3069	.3027	.2986	.2944	.2904	.2863	.2824	.2784	.2745	.2706
.3	.2668	.2630	.2592	.2555	.2518	.2481	.2445	.2409	.2374	.2339
.4	.2304	.2270	.2236	.2203	.2169	.2137	.2104	.2072	.2040	.2009
.5	.1978	.1947	.1917	.1887	.1857	.1828	.1799	.1771	.1742	.1714
.6	.1687	.1659	.1633	.1606	.1580	.1554	.1528	.1503	.1478	.1453
.7	.1429	.1405	.1381	.1358	.1334	.1312	.1289	.1267	.1245	.1223
.8	.1202	.1181	.1160	.1140	.1120	.1100	.1080	.1061	.1042	.1023
.9	.1004	.09860	.09680	.09503	.09328	.09156	.08986	.08819	.08654	.08491
1.0	.08332	.08174	.08019	.07866	.07716	.07568	.07422	.07279	.07138	.06999
1.1	.06862	.06727	.06595	.06465	.06336	.06210	.06086	.05964	.05844	.05726
1.2	.05610	.05496	.05384	.05274	.05165	.05059	.04954	.04851	.04750	.04650
1.3	.04553	.04457	.04363	.04270	.04179	.04090	.04002	.03916	.03831	.03748
1.4	.03667	.03587	.03508	.03431	.03356	.03281	.03208	.03137	.03067	.02998
1.5	.02931	.02865	.02800	.02736	.02674	.02612	.02552	.02494	.02436	.02380
1.6	.02324	.02270	.02217	.02165	.02114	.02064	.02015	.01967	.01920	.01874
1.7	.01829	.01785	.01742	.01699	.01658	.01617	.01578	.01539	.01501	.01464
1.8	.01428	.01392	.01357	.01323	.01290	.01257	.01226	.01195	.01164	.01134
1.9	.01105	.01077	.01049	.01022	$.0^{2}9957$	$.0^{2}9698$	$.0^{2}9445$	$.0^{2}9198$	$.0^{2}8957$	$.0^{2}8721$
2.0	$.0^{2}8491$	$.0^{2}8266$	$.0^{2}8046$	$.0^{2}7832$	$.0^{2}7623$	$.0^{2}7418$	$.0^{2}7219$	$.0^{2}7024$	$.0^{2}6835$	$.0^{2}6649$
2.1	$.0^{2}6468$	$.0^{2}6292$	$.0^{2}6120$	$.0^{2}5952$	$.0^{2}5788$	$.0^{2}5628$	$.0^{2}5472$	$.0^{2}5320$	$.0^{2}5172$	$.0^{2}5028$
2.2	$.0^{2}4887$	$.0^{2}4750$	$.0^{2}4616$	$.0^{2}4486$	$.0^{2}4358$	$.0^{2}4235$	$.0^{2}4114$	$.0^{2}3996$	$.0^{2}3882$	$.0^{2}3770$
2.3	$.0^{2}3662$	$.0^{2}3556$	$.0^{2}3453$	$.0^{2}3352$	$.0^{2}3255$	$.0^{2}3159$	$.0^{2}3067$	$.0^{2}2977$	$.0^{2}2889$	$.0^{2}2804$
2.4	$.0^{2}2720$	$.0^{2}2640$	$.0^{2}2561$	$.0^{2}2484$	$.0^{2}2410$	$.0^{2}2337$	$.0^{2}2267$	$.0^{2}2199$	$.0^{2}2132$	$.0^{2}2067$

u	0	1	2	3	4	5	6	7	8	9
2.5	$.0^{2}2004$	$.0^{2}1943$	$.0^{2}1883$	$.0^{2}1826$	$.0^{2}1769$	$.0^{2}1715$	$.0^{2}1662$	$.0^{2}1610$	$.0^{2}1560$	$.0^{2}1511$
2.6	$.0^{2}1464$	$.0^{2}1418$	$.0^{2}1373$	$.0^{2}1330$	$.0^{2}1288$	$.0^{2}1247$	$.0^{2}1207$	$.0^{2}1169$	$.0^{2}1132$	$.0^{2}1095$
2.7	$.0^{2}1060$	$.0^{2}1026$	$.0^{3}9928$	$.0^{3}9607$	$.0^{3}9295$	$.0^{3}8992$	$.0^{3}8699$	$.0^{3}8414$	$.0^{3}8138$	$.0^{3}7870$
2.8	$.0^{3}7611$	$.0^{3}7359$	$.0^{3}7115$	$.0^{3}6879$	$.0^{3}6650$	$.0^{3}6428$	$.0^{3}6213$	$.0^{3}6004$	$.0^{3}5802$	$.0^{3}5606$
2.9	$.0^{3}5417$	$.0^{3}5233$	$.0^{3}5055$	$.0^{3}4883$	$.0^{3}4716$	$.0^{3}4555$	$.0^{3}4398$	$.0^{3}4247$	$.0^{3}4101$	$.0^{3}3959$
3.0	$.0^{3}3822$	$.0^{3}3689$	$.0^{3}3560$	$.0^{3}3436$	$.0^{3}3316$	$.0^{3}3199$	$.0^{3}3087$	$.0^{3}2978$	$.0^{3}2873$	$.0^{3}2771$
3.1	$.0^{3}2673$	$.0^{3}2577$	$.0^{3}2485$	$.0^{3}2396$	$.0^{3}2311$	$.0^{3}2227$	$.0^{3}2147$	$.0^{3}2070$	$.0^{3}1995$	$.0^{3}1922$
3.2	$.0^{3}1852$	$.0^{3}1785$	$.0^{3}1720$	$.0^{3}1657$	$.0^{3}1596$	$.0^{3}1537$	$.0^{3}1480$	$.0^{3}1426$	$.0^{3}1373$	$.0^{3}1322$
3.3	$.0^{3}1273$	$.0^{3}1225$	$.0^{3}1179$	$.0^{3}1135$	$.0^{3}1093$	$.0^{3}1051$	$.0^{3}1012$	$.0^{4}9734$	$.0^{4}9365$	$.0^{4}9009$
3.4	$.0^{4}8666$	$.0^{4}8335$	$.0^{4}8016$	$.0^{4}7709$	$.0^{4}7413$	$.0^{4}7127$	$.0^{4}6852$	$.0^{4}6587$	$.0^{4}6331$	$.0^{4}6085$
3.5	$.0^{4}5848$	$.0^{4}5620$	$.0^{4}5400$	$.0^{4}5188$	$.0^{4}4984$	$.0^{4}4788$	$.0^{4}4599$	$.0^{4}4417$	$.0^{4}4242$	$.0^{4}4073$
3.6	$.0^{4}3911$	$.0^{4}3755$	$.0^{4}3605$	$.0^{4}3460$	$.0^{4}3321$	$.0^{4}3188$	$.0^{4}3059$	$.0^{4}2935$	$.0^{4}2816$	$.0^{4}2702$
3.7	$.0^{4}2592$	$.0^{4}2486$	$.0^{4}2385$	$.0^{4}2287$	$.0^{4}2193$	$.0^{4}2103$	$.0^{4}2016$	$.0^{4}1933$	$.0^{4}1853$	$.0^{4}1776$
3.8	$.0^{4}1702$	$.0^{4}1632$	$.0^{4}1563$	$.0^{4}1498$	$.0^{4}1435$	$.0^{4}1375$	$.0^{4}1317$	$.0^{4}1262$	$.0^{4}1208$	$.0^{4}1157$
3.9	$.0^{4}1108$	$.0^{4}1061$	$.0^{4}1016$	$.0^{5}9723$	$.0^{5}9307$	$.0^{5}8908$	$.0^{5}8525$	$.0^{5}8158$	$.0^{5}7806$	$.0^{5}7469$
4.0	$.0^{5}7145$	$.0^{5}6835$	$.0^{5}6538$	$.0^{5}6253$	$.0^{5}5980$	$.0^{5}5718$	$.0^{5}5468$	$.0^{5}5227$	$.0^{5}4997$	$.0^{5}4777$
4.1	$.0^{5}4566$	$.0^{5}4364$	$.0^{5}4170$	$.0^{5}3985$	$.0^{5}3807$	$.0^{5}3637$	$.0^{5}3475$	$.0^{5}3319$	$.0^{5}3170$	$.0^{5}3027$
4.2	$.0^{5}2891$	$.0^{5}2760$	$.0^{5}2635$	$.0^{5}2516$	$.0^{5}2402$	$.0^{5}2292$	$.0^{5}2188$	$.0^{5}2088$	$.0^{5}1992$	$.0^{5}1901$
4.3	$.0^{5}1814$	$.0^{5}1730$	$.0^{5}1650$	$.0^{5}1574$	$.0^{5}1501$	$.0^{5}1431$	$.0^{5}1365$	$.0^{5}1301$	$.0^{5}1241$	$.0^{5}1183$
4.4	$.0^{5}1127$	$.0^{5}1074$	$.0^{5}1024$	$.0^{6}9756$	$.0^{6}9296$	$.0^{6}8857$	$.0^{6}8437$	$.0^{6}8037$	$.0^{6}7655$	$.0^{6}7290$
4.5	$.0^{6}6942$	$.0^{6}6610$	$.0^{6}6294$	$.0^{6}5992$	$.0^{6}5704$	$.0^{6}5429$	$.0^{6}5167$	$.0^{6}4917$	$.0^{6}4679$	$.0^{6}4452$
4.6	$.0^{6}4236$	$.0^{6}4029$	$.0^{6}3833$	$.0^{6}3645$	$.0^{6}3467$	$.0^{6}3297$	$.0^{6}3135$	$.0^{6}2981$	$.0^{6}2834$	$.0^{6}2694$
4.7	$.0^{6}2560$	$.0^{6}2433$	$.0^{6}2313$	$.0^{6}2197$	$.0^{6}2088$	$.0^{6}1984$	$.0^{6}1884$	$.0^{6}1790$	$.0^{6}1700$	$.0^{6}1615$
4.8	$.0^{6}1533$	$.0^{6}1456$	$.0^{6}1382$	$.0^{6}1312$	$.0^{6}1246$	$.0^{6}1182$	$.0^{6}1122$	$.0^{6}1065$	$.0^{6}1011$	$.0^{7}9588$
4.9	$.0^{7}9096$	$.0^{7}8629$	$.0^{7}8185$	$.0^{7}7763$	$.0^{7}7362$	$.0^{7}6982$	$.0^{7}6620$	$.0^{7}6276$	$.0^{7}5950$	$.0^{7}5640$

$$L_{N*}(-u) = u + L_{N*}(u)$$

Examples: $L_{N*}(3.57) = .0^{4}4417 = .00004417$

$$L_{N*}(-3.57) = 3.57004417$$

Table V
Random Digits

10	09	73	25	33	76	52	01	35	86	34	67	35	48	76	80	95	90	91	17	39	29	27	49	45
37	54	20	48	05	64	89	47	42	96	24	80	52	40	37	20	63	61	04	02	00	82	29	16	65
08	42	26	89	53	19	64	50	93	03	23	20	90	25	60	15	95	33	47	64	35	08	03	36	06
99	01	90	25	29	09	37	67	07	15	38	31	13	11	65	88	67	67	43	97	04	43	62	76	59
12	80	79	99	70	80	15	73	61	47	64	03	23	66	53	98	95	11	68	77	12	17	17	68	33
66	06	57	47	17	34	07	27	68	50	36	69	73	61	70	65	81	33	98	85	11	19	92	91	70
31	06	01	08	05	45	57	18	24	06	35	30	34	26	14	86	79	90	74	39	23	40	30	97	32
85	26	97	76	02	02	05	16	56	92	68	66	57	48	18	73	05	38	52	47	18	62	38	85	79
63	57	33	21	35	05	32	54	70	48	90	55	35	75	48	28	46	82	87	09	83	49	12	56	24
73	79	64	57	53	03	52	96	47	78	35	80	83	42	82	60	93	52	03	44	35	27	38	84	35
98	52	01	77	67	14	90	56	86	07	22	10	94	05	58	60	97	09	34	33	50	50	07	39	98
11	80	50	54	31	39	80	82	77	32	50	72	56	82	48	29	40	52	42	01	52	77	56	78	51
83	45	29	96	34	06	28	89	80	83	13	74	67	00	78	18	47	54	06	10	68	71	17	78	17
88	68	54	02	00	86	50	75	84	01	36	76	66	79	51	90	36	47	64	93	29	60	91	10	62
99	59	46	73	48	87	51	76	49	69	91	82	60	89	28	93	78	56	13	68	23	47	83	41	13
65	48	11	76	74	17	46	85	09	50	58	04	77	69	74	73	03	95	71	86	40	21	81	65	44
80	12	43	56	35	17	72	70	80	15	45	31	82	23	74	21	11	57	82	53	14	38	55	37	63
74	35	09	98	17	77	40	27	72	14	43	23	60	02	10	45	52	16	42	37	96	28	60	26	55
69	91	62	68	03	66	25	22	91	48	36	93	68	72	03	76	62	11	39	90	94	40	05	64	18
09	89	32	05	05	14	22	56	85	14	46	42	75	67	88	96	29	77	88	22	54	38	21	45	98
91	49	91	45	23	68	47	92	76	86	46	16	28	35	54	94	75	08	99	23	37	08	92	00	48
80	33	69	45	98	26	94	03	68	58	70	29	73	41	35	53	14	03	33	40	42	05	08	23	41
44	10	48	19	49	85	15	74	79	54	32	97	92	65	75	57	60	04	08	81	22	22	20	64	13
12	55	07	37	42	11	10	00	20	40	12	86	07	46	97	96	64	48	94	39	28	70	72	58	15
63	60	64	93	29	16	50	53	44	84	40	21	95	25	63	43	65	17	70	82	07	20	73	17	90
61	19	69	04	46	26	45	74	77	74	51	92	43	37	29	65	39	45	95	93	42	58	26	05	27
15	47	44	52	66	95	27	07	99	53	59	36	78	38	48	82	39	61	01	18	33	21	15	94	66
94	55	72	85	73	67	89	75	43	87	54	62	24	44	31	91	19	04	25	92	92	92	74	59	73
42	48	11	62	13	97	34	40	87	21	16	86	84	87	67	03	07	11	20	59	25	70	14	66	70
23	52	37	83	17	73	20	88	98	37	68	93	59	14	16	26	25	22	96	63	05	52	28	25	62
04	49	35	24	94	75	24	63	38	24	45	86	25	10	25	61	96	27	93	35	65	33	71	24	72
00	54	99	76	54	64	05	18	81	59	96	11	96	38	96	54	69	28	23	91	23	28	72	95	29
35	96	31	53	07	26	89	80	93	54	33	35	13	54	62	77	97	45	00	24	90	10	33	93	33
59	80	80	83	91	45	42	72	68	42	83	60	94	97	00	13	02	12	48	92	78	56	52	01	06
46	05	88	52	36	01	39	09	22	86	77	28	14	40	77	93	91	08	36	47	70	61	74	29	41
32	17	90	05	97	87	37	92	52	41	05	56	70	70	07	86	74	31	71	57	85	39	41	18	38
69	23	46	14	06	20	11	74	52	04	15	95	66	00	00	18	74	39	24	23	97	11	89	63	38
19	56	54	14	30	01	75	87	53	79	40	41	92	15	85	66	67	43	68	06	84	96	28	52	07
45	15	51	49	38	19	47	60	72	46	43	66	79	45	43	59	04	79	00	33	20	82	66	95	41
94	86	43	19	94	36	16	81	08	51	34	88	88	15	53	01	54	03	54	56	05	01	45	11	76
98	08	62	48	26	45	24	02	84	04	44	99	90	88	96	39	09	47	34	07	35	44	13	18	80
33	18	51	62	32	41	94	15	09	49	89	43	54	85	81	88	69	54	19	94	37	54	87	30	43
80	95	10	04	06	96	38	27	07	74	20	15	12	33	87	25	01	62	52	98	94	62	46	11	71
79	75	24	91	40	71	96	12	82	96	69	86	10	25	91	74	85	22	05	39	00	38	75	95	79
18	63	33	25	37	98	14	50	65	71	31	01	02	46	74	05	45	56	14	27	77	93	89	19	36
74	02	94	39	02	77	55	73	22	70	97	79	01	71	19	52	52	75	80	21	80	81	45	17	48
54	17	84	56	11	80	99	33	71	43	05	33	51	29	69	56	12	71	92	55	36	04	09	03	24
11	66	44	98	83	52	07	98	48	27	59	38	17	15	39	09	97	33	34	40	88	46	12	33	56
48	32	47	79	28	31	24	96	47	10	02	29	53	68	70	32	30	75	75	46	15	02	00	99	94
69	07	49	41	38	87	63	79	19	76	35	58	40	44	01	10	51	82	16	15	01	84	87	69	38

Reproduced by permission from The RAND Corporation, "A Million Random Digits," Free Press, Glencoe, Ill., 1955.

Table VI
Square Roots

n	0	1	2	3	4	5	6	7	8	9	10	Tenths of the tabular difference 1	2	3	4	5
.1	.316	.332	.346	.361	.374	.387						1	3	4	6	7
						.387	.400	.412	.424	.436	.447	1	2	4	5	6
.2	.447	.458	.469	.480	.490	.500	.510	.520	.529	.539	.548	1	2	3	4	5
.3	.548	.557	.566	.574	.583	.592	.600	.608	.616	.624	.632	1	2	3	3	4
.4	.632	.640	.648	.656	.663	.671	.678	.686	.693	.700	.707	1	1	2	3	4
.5	.707	.714	.721	.728	.735	.742	.748	.755	.762	.768	.775	1	1	2	3	3
.6	.775	.781	.787	.794	.800	.806	.812	.819	.825	.831	.837	1	1	2	2	3
.7	.837	.843	.849	.854	.860	.866	.872	.877	.883	.889	.894	1	1	2	2	3
.8	.894	.900	.906	.911	.917	.922	.927	.933	.938	.943	.949	1	1	2	2	3
.9	.949	.954	.959	.964	.970	.975	.980	.985	.990	.995	1.000	1	1	2	2	3
1.0	1.000	1.005	1.010	1.015	1.020	1.025	1.030	1.034	1.039	1.044	1.049	0	1	1	2	2
1.1	1.049	1.054	1.058	1.063	1.068	1.072	1.077	1.082	1.086	1.091	1.095	0	1	1	2	2
1.2	1.095	1.100	1.105	1.109	1.114	1.118	1.122	1.127	1.131	1.136	1.140	0	1	1	2	2
1.3	1.140	1.145	1.149	1.153	1.158	1.162	1.166	1.170	1.175	1.179	1.183	0	1	1	2	2
1.4	1.183	1.187	1.192	1.196	1.200	1.204	1.208	1.212	1.217	1.221	1.225	0	1	1	2	2
1.5	1.225	1.229	1.233	1.237	1.241	1.245	1.249	1.253	1.257	1.261	1.265	0	1	1	2	2
1.6	1.265	1.269	1.273	1.277	1.281	1.285	1.288	1.292	1.296	1.300	1.304	0	1	1	2	2
1.7	1.304	1.308	1.311	1.315	1.319	1.323	1.327	1.330	1.334	1.338	1.342	0	1	1	2	2
1.8	1.342	1.345	1.349	1.353	1.356	1.360	1.364	1.367	1.371	1.375	1.378	0	1	1	1	2
1.9	1.378	1.382	1.386	1.389	1.393	1.396	1.400	1.404	1.407	1.411	1.414	0	1	1	1	2
2.0	1.414	1.418	1.421	1.425	1.428	1.432	1.435	1.439	1.442	1.446	1.449	0	1	1	1	2
2.1	1.449	1.453	1.456	1.459	1.463	1.466	1.470	1.473	1.476	1.480	1.483	0	1	1	1	2
2.2	1.483	1.487	1.490	1.493	1.497	1.500	1.503	1.507	1.510	1.513	1.517	0	1	1	1	2
2.3	1.517	1.520	1.523	1.526	1.530	1.533	1.536	1.539	1.543	1.546	1.549	0	1	1	1	2
2.4	1.549	1.552	1.556	1.559	1.562	1.565	1.568	1.572	1.575	1.578	1.581	0	1	1	1	2
2.5	1.581	1.584	1.587	1.591	1.594	1.597	1.600	1.603	1.606	1.609	1.612	0	1	1	1	2
2.6	1.612	1.616	1.619	1.622	1.625	1.628	1.631	1.634	1.637	1.640	1.643	0	1	1	1	2
2.7	1.643	1.646	1.649	1.652	1.655	1.658	1.661	1.664	1.667	1.670	1.673	0	1	1	1	2
2.8	1.673	1.676	1.679	1.682	1.685	1.688	1.691	1.694	1.697	1.700	1.703	0	1	1	1	1
2.9	1.703	1.706	1.709	1.712	1.715	1.718	1.720	1.723	1.726	1.729	1.732	0	1	1	1	1
3.0	1.732	1.735	1.738	1.741	1.744	1.746	1.749	1.752	1.755	1.758	1.761	0	1	1	1	1
3.1	1.761	1.764	1.766	1.769	1.772	1.775	1.778	1.780	1.783	1.786	1.789	0	1	1	1	1
3.2	1.789	1.792	1.794	1.797	1.800	1.803	1.806	1.808	1.811	1.814	1.817	0	1	1	1	1
3.3	1.817	1.819	1.822	1.825	1.828	1.830	1.833	1.836	1.838	1.841	1.844	0	1	1	1	1
3.4	1.844	1.847	1.849	1.852	1.855	1.857	1.860	1.863	1.865	1.868	1.871	0	1	1	1	1
3.5	1.871	1.873	1.876	1.879	1.881	1.884	1.887	1.889	1.892	1.895	1.897	0	1	1	1	1
3.6	1.897	1.900	1.903	1.905	1.908	1.910	1.913	1.916	1.918	1.921	1.924	0	1	1	1	1
3.7	1.924	1.926	1.929	1.931	1.934	1.936	1.939	1.942	1.944	1.947	1.949	0	1	1	1	1
3.8	1.949	1.952	1.954	1.957	1.960	1.962	1.965	1.967	1.970	1.972	1.975	0	1	1	1	1
3.9	1.975	1.977	1.980	1.982	1.985	1.987	1.990	1.992	1.995	1.997	2.000	0	1	1	1	1
4.0	2.000	2.002	2.005	2.007	2.010	2.012	2.015	2.017	2.020	2.022	2.025	0	0	1	1	1
4.1	2.025	2.027	2.030	2.032	2.035	2.037	2.040	2.042	2.045	2.047	2.049	0	0	1	1	1
4.2	2.049	2.052	2.054	2.057	2.059	2.062	2.064	2.066	2.069	2.071	2.074	0	0	1	1	1
4.3	2.074	2.076	2.078	2.081	2.083	2.086	2.088	2.090	2.093	2.095	2.098	0	0	1	1	1
4.4	2.098	2.100	2.102	2.105	2.107	2.110	2.112	2.114	2.117	2.119	2.121	0	0	1	1	1
4.5	2.121	2.124	2.126	2.128	2.131	2.133	2.135	2.138	2.140	2.142	2.145	0	0	1	1	1
4.6	2.145	2.147	2.149	2.152	2.154	2.156	2.159	2.161	2.163	2.166	2.168	0	0	1	1	1
4.7	2.168	2.170	2.173	2.175	2.177	2.179	2.182	2.184	2.186	2.189	2.191	0	0	1	1	1
4.8	2.191	2.193	2.195	2.198	2.200	2.202	2.205	2.207	2.209	2.211	2.214	0	0	1	1	1
4.9	2.214	2.216	2.218	2.220	2.223	2.225	2.227	2.229	2.232	2.234	2.236	0	0	1	1	1
5.	2.236	2.258	2.280	2.302	2.324	2.345	2.366	2.387	2.408	2.429	2.449	2	4	6	9	11
6.	2.449	2.470	2.490	2.510	2.530	2.550	2.569	2.588	2.608	2.627	2.646	2	4	6	8	10
7.	2.646	2.665	2.683	2.702	2.720	2.739	2.757	2.775	2.793	2.811	2.828	2	4	5	7	9
8.	2.828	2.846	2.864	2.881	2.898	2.915	2.933	2.950	2.966	2.983	3.000	2	3	5	7	9
9.	3.000	3.017	3.033	3.050	3.066	3.082	3.098	3.114	3.130	3.146	3.162	2	3	5	6	8

Reproduced by permission from E. V. Huntington, "Four-place Tables," Houghton Mifflin Company, Boston, 1931.

Table VII
Cube Roots

n	0	1	2	3	4	5	6	7	8	9	10	Tenths of the tabular difference				
												1	2	3	4	5
.010	.2154	.2162	.2169	.2176	.2183	.2190	.2197	.2204	.2210	.2217	.2224	1	1	2	3	3
.011	.2224	.2231	.2237	.2244	.2251	.2257	.2264	.2270	.2277	.2283	.2289	1	1	2	3	3
.012	.2289	.2296	.2302	.2308	.2315	.2321	.2327	.2333	.2339	.2345	.2351	1	1	2	2	3
.013	.2351	.2357	.2363	.2369	.2375	.2381	.2387	.2393	.2399	.2404	.2410	1	1	2	2	3
.014	.2410	.2416	.2422	.2427	.2433	.2438	.2444	.2450	.2455	.2461	.2466	1	1	2	2	3
.015	.2466	.2472	.2477	.2483	.2488	.2493	.2499	.2504	.2509	.2515	.2520	1	1	2	2	3
.016	.2520	.2525	.2530	.2535	.2541	.2546	.2551	.2556	.2561	.2566	.2571	1	1	2	2	2
.017	.2571	.2576	.2581	.2586	.2591	.2596	.2601	.2606	.2611	.2616	.2621	0	1	1	2	2
.018	.2621	.2626	.2630	.2635	.2640	.2645	.2650	.2654	.2659	.2664	.2668	0	1	1	2	2
.019	.2668	.2673	.2678	.2682	.2687	.2692	.2696	.2701	.2705	.2710	.2714	0	1	1	2	2
.020	.2714	.2719	.2723	.2728	.2732	.2737	.2741	.2746	.2750	.2755	.2759	0	1	1	2	2
.021	.2759	.2763	.2768	.2772	.2776	.2781	.2785	.2789	.2794	.2798	.2802	0	1	1	2	2
.022	.2802	.2806	.2811	.2815	.2819	.2823	.2827	.2831	.2836	.2840	.2844	0	1	1	2	2
.023	.2844	.2848	.2852	.2856	.2860	.2864	.2868	.2872	.2876	.2880	.2884	0	1	1	2	2
.024	.2884	.2888	.2892	.2896	.2900	.2904	.2908	.2912	.2916	.2920	.2924	0	1	1	2	2
.025	.2924	.2928	.2932	.2936	.2940	.2943	.2947	.2951	.2955	.2959	.2962	0	1	1	2	2
.026	.2962	.2966	.2970	.2974	.2978	.2981	.2985	.2989	.2993	.2996	.3000	0	1	1	2	2
.027	.3000	.3004	.3007	.3011	.3015	.3018	.3022	.3026	.3029	.3033	.3037	0	1	1	1	2
.028	.3037	.3040	.3044	.3047	.3051	.3055	.3058	.3062	.3065	.3069	.3072	0	1	1	1	2
.029	.3072	.3076	.3079	.3083	.3086	.3090	.3093	.3097	.3100	.3104	.3107	0	1	1	1	2
.03	.311	.314	.317	.321	.324	.327	.330	.333	.336	.339	.342	0	1	1	1	2
.04	.342	.345	.348	.350	.353	.356	.358	.361	.363	.366	.368	0	1	1	1	1
.05	.368	.371	.373	.376	.378	.380	.383	.385	.387	.389	.391	0	0	1	1	1
.06	.391	.394	.396	.398	.400	.402	.404	.406	.408	.410	.412	0	0	1	1	1
.07	.412	.414	.416	.418	.420	.422	.424	.425	.427	.429	.431	0	0	1	1	1
.08	.431	.433	.434	.436	.438	.440	.441	.443	.445	.446	.448	0	0	1	1	1
.09	.448	.450	.451	.453	.455	.456	.458	.459	.461	.463	.464	0	0	0	1	1
.1	.464	.479	.493	.507	.519	.531						1	3	4	5	7
						.531	.543	.554	.565	.575	.585	1	2	3	4	5
.2	.585	.594	.604	.613	.621	.630	.638	.646	.654	.662	.669	1	2	3	3	4
.3	.669	.677	.684	.691	.698	.705	.711	.718	.724	.731	.737	1	1	2	3	3
.4	.737	.743	.749	.755	.761	.766	.772	.777	.783	.788	.794	1	1	2	2	3
.5	.794	.799	.804	.809	.814	.819	.824	.829	.834	.839	.843	0	1	1	2	2
.6	.843	.848	.853	.857	.862	.866	.871	.875	.879	.884	.888	0	1	1	2	2
.7	.888	.892	.896	.900	.905	.909	.913	.917	.921	.924	.928	0	1	1	2	2
.8	.928	.932	.936	.940	.944	.947	.951	.955	.958	.962	.965	0	1	1	1	2
.9	.965	.969	.973	.976	.980	.983	.986	.990	.993	.997	1.000	0	1	1	1	2
1.0	1.000	1.003	1.007	1.010	1.013	1.016	1.020	1.023	1.026	1.029	1.032	0	1	1	1	2
1.1	1.032	1.035	1.038	1.042	1.045	1.048	1.051	1.054	1.057	1.060	1.063	0	1	1	1	1
1.2	1.063	1.066	1.069	1.071	1.074	1.077	1.080	1.083	1.086	1.089	1.091	0	1	1	1	1
1.3	1.091	1.094	1.097	1.100	1.102	1.105	1.108	1.111	1.113	1.116	1.119	0	1	1	1	1
1.4	1.119	1.121	1.124	1.127	1.129	1.132	1.134	1.137	1.140	1.142	1.145	0	1	1	1	1
1.5	1.145	1.147	1.150	1.152	1.155	1.157	1.160	1.162	1.165	1.167	1.170	0	0	1	1	1
1.6	1.170	1.172	1.174	1.177	1.179	1.182	1.184	1.186	1.189	1.191	1.193	0	0	1	1	1
1.7	1.193	1.196	1.198	1.200	1.203	1.205	1.207	1.210	1.212	1.214	1.216	0	0	1	1	1
1.8	1.216	1.219	1.221	1.223	1.225	1.228	1.230	1.232	1.234	1.236	1.239	0	0	1	1	1
1.9	1.239	1.241	1.243	1.245	1.247	1.249	1.251	1.254	1.256	1.258	1.260	0	0	1	1	1
2.	1.260	1.281	1.301	1.320	1.339	1.357						2	4	6	8	10
						1.357	1.375	1.392	1.409	1.426	1.442	2	3	5	7	9
3.	1.442	1.458	1.474	1.489	1.504	1.518	1.533	1.547	1.560	1.574	1.587	1	3	4	6	7
4.	1.587	1.601	1.613	1.626	1.639	1.651	1.663	1.675	1.687	1.698	1.710	1	2	4	5	6
5.	1.710	1.721	1.732	1.744	1.754	1.765	1.776	1.786	1.797	1.807	1.817	1	2	3	4	5
6.	1.817	1.827	1.837	1.847	1.857	1.866	1.876	1.885	1.895	1.904	1.913	1	2	3	4	5
7.	1.913	1.922	1.931	1.940	1.949	1.957	1.966	1.975	1.983	1.992	2.000	1	2	3	3	4
8.	2.000	2.008	2.017	2.025	2.033	2.041	2.049	2.057	2.065	2.072	2.080	1	2	2	3	4
9.	2.080	2.088	2.095	2.103	2.110	2.118	2.125	2.133	2.140	2.147	2.154	1	1	2	3	4

Reproduced by permission from E. V. Huntington, "Four-place Tables," Houghton Mifflin Company, Boston, 1931.

Index of Symbols

Index includes those symbols which are used in more than one chapter

0   as subscript, denotes *prior* value, 196, 298
1   as subscript, denotes *posterior* value, 196, 298
α = maximum conditional probability of error of first kind, 165
α = specified value of producer's risk, 158
β = specified value of consumer's risk, 158
c = rejection or critical number, 153, 272
C_r^n = number of possible orders in which r successes can occur in a sequence of n trials, 138
$D = \dfrac{|\mu_b - \mathrm{E}(\tilde{\mu})|}{\sigma(\tilde{\mu})}$, where μ stands for *any* random variable, 320
$D_B = \dfrac{|\mu - \mathrm{E}_0(\tilde{\mu})|}{\sigma(\tilde{E}_1)}$, 324
$D_0 = \dfrac{|\mu_b - \mathrm{E}_0(\tilde{\mu})|}{\sigma_0(\tilde{\mu})}$, 324
E = expectation, 97
$F._f$ = point-f fractile, 91
γ = fraction of false statements in repeated application of confidence-interval procedure, 214
I = quantity of information, 304–305
k_o = loss per unit of overage, 85
k_s = variable sampling cost, per item in sample, 329
K_s = fixed element in sampling cost, independent of sample size, 329
k_t = terminal loss constant in two-action problems with linear costs or profits, 318
k_u = loss per unit of underage, 85
$L_{N^*}(u) = \mathrm{P}'_{N^*}(u) - u\,\mathrm{P}_{N^*}(\tilde{u} > u)$, unit Normal loss integral, 320, 370–371
M = mean, of Normal distribution, 233
μ = mean, of many-valued population, 249
μ_b = break-even value of μ, 269, 318
n = number of Bernoulli trials, 137–138
n = number of items in sample, 112
N = population size, 144, 259
ν = number of degrees of freedom, 267
p = long-run fraction successful in Bernoulli process, 137–138
p_b = break-even value of p, 151
$\mathrm{P}(A)$ = probability of A, 60, 127

375

$P(A,B)$ = joint probability of A and B, 128

$P(A|B)$ = conditional probability of A given B, 127

$P'(z)$ = probability per unit width at value z of $\tilde{z}$, 60–61

$P_b(\tilde{r} \geq r|n,p)$ = binomial probability, 141–142

$P_{N^\bullet}(\tilde{u} > u)$ = standardized Normal probability, 236–238

q = long-run fraction unsuccessful in a Bernoulli process, 137–138

Q = number of units stocked, 68

r = number of Bernoulli successes, 137–138

r_o = observed number of Bernoulli successes, 166

$$s = \sqrt{\frac{1}{\nu} \Sigma(x - \bar{x})^2}, \; 264$$

S = standard deviation of Normal distribution, 233

σ = standard deviation, 227

σ^2 = variance, 227

σ^2 = variance of process or population or of an individual sample item, 257

$$\sigma^2(\tilde{E}_1) = \sigma_0^2(\tilde{\mu}) \frac{\sigma_0^2(\tilde{\mu})}{\sigma_0^2(\tilde{\mu}) + \sigma^2(\tilde{x})}, \; 324$$

t = total value of sample from many-valued population, 249

$$u = \frac{z - M}{S}, \; 236$$

mean and variance of, 235

$$\hat{u} = \frac{\bar{x} - \mu}{s/\sqrt{n}}, \; 265$$

distribution of, 265–267

x = value of individual member of population or of individual sample item, 249

$$\bar{x} = \frac{r}{n} \text{ or } \frac{t}{n}, \text{ sample mean, } 260$$

distribution of, 261–262

when population is incompletely specified, 254–257

when population is Normal, 254

when population is rectangular or skew, 254

$\bar{x}_o$ = observed value of $\bar{x}$, 278

$$Z_0 = \frac{\sigma_0(\tilde{\mu})}{\sigma} \sqrt[3]{\frac{k_t \sigma}{k_s}}, \; 330$$

Subject Index

Boldface numbers shown in parentheses refer to problems on the pages indicated

Acts, 4
  comparison of, under uncertainty, 5–7
    in terms of loss, 75, 173–176
Additivity of means, variances, and
  standard deviations, 227–228
Advertising agency (4), 168
Assignable causes, of irregularities in his-
  torical frequency distributions, 106,
  109
Average, weighted, 10, 96
  (*See also* Location, measures of)

Ball bearings, sorting of (3), 134
Bayes' decision rules, 176–178
Bayes' postulate, 307n.
Bayes' theorem, 191, 202, 322
  when prior distribution is continuous,
    207–209, 296
  when prior distribution is discrete, 192–
    195
Beacon Catering Corporation (2), 78; (1),
  87
Bernoulli process, 136, 249
  conditions defining, 136
  parameter of, 136
    assessment of distribution of, 175–
      176, 179–181
  sampling from, 142–143
Bernoulli trial, 228–229
Binomial distribution, 137–140
  approximated, by Normal distribution,
    238–246
  mean of, 140, 229
  tables of, explained, 141
  variance of, 229
Book club, 159

Break-even probability, 39; (3), 48
Break-even value of basic random variable, 151, 269, 317–318

Central limit theorem, 252–253
Central tendency, measure of, 102
Confidence intervals, 214–219, 312–315
  for μ when $\bar{x}$ is Normally distributed,
    312–313
  for p of Bernoulli process, 214–215
  proof of essential property of, 217–219,
    313–314
  purpose and nature of, 214–215
  relation to posterior probability, 215–
    217, 314
Consequences, 24
  evaluation of, in terms of reference
    lottery, 34–37
  reference, 33
Correlation, 228n.
Cost, good-will, 88
  of irrationality, 76
  of uncertainty, 76, 320
    (*See also* Loss, expected)
  variable versus fixed, 68
Cost or profit, conditional, 97–102
  expected, 98–100, 316–317
  incremental (*see* Incremental analysis)
  linear (*see* Linear cost or profit)
  unaffected by decision, exclusion of,
    67–69
Critical ratio, 87
  (*See also* Fractiles, critical)

Daily Racing Form (2), 87
D'Alembert's paradox, 15–16, 18

Decision rules, Bayes', 176–178
  choice by specification of α and β, 157–159, 275–277
  conditional performance described, by probabilities of error, 154–157, 273–275
  by terminal loss, 169–173, 289–290
  equivalent to test of significance, 166–167, 284–285
  error characteristics of, 154–155, 273–275, 281–282
  expected terminal loss under, 177–178, 290–292
  expected total cost, profit, or loss under, 183, 292–293
  expected value of sample information under, 322–326
  minimax, 173–174
  net gain of sampling under, 326
  unconditional performance evaluated in terms of loss, 173–186, 290–292
  when sample size is fixed, 162–163, 279
    choice by limitation of risks of type I error, 164–166, 282–284
    conditional performance described by probability of error, 163–164
    error characteristics of, 163–164
  when sampling is binomial, 150–167
  when sampling is Normal, 268–285
  expected losses under, 289–295
  (*See also* Errors of first and second kind; Tests of hypotheses)
Degrees of freedom, 264, 267
Differences, populations and samples of, 278, 279
Discrepancy, forecast (*see* Forecast discrepancies)
Distribution, binomial (*see* Binomial distribution)
  continuous, 230
  cumulative, 57–60
  discrete, 230–231
  frequency, 52–54
    smoothing of, 108–111
  graphic representation of, 54–57, 58–60
    relation between shapes of cumulative and ordinary, 113–115
  grouped, 56–57
  posterior, when prior is rectangular and sampling is binomial, 207
  prior, continuous, 206, 296

Distribution, prior, discrete, 178–179, 296
  effect of, compared with effect of sample, 207–209, 305–309
  "gentle," 207, 208
  rectangular, 205–209
  when statistic is Normally distributed (*see* Normal distribution)
  probability, 52–53
    based directly on betting odds (5), 118; 300–302
    relation to frequency, 52–54, 104–111, 121
  of sample mean, 260–262, 297
    relation to distribution of $\bar{l}$, 260–261
  sampling, 250–251
  of sums, of independent identically distributed random variables (*see* Normal distribution)
  (*See also* names of specific mathematical distributions)

Equally likely, 13, 307
Error characteristic (*see* Decision rules)
Errors of first and second kind, 162
  graphical description of, 163–164
Estimation, of long-run cumulative frequencies (fractiles), 111–113
  of long-run frequencies, 106–107, 110
  of population variance, 262–267, 280
  (*See also* Confidence intervals)
Events, 4
  collectively exhaustive, 7
  compound, 9
  elementary, 9
  graphic representation of, 9
  grouping of, 7–9
  mutually exclusive, 7–8
Expectation, 97
  applications of, 97–102
  of random variables, binomial, 140, 228–229
    continuous, 230–231
    Normal, 235
  of sample mean, 261–262
  of sum of random variables, 227
Expected value, of an act (*see* Value)
  of a random variable (*see* Expectation)
Experience as basis for assigning subjective probabilities (*see* Probability, subjective)

Factorial n, 138

Family-Fare Plan (2), 286

Finite population, effect of, on distribution, of $\bar{r}$, 143–148
  of $\bar{l}$, 258–260

Finite population correction (*see* Variance)

Forecast discrepancies (3), 61
  as basis for probability distribution of demand, 117

Fractiles, 91–93
  critical, in many-action problems with proportional losses, 93–95
  estimation of, 111–113

Freedom, degrees of, 264, 267

Frequency always denotes relative frequency, 53
  (*See also* Relative frequency)

Frequency distribution (*see* Distribution)

Grand Western Railroad (2), 286

Histogram, 54–56

Hypergeometric distribution, 144–145
  approximated, by binomial, 145–147
  compared with binomial, 145–147

Hypotheses, null, versus alternate, 161–162, 201
  tests of (*see* Tests of hypotheses)
  use of null versus break-even value in defining, 201, 309–310

Ignorance, total, 307

Incremental analysis, basic principle of, 80–81
  compared with direct analysis, 83–85
  problems to which applicable, 80–81

Independence, statistical, 130–131
  of Bernoulli trials, 229, 271

Infinite means or standard deviations, 253n.

Information, disregard of negligible prior, 208, 305–307
  quantity of, 304–305
  sample, value of, 325–326
  summarization of, 212–214, 312–315
  (*See also* Two-action problems)

Insurance, self-, 28, 43

Inventory control, described, by loss table, 71–73
  by payoff table, 4–5, 67–70
  direct analysis of, 73–75
  incremental analysis of, 81–87
  optimal stock in, 85–87

Irrationality, cost of, 76

Large-sample theory, 249–267

Likelihood, definition of, 196

Linear cost or profit, definition of, 98, 101–102, 316
  expectation of, 98–100, 316–317

Location, measures of, 89–97
  dangers in use of, 89–90, 102

Loss, always denotes opportunity loss, 70–71
  conditional, 71
    computed directly, 73–74
    under a decision rule, 169–173, 289–290
    derived from payoff table, 71–73
  of overage, 73, 85
  of underage, 73, 85
  expected, comparison of acts in terms of, 75
    as expectation of conditional losses, 74–75, 177–178
  incremental (*see* Incremental analysis)
  terminal, of a decision rule, 170, 173–178
  total, of a decision rule, 183
    of decision to sample and then act, 324–325
    (*See also* Two-action problems)

Loss constant, 318

Loss table, 71–73

Lottery, equivalent, 34
  reduction to reference lottery, 37–38
  reference, 35–38
    evaluation of consequences by means of, 34–37
  standard, 13–14

Mar-Pruf Finishes, Inc. (1), 285

Mean, 95–97
  of sample, 263
    (*See also* $\bar{x}$ in Index of Symbols)
  (*See also* Expectation)

Measuring process, as source of uncertainty, 270–271
Median, 90–91
Minimax decision rules, 173–174
Minimax-loss, principle of, 76–77
Minimax principle, 5
Multiplication rule, 129–130
    for independent events, 131

Net gain of sampling, 326
    (*See also* Two-action problems)
Normal distribution, 233–238
    as approximation, to binomial, 238–246
        to distribution of sums or means of independent indentically distributed random variables, 253–267
    as expression of purely subjective betting odds (5), 118; 300–302
    graphic representation of, 233–235
    parameters of, 233–235, 296
        assessment of distribution of, 298–302
    as posterior, 302–305
    as prior, 298–307
        based on historical frequencies, 298–300
    as prior or posterior, when true prior is nonnormal, 307–309, 339
    tables of, explained, 237–238
    unit or standardized, 235–237
Normal-probability paper, 115

Operating characteristic (5), 168
Opportunity loss (*see* Loss)

Parameter, 139, 234, 330
Payoff table, 4–5
    construction of, 67–70
    exclusion of irrelevant costs from, 67
Percentage samples, 147
Performance characteristic (6), 168
Poisson approximation to binomial distribution, 242
Population, 297
    of differences, 278
    exponential (4), 267
    finite (*see* Finite population)

Population, gamma (4), 267
    many-valued, 249
    rectangular (4), 267
    two-valued, 143–144
Power curve (6), 168
Preference, personal, as basis for decision under uncertainty, 26–28
Probability, break-even (*see* Break-even probability)
    conditional, of compound events, 125–129
        of elementary events, 121–125
        mathematical definition of, 128
        (*See also* Bayes' theorem)
    joint, 121–122, 191
        multiplication rule for, 129–131
    marginal, 131–132
        of sample outcome, 191
    mathematical theory of, 16
        as aid in assignment of subjective probabilities, 18–19, 191–192
    posterior, as guide to suspension of judgment, 209–210
        in relation, to confidence intervals, 215–217, 314
            to statistical significance, 211–212, 310–312
    prior and posterior, 195–196
    revision of, in light of new information, 188–197
    subjective (or "weight"), 6–7, 17, 294
        assignment of, basic rules for, 10–13
        check for consistency of, 15–16
        indirect, 19
        use in, of experience with relative frequency, 17–22, 104–113, 121, 178–181
            of standard lottery, 13–14
    unconditional, 122–123
    (*See also* Distribution; Relative frequency)
Probability paper (*see* Normal-probability paper)
Process, exponential, 254
    gamma, 254
    Normal, 252, 270–271
    random, 108, 249
    rectangular, 254

Process, skewed, 254
two-valued, 252
unknown or incompletely specified,
254
(*See also* Bernoulli process; Measuring
process)
Profit (*see* Cost or profit)

Random process, 108, 249
Random variable, 50–52
basic, 52
notation for, 60–61
value of, distinguished, from an event,
51
from random variable itself, 60
(*See also* Distribution; names of specific
random variables in Index of Symbols)
Relative frequency, calculated by theory
of probability, 22–23
conditional, of compound events, 128–
129
of elementary events, 124–125
guide to assignment of probabilities,
17–22, 53–54, 104–113, 121, 175
versus other evidence, 20
joint, 122
of mental phenomena, 21–22
unconditional, 128
(*See also* Distribution; Probability)
Reporting of sample information for un-
specified use, 312–313
Risk, attitude of individual toward, 26–
28, 41–43
dependence on situation, 44
producer's and consumer's, 153–154
choice of decision rule by specification of, 157–159
graphic description of, 154–155
reduction of, 155–157
(*See also* Errors of first and second
kind)
sharing of (8), 48
Robinson Abrasive Company (8), 186
Roulette (2), 47

Sample, as basis, for original assessment
of complete probability distribution, 104–113

Sample, as basis, for revision of previously assigned probabilities, 192–
197, 202–203
Sample mean, 263
(*See also* $\bar{x}$ in Index of Symbols)
Sample size, classical theory for choice of,
157–159, 275–277
nonoptimal, effect of, 336–337
optimal, 183–186
approximation of, 337–341
in two-action problems with linear
costs and Normal distributions,
329–341
Sample variance, 263–264
Sampling, cost of, 152–153
unknown, depending on value of
basic random variable, 185–186
from finite population, 143–148
independent versus dependent drawings, 251–252
net gain of, 326
(*See also* Two-action problems)
percentage, 147
simple, 144, 147–148
value of (*see* Information, sample)
Sampling distributions, 250–251
Sampling error, in historical frequency
distributions, 104–107
Sampling plan (5), 168
(*See also* Decision rules)
Sampling ratio, 259
Significance, statistical, 167
relation to posterior probability,
211–212, 310–312
tests of (*see* Tests of hypotheses)
two-tail, 200, 310
Smoothing, of cumulative distributions,
110–113
of frequency distributions, 108–109
Sparse data, use of, to assess probability
distributions, 110–113
Standard deviation, 225
(*See also* Variance)
Standardization, of Normal distribution,
235–237
Statistical decision rules (*see* Decision
rules)
Student distribution, 265–267
Sums of random variables (*see* Distribution)
Superprocess, 299

Suspension of judgment on terminal action, 198–212
  analysis, in terms of expected loss, 201–212
    by test of significance, 199–201, 309–310
    posterior probability as guide to, 209–210

Tables, probability, use of, in general, 142
  (*See also* specific distributions)
Tail of a distribution, 58
Telephone surveys, 204–205
Terminal, 170
  (*See also* Cost or profit; Loss)
Tests of hypotheses, 166–167, 199–201, 282–285
  may be misleading in some uses, 203, 211, 212*n*.
  use of, in choosing between two terminal acts, 166–167, 282–285
  (*See also* Decision rules; Hypotheses; Significance)
Tests of significance (*see* Tests of hypotheses)
Two-action problems with linear costs or profits, examples of, in chemical processing, 268–277
  in choice of package design, 277–285
  in marketing of paperback books, 159–167
  in process control for fraction defective, 150–159
  expected cost or profit in, 316–317
  expected loss of optimal terminal action in, 320–321
    under Normal distribution, 319–322
  expected value of sample information in, 322–325
    under Normal distribution, 325
  net gain of sampling in, 326
    under Normal distribution, 329
      behavior of, as *n* increases, 329–333
  optimal sample size in, under Normal distribution, 333–335
  under other distributions, 337–341

Two-action problems with linear costs or profits (*See also* Decision rules; Tests of hypotheses)

Uncertainty, cost of (*see* Cost)
Utility, alternate scales for measuring, 45–46
  analysis in terms of, 31–32, 181–182
  conditional, assessment of, 38–41
    interpretation of, 43–45
    zero assigned to consequence $0 (7), 48
  curves, establishment of, 39–41
  expected, as guide to action, 38–39
  of money, dependent on situation, 44

Value, of an act, conditional, 24
  expected, 24–25
    monetary, as guide to action, 25–31, 46–47
  break-even, of basic random variable, 151, 269, 317–318
  of a random variable, 50–61
  expected (*see* Expectation)
Variability, measures of, 223–232
Variable (*see* Random variable)
Variance, 224–227
  correction for effect of finite population on, 259–260
  effect of sampling ratio on, 259–260
  population or process, effect of unknown, 265–267
  estimation of, 262–267
  of random variables, binomial, 228–229
    continuous, 230–231
    normal, 235
  sample, 263–264
  of sample mean, 262
  of sum of random variables, 227–228

Weighted average, computation of, 10
  mean as, 96
Weights, subjective (*see* Probability)